GREEK COINS AND THEIR VALUES

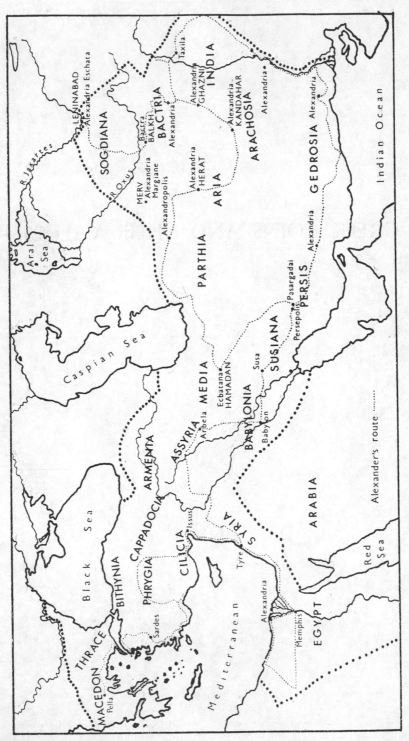

THE EMPIRE OF ALEXANDER THE GREAT AND HIS SUCCESSORS

GREEK COINS
AND THEIR VALUES

2nd EDITION

H. A. SEABY

B. A. SEABY, LTD.,
61-65 GREAT PORTLAND STREET,
LONDON, W.1.

1966

A Catalogue of Greek Coins by G. Askew ,1951

Greek Coins and Their Values by H. A. Seaby and Lieut.-Col. Kozolubski, 1959

Greek Coins and Their Values, 2nd Edition by H. A. Seaby, 1966

PRINTED IN ENGLAND BY ROBERT STOCKWELL LTD., LONDON S.E.I

CONTENTS.

PREFACE TO FIRST EDITION.

Just before he died in 1950, Gilbert Askew compiled *A Catalogue of Greek Coins* which we published in 1951. A year or two previously we had purchased an extensive collection of Greek coins formed by Professor A. B. Cook and this work was a catalogue of our stock including this collection.

I have taken this old catalogue as a basis for this new work and have made it much more comprehensive by adding many additional items especially of towns and rulers not included in the earlier work. I have included most of the coins that we have had through our hands in the last two or three years and have completely repriced each coin at 1958 collectors' value. Lieut.-Col. Kozolubski, who is in charge of the Ancient Department of our firm, has checked and edited it throughout, and, in fact, has rewritten parts of it.

Gilbert Askew wrote pages 4-22, except for minor revisions and the section on Deities and Personifications which is new. The additional maps were drawn by Peter Seaby, who also read the proofs and offered much useful advice. The plates were photographed by Frank Purvey.

The original catalogue proved quite popular and I trust that this revised work will be even more useful to the student and the collector.

Dorking   H. A. SEABY
March, 1959

PREFACE TO SECOND EDITION.

I had hoped that Lieut.-Col. Kozolubski would prepare this edition by the time the first edition went out of print but unfortunately he died in November 1964. Therefore, I have had to undertake this revision in my spare time. Firstly I obtained a large number of additional line blocks and this has necessitated rewriting part of the text and I have added a considerable number of coins, especially of places not represented before. Then with the help of David Sear, the present head of our Ancient Dept., I have revised the prices throughout with 1965 values. Peter Seaby has drawn a whole series of new and additional maps. Frank Purvey has provided eight plates in place of the original four.

London   H. A. SEABY
Dec., 1965

ON COLLECTING GREEK COINS.

This catalogue is not to be considered as a sale list, but rather a help to the student and a guide to the valuation of Greek coins, within the limits of the material dealt with. As to valuation, it should be remembered that in no department of ancient coinage is condition so great a factor; a worn tetradrachm of Syracuse may be worth only the same number of shillings as its " extremely fine " counterpart may be worth pounds. The chief points to be kept in mind by the collector in choosing Greek coins are, in order, authenticity, conservation and style: of these, it is obvious why the first is given that place, because a forgery, however beautiful (and there are some really lovely " fakes "), should never be admitted to a collection of genuine pieces except perhaps in a special section or " Black Museum." Conservation comes second because only in a well-preserved coin can the beauty of the work-manship be fully appreciated: style has been given third place, but it is a " close " third, and some judges might prefer to give it second place leaving the condition till last.

To revert to the subject of forgeries, we are sometimes asked how such pieces are detected, and really this is a difficult question to answer off-hand. To say that a certain coin " didn't look right " seems no answer at all, and yet that answer con-tains the truth. After handling and examining large numbers of genuine coins, the forgery seems to stand out at once in most instances; but not always, as there are " borderline " cases in which much study and comparison with illustrations in catalogues are required. There is, however, one test that can be applied by the beginner, and should indeed be used by anyone faced with a doubtful coin: the weight should be checked. If all the recorded specimens of a particular coin show a weight of, say, 130 grains each, and the subject of an enquiry only turns the scale at 100 grains whilst yet appearing to be in good condition without much wear, there is something extremely wrong with it, and it is probably a cast in base metal, cleaned up to deceive the collector. Weight should always be the first check, and if the collector has no scales delicate enough for the work, is should be remembered that the man in the chemist's shop has, and if he is politely approached he will usually make no difficulty about assisting in this way. To show the importance of weight, one instance may suffice: a Greek coin of Heraklea Lucaniae had been purchased in a sale lot, and the writer when cataloguing the pieces felt that there was something wrong about this one. The scales proved that there was, for whereas the coin should have weighed about 120 grains, it was actually 240. It was, in fact, a " Becker " forgery and had been struck on a flan much too heavy for a genuine coin.

Experience is the best instructor on the art of detecting forgeries, but the author suggests that by buying only from a firm which has a reputation to keep up such experience need not be acquired. Beware the Greek silver coins offered by the junk-shop. They are probably electrotypes at the best and sheer rank forgeries at the worst, and the prices asked will generally be outrageously high or absurdly low. Either extreme should be suspected.

It is seldom that we are asked " How should a collection of Greek coins be built up? " because most collectors who take an interest in the series have graduated through experience in others. Supposing, however, the question were asked, it would not be easy to answer, but one point could be emphasised. Buy the best you can afford. " Costly thy habit as thy purse can buy," said Polonius to his son, and similar advice should be offered to the would-be collector of Greek coins. This is not to say that only the expensive silver pieces should be sought. The collector should bear in mind that the bronze issues struck contemporaneously with the finest silver coins of certain mints were probably designed by the same artists, and a bronze piece, if available in " extremely fine " condition, can be a very lovely thing, especially if patinated. The difficulty is, of course, that the bronze coins, being of lower denomination, circulated to a greater extent, and therefore tend to show more wear than those of silver. The scope of the Greek coinage is, however, so great that specialisation is almost inevitable. One collector will concentrate on the silver of the Graeco-Italian city states, whereas another will be attracted by, say, the Athenian series. Yet another will pass these by to seek out the Imperial bronze issues of the Greek mints of Asia Minor; and all will find a wealth of interest in their collections. It is not possible, within the limits of the present work, to give a bibliography of the Greek coinage, because the subject has attracted the attention of many writers who have produced an extensive literature; moreover, many of the best works are out of print. It is only right, however, that a few books should be recommended, and the present writer suggests that the following might be acquired in the order given. First, as a good introduction to the subject, might come *Coin Collecting* by J. G. Milne, C. H. V. Sutherland and J. D. A. Thompson (Oxford, 1950; price 15/–). This is particularly good on the Greek series—indeed it is an extremely useful ' all-round ' book—and the plates are of a very high standard. Next, one would suggest *Greek Coins* by Charles Seltman (2nd edition, London, 1955; new reprint available shortly) in the Handbooks of Archaeology series. It is probably the most readable of all the authoritative works on the subject and it has many fine plates of illustrations. Another book by Seltman is *Masterpieces of Greek Coinage* (Oxford, 1949; price 21/–) but it is more suitable for the advanced collector and art connoisseur than for the beginner. The book that is virtually indispensable to the serious collector is *Historia Numorum* (Oxford, 1911) recently reprinted, price £9 9s. This work, in which a high standard of scholarship and most judicious condensation are united, is a guide to the whole Greek coinage, and the wealth of information contained in its pages is little short of marvellous. Zander H. Klawans' *An Outline of Ancient Greek Coins* (U.S.A., 1959) is also available, price 30/–.

The standard work on Greek coins, the British Museum Catalogue comprising of 29 volumes, has recently been reprinted. Individual volumes are priced at £9 5s each including postage, and the entire set at £225 including postage. Details of the contents of each volume available on request. (See also p. 24). The following books, all out of print, but sometimes available at second-hand, are all worthy of acquisition:—Sir George Macdonald's *Coin Types, their Origin and Development* (Glasgow, 1905), which is largely devoted to the Greek series; Sir George Hill's *Historical Greek Coins* and *Coins of Ancient Sicily*, both useful studies of a limited section of material; and Percy Gardner's *History of Ancient Coinage*, 700-300 B.C. (Oxford, 1918). Finally, we must not forget J. G. Milne's *Greek and Roman Coins and the Study of History* (London, 1936) and the British Museum publication *A Guide to the Principal Coins of the Greeks* by Sir George Hill. For the fairly advanced collector who can afford it, the three volume *Catalogue of the McClean Collection of Greek Coins* by S. W. Grose (Cambridge, 1923; price £12 12s per volume) can be recommended as a most useful work of reference.

In conclusion, the present writer would offer the opinion that no coins can compare with the Greek for historical interest or beauty of workmanship, and he hopes that this Catalogue will, despite its admitted limitations and imperfections, be some help to those collectors and students who find themselves attracted to the study of Greek numismatics.

London.   GILBERT ASKEW.

December, 1950.
[*Revised* 1965].

THE ORIGINS OF GREEK COINAGE.

So accustomed is our modern world to the use of coined money, or its paper equivalent, that it is difficult to imagine a time when trade was not carried on through the medium of coinage; but such a time there was. In the prehistoric period any trading was done by barter, a system quite suitable for primitive communities, but as soon as the primitive stage was passed the process of bartering goods in exchange for others proved itself inconvenient and often unpractical. As Sir George Macdonald says, " However narrow the limits of a district, however small the population of a village, those mutual wants by which the necessity for exchange is conditioned, are bound to make themselves felt at different times and seasons; the odds are all against the tailor being down at heel at the exact moment when the shoemaker is out at elbow."[1] Thus even primitive people early recognised the necessity for some medium of exchange: the medium varied from place to place and from time to time, sometimes being in the form of cattle—as in South Africa within living memory—or sometimes in some more portable shape. The precious metals, gold and silver, must soon have been discovered to be most suitable as a basis for trade, being durable, portable, homogeneous and readily divisible. Bronze also fulfils these conditions, and, indeed, was used in North and Central Italy before those districts were forced by economic causes to adopt silver. Gold and silver, however, were prized for their beauty as well as for their other qualities, and therefore they soon became the measure of value. But at first they passed by weight in the same way as any other commodity, as references to them in the Old Testament will show: witness Abraham's purchase of the cave of Machpelah from Ephron the Hittite, when he " weighed to Ephron the silver, which he had named in the audience of the sons of Heth, four hundred shekels of silver, current money with the merchant." (*Genesis*, 23, 16). Note that the word " shekel," although later the name of a coin, was at this time a weight; our own word " pound " has similarly acquired the double meaning. Thus began the use of the precious metals as mediums of exchange, passing by weight and not by tale, and some of the most highly civilized peoples of the ancient world—the Egyptians, Babylonians and Assyrians—progressed no further.

The earliest coins are merely small pieces of electrum—a natural alloy of gold and silver—bearing a stamp which must have been intended to guarantee the purity of the metal. No question of any standard weight seems to have been contemplated at first, as the weights of the surviving specimens are irregular. Soon, however, it must have been discovered that the adoption of a standard weight-system would do away with the old and cumbrous method of weighing the ingots in the balances, and so we get the first true coins, agreeing with the definition that a coin " is a piece of some recognised precious metal bearing the stamp of an issuing authority to guarantee its weight and fineness." To whom the credit is due for this advance is uncertain, for even the ancient writers could not agree about it; but it must be to either the Lydians or the Greeks of Ionia that we have to allow it. Herodotus says " So far as we have any knowledge, they (the Lydians) were the first nation to introduce the use of gold and silver coin, and the first who sold goods by retail." (Book i, 94). Although it is too late now for us to attempt to assess the value of the different claims, it seems certain that the mainland of Asia Minor was the birth-

---

[1] In " The Evolution of Coinage." Ch. I.

place of coined money insofar as the western world is concerned. The possibility of a yet earlier system in the Far East is outside the scope of this essay.

Fig. 1.

About 700 B.C., therefore, either the Lydians or the Ionian Greeks produced the first coinage, electrum being the earliest medium. Figure 1 illustrates a piece of this early money, one of the chief rarities of the British Museum collection: its weight is 166.8 grains and the obverse shows merely a striated surface, the reverse bearing three rough punch-marks or " incuses."

Under what authority these earliest coins were issued cannot now be ascertained, but it has been suggested that merchants may have been responsible. It was not long, however, before the rulers of the coin-using states and cities recognised that here was something that ought not be left in the hands of individual traders, but that it should be under the control of the supreme authorities, who were in a better position to guarantee the weight and fineness of the issues, particularly when the money began to circulate, as it soon did, outside the place of mintage.

The use of electrum was soon discovered to be unsatisfactory, as the mixture of the two component metals was by no means constant; and thus we find that Croesus, who began to reign in Lydia in 561 B.C., soon abandoned the electrum coinage for a double system of gold and silver pieces, the weights of the various coins being

Fig. 2.

adjusted to each other for purposes of ready exchange. Figure 2 illustrates the type used in this coinage, the foreparts of a lion and a bull confronting each other.

Although the inscription on any coin seems to us to be indispensable, it was long before coins were other than anepigraphical; but there is one early piece

Fig. 3.

which bears a legend and is illustrated in Fig. 3. As will be seen, the obverse type is a stag, and above it is the legend, in archaic Greek characters, retrograde, ΦΑΝΟΣ ΕΜΙ ΣΗΜΑ, which has been translated " I am the badge of Phanes." Who this Phanes was is not known, but the coin was found at Halicarnassus, and a citizen of this place, named Phanes, is known to have been in the service of Cambyses, king of Persia, sometime before 525 B.C. It has been suggested that an ancestor of this Phanes may be responsible for this interesting and unique coin, the minting of which has been ascribed to Ephesus on account of the type, the stag being a symbol of the worship of the Ephesian Diana.

Before, however, the bimetallic system of Croesus had been introduced, knowledge of the invention of coined money had spread beyond the confines of Asia

Minor. About the middle of the seventh century B.C. the island of Aegina, then one of the most important trading stations in the Eastern Mediterranean, began to issue silver coins bearing the island's device of the turtle. Others of the Greek islands followed with coinage of their own, and soon Athens and Corinth had joined the ranks of the silver-issuing cities. Mints increased in Asia Minor, and arose in North Africa and the Greek colonies of Southern Italy. Although the western cities, including those of Sicily, issued their first coins many years after minting had begun in places farther east, the artistic development of coinage was brought by them to a level of beauty attained neither before nor since.

GREEK COIN TYPES.

To do justice to this subject a complete book would be necessary; and, indeed, books have been written on it, the best English works probably being Professor Percy Gardner's " Types of Greek Coins " (1883) and Sir George Macdonald's " Coin Types: their Origin and Development " (1905). The latter is not devoted solely to the Greek coinage, but inevitably this provides a large proportion of the examples discussed. The subject is complicated, of course, by the immense variety of such types. Any good catalogue of Greek coins has to devote many pages to the mere indexing of them.

Although the origin of many of the types is uncertain, it is fair to say that most of them, particularly the earlier ones, have some religious significance. The very earliest coins, of course, were without type of any kind, and when types came into use they appeared on the obverse of the coin, the reverse showing only the mark of the punch used to force the metal into the die. Amongst the earlier coins some examples may bear types which were heraldic in nature, but even these may derive from some religious source much anterior to the invention of coinage. There is still room for much research in this direction.

Let us now consider some concrete examples, beginning with the coinage of Athens. The earliest coins of the city bear types having no apparent relation to those of later pieces, such as a pomegranate, a wheel or a Gorgon-head: the reverse at this time bears only the incuse square. The types cited may be the particular marks or badges of the officials responsible for the issue of the coins, and therefore should probably be classified as " heraldic "; but when the Athenian coinage assumes a regular style, some time early in the sixth century B.C., the types used are certainly religious. The obverse type of the tetradrachm is the helmeted head of Pallas Athena, of rude style, with the " archaic " eye, i.e., depicted as if seen from the front. The fabric of the coins is globular, and the face of Athena seems, usually, to wear a sinister smile. The helmet is crested and almost free from decoration. About the beginning of the fifth century, however, the tetradrachm becomes a flatter and thinner coin, and although the head of Athena is still of archaic style it is somewhat more natural in appearance, except for the eye. The helmet is now decorated with olive leaves, an addition commemorating the victory of Marathon in 490 B.C. The reverse of both series depict the owl, sacred to Athena, a spray of olive (the tree being, traditionally, Athena's gift to mankind) and the letter *AΘE*. The later reverses bear a small crescent in the field, behind the owl. (See No. 984). This coinage continued until, or almost until, the fall of Athens in 404 B.C., after which the Athenian mint was closed, or almost inactive, for some years. When it re-opened, about 393 B.C., the tetradrachms it issued were similar in style to those of the previous period, except for the eye of Athena being correctly represented in profile. The workmanship is rough and careless, but the coins were struck in large numbers, the issue continuing to about 338 B.C., when the rise of the Macedonian power caused the coinage of Philip II and Alexander the Great to supersede the Athenian as the chief currency of the Greek world.

When, in about 220 B.C., the Athenian mint re-opened, the coins were of a much different style. A tetradrachm of this kind is illustrated here, and although

there are many points of difference from the earlier series, the types remain the same, Athena and her owl. The tetradrachms of this " new style " were struck until 86 B.C., when Sulla's capture of Athens once more closed the mint. No further silver coins were ever issued, and when, in the second century A.D., Athens was once more permitted to strike bronze coins for local use, the head of Athena is almost always the obverse type. The reverses are many and various, but most of them are religious or relating to exploits of Athenian heroes. An exception to this

is the reverse here depicted (about twice natural size) which shows a view of the Acropolis, with the Parthenon, the statue of Athena, and the Propylaea approached by stairs: below, in the rock, is the grotto of Pan; but even this type can be classi-fied as religious, as what is represented was the chief sanctuary of the Athenian people.

From these examples it will be seen that the Athenians placed their coinage under the protection of the goddess whom they beleived to be their particular friend and helper. It may be argued that the continuance of the Athena-types for so long was as much commercial as religious, for the Athenian " silver owls " were so well known throughout the Greek world that the types were suffered to remain com-paratively unchanged to ensure the continued acceptance of the coins in trade, it being well known, then as later, that people prefer the coins to which they are accustomed. But commercial reasons cannot have operated in regard to the local copper coinage of the Imperial period. The use of the Athena-types then is religious and traditional.

Some of the best examples of religious types are found in the coinage of Elis, which land was particularly sacred to Zeus. Some of the pieces of finest style depict the head of the god on the obverse, with a thunderbolt on the reverse, others show the head of Hera on the obverse and also have the thunderbolt reverse. A later series associates a reverse type of the eagle with the head of Zeus on the obverse.

We may now consider some of the types best classified as " heraldic." These are such devices as the griffin of Abdera, the sphinx of Chios, the ear of barley of Metapontum, and the selinon leaf of Selinus. The well-known bee on the coins of Ephesus is probably an example of a religious type becoming heraldic, as although it was first used as a symbol of Artemis—the bee being sacred to that goddess—it seems to be treated later as the heraldic badge of the city. The case of Sicyon is peculiar. Here the dove, usually depicted flying, is used as obverse or reverse type intermittently throughout the whole series; but Xenophon* tells us that in the Corinthian war (394-387 B.C.) the Sicyonian soldiers were distinguished by a large Σ upon their shields; and this same Σ forms the reverse type of the earliest silver drachms of the city, drachms which must have been in use at the period of which Xenophon writes.

A type which is heraldic but of commercial origin is the silphium plant of Cyrene. Upon the production and export of this famous herb the prosperity of the city was founded, an excellent reason for its being chosen as the city's badge.

The mint of Aegina, from which the earliest coins of Greece proper were issued, used for its chief type the sea-turtle, for all denominations, until 431 B.C. In this year the inhabitants of the island were expelled by the Athenians, who maintained a garrison there until 404 B.C., when Lysander of Sparta restored the remnant of the Aeginetans to their former home. The mint was soon reopened, and the obverse type of the silver coins issued was similar to that previously used, but was now clearly a land-tortoise and not a turtle. The reason for the change is not clear: the twenty-seven years of exile might be the cause, or perhaps the type had always been a tortoise and its somewhat crude representation on the early coins has been mistaken for a turtle. It is certain that the latest issues of the mint before its closing in 431 B.C. bear a type very closely resembling that used when it reopened after 404. Coins of the early and late styles are illustrated at Nos. 1050 and 1065.

The beautiful tetradrachms of Amphipolis, current between 424 and 358 B.C., are good examples of a combination of religious and heraldic types. The obverse type of the facing head of Apollo is one of the finest examples of Greek celature, and the reverse shows the race-torch which was the badge of the city. Another fine coin, which bears religious types on both faces, is the tetradrachm of Pyrrhus, King of Epirus (295-272 B.C.); here we see the head of Zeus Dodonaos on the obverse and Dione enthroned on the reverse.

The best comment on religious types is provided by Barclay Head (in *Historia Numorum*, 1st Edn., p. lvii), who says " All through the history of free and inde-

*Hellenics, book iv, ch. 4, 10.

pendent Greece, and even until the death of Alexander the Great, the main object of the coin-type was to place before the people an ideal representation of the divinity most honoured in the district in which the coin was intended to circulate. No tyrant, however despotic, no general, however splendid his achievements by land or sea, no demagogue, however inflated his vanity, ever sought to perpetuate his features on the current coin. Hence the mythological interest of the coin-types is paramount, from the first introduction of the art of coining down to the age of the successors of Alexander."

The various series of portrait coins, therefore, begin after 323 B.C., and it will be proper to conclude this chapter by giving a few examples. The first is a didrachm of Philip V of Macedon (220-179 B.C.) with obverse type of the king's head diademed,

and the club of Herakles on the reverse. Another king of Macedon, Perseus (178-168 B.C.) has left us his portrait on both tetradrachms, one of which is illus-

trated here, and didrachms. These fine and well-struck coins are good examples of the moneyer's art of the second century B.C. It will be noticed that the religious types are now relegated to an inferior place, the reverse, and the image of the king depicted on the obverse without any name or title to break the artistic effect.

The coins of the kings of Pergamum are also portrait pieces, but most of them depict, not the head of the reigning monarch, but that of Philetaerus, who was trea-

surer of Lysimachus King of Thrace, and who made himself independent in 283 B.C., although probably recognising Seleucus I of Syria (312-280 B.C.) as his suzerain. Thus it is the founder of the dynasty who affords the chief type of the series, and the same practice operated in Egypt, where the most frequent obverse type of the tetradrachm is the head of Ptolemy I (323-284 B.C.) who ruled Egypt independently

from 311 and styled himself king after 305, placing his own portrait on his coins. The example illustrated is a coin of Ptolemy VIII (170-117 B.C.) but the head is intended to represent Ptolemy I.

We close these notes with an illustration, somewhat larger than natural size, of

the famous tetradrachm of Antony and Cleopatra. The place of mintage of this rare coin is not certain, but is has been attributed to Antioch with reasonable likelihood.

DEITIES, PERSONIFICATIONS, &c.

A list of some of the principal deities and personifications
portrayed on Greek coin types.

The names in parenthesis are the equivalent Roman deities.

Agathodaimon. The " Good God," or good genius, was a divinity in honour of whom the Greeks drank a cup of unmixed wine at the end of each repast. He was worshipped in Egypt and had a special name in each town. On the coins of Alexandria he is represented as an erect serpent wearing the skhent or crown of Pharaoh, generally with a caduceus.

Ammon. Originally a Libyan divinity, probably protecting and leading the flocks, Ammon was later introduced into Egypt and Greece, where he was identified with Zeus. The head of Zeus Ammon is represented on Egyptian coins as a bearded man, diademed and with a ram's horn at the temple (Ammon's horn). The ram was sacred to him and on a coin of Alexandria he is shown driving a biga of rams.

Aphrodite (Venus). One of the twelve great Olympian divinities, Aphrodite was goddess of love and beauty. She was believed to have been created from the foam of the sea, hence she sometimes appears on coins with a sea-horse or dolphin. Others of her attributes are the myrtle, rose, apple, poppy; and doves, swans and sparrows were sacred to her. She is represented on coins nude, semi-nude or dressed and crowned, often accompanied by Eros, her child attendant. The apple she sometimes holds in her hand is the prize awarded her by Paris in the contest with Hera and Athena on Mount Ida.

Apollo. He was the sun-god, one of the great gods of the Greeks, and was the son of Zeus and Leto; he was also the god of prophecy, of song, music and the arts, and protector of flocks and herds. He punished and destroyed the wicked and overbearing, but afforded help to men in distress by warding off evil. He exercised his power of prophecy through various oracles, of which that at Delphi was the most important. The head of Apollo and his attribute the lyre are common types on early Greek coinage. On Greek coins of Imperial times he appears in many scenes of mythology, and he has various titles, such as *Aktios*, *Pythios* and *Embasios*.

Ares (Mars). God of war and another of the great Olympian deities, Ares was the son of Zeus and Hera. He loved war for its own sake and often changed sides in assisting one or the other combatant parties, but he could be worsted in battle and even be wounded by mortals. His helmeted head, beardless or bearded, appears on many coins, and his full-length figure is sometimes depicted helmeted but naked, or wearing a cuirass, and shield, spear or trophy. He is sometimes shown in the company of Aphrodite, whose lover he was.

Artemis (Diana). One of the great divinities and sister of Apollo, Artemis was the deity of the chase, goddess of the Moon, and protectress of the young. In Ionia, and in particular as goddess of the famous temple of Ephesus, she took over the fructifying and all-nourishing powers of nature from an older Asiatic divinity whom the Greeks, who settled in that area, renamed Artemis. The coin types representing Artemis are very varied for she is represented as a huntress with bow and arrow, running with a hound or killing a stag. As Artemis Tauropolos she is portrayed riding a bull holding a veil over her head. Yet another type is the cultus-statue of the Ephesian Artemis, standing facing, which is used on the coinage of forty different cities in Imperial times. Artemis is also shown carrying one or two torches.

Asklepios (Aesculapius). God of medicine and healing, he is shewn as a man of mature years, leaning on a staff about which a serpent is entwined. Sometimes the boy Telesphorus, the personification of the genius of recovery, stands by his side. Serpents, symbols of prudence and renovation, were sacred to Asklepios for they were believed to have the power of guarding wells and discovering healing herbs.

Atargatis. The Aramaic Atar-Ata (" divine Ata ") or Derketo, a Syrian fertility goddess, was considered by the Greeks to be Aphrodite, but was generally known by them simply as *Thea Syria* (the " Syrian Goddess "). On coins of Hieropolis she is represented with a turreted crown, like Kybele, and a tympanon, enthroned or riding a lion.

Athena (Minerva). Surnamed Pallas, and sometimes known by this name alone, Athena was goddess of wisdom, patroness of agriculture, industry and the arts. She guided men through the dangers of war, where victory was gained by prudence, courage and perseverance. Her full-length image, or bust or head only, are amongst the commonest of Greek coin types. She is usually wearing the Spartan sleeveless chiton, peplos, and helmet, and holds spear and shield. She is sometimes shown hurling a thunderbolt, covering her left arm with an aegis, or holding Nike. Sacred to her were the owl, serpent, cock and olive, and these attributes often appear with her on coins. She had many additional titles, such as Areia (at Pergamum), Ilias (at Ilium), Argeia (at Alexandria), Itonia (in Thessaly), etc.

Baal. A Semitic god, lord (deity) of a locality, Baal was usually identified by the Greeks with Zeus.

Bakchos. *See* Dionysos.

Demeter (Ceres). Goddess of fertility, agriculture and marriage, Demeter was sister to Zeus. When her daughter Persephone was carried off to the underworld by Hades, Demeter, by her mourning, withheld fertility from the earth until, through the mediation of Zeus, it was arranged that Persephone should spend half the year (winter) with Hades and the other half with her mother. The myth of Demeter and her daughter embodies the idea that the productive powers of nature are rested and concealed during the winter season. The head of Demeter on coins is wreathed with corn or veiled. She sometimes carries a sceptre or ears of corn, or searches for her daughter with a torch. She is also represented holding two torches and standing in a chariot drawn by two winged and crested serpents.

Derketo. *See* Atargatis.

Dione. The consort of Zeus at Dodona, Dione was probably a sky-goddess. She appears on coins of Epirus together with Zeus, with a laureate stephanos and veil, or alone, laureate and veiled.

Dionysos (Liber). Sometimes known as Bakchos (Bacchus), Dionysos was god of vegetation and the fruits of the trees, particularly the vine. Represented on coins as a youth holding a bunch of grapes, or with his head crowned with ivy or vine leaves, or riding or accompanied by a panther. Vine branches, kantharos and thyrsos are symbols of Dionysos.

Dikaiosyne (Aequitas). The personification of equity and fair dealing, Dikaiosyne is represented as a woman holding scales in one hand and a sceptre, later a cornucopiae, in the other.

Dioskouroi (Dioscuri). Kastor (Castor) and Polydeukes (Pollux), sons of Zeus and Leda and brothers of Helen of Troy, were protectors of travellers, particularly sailors, and helpers of those in distress. They received divine honours at Sparta and their worship spread from the Peloponnesus over the whole of Greece, Sicily and Italy. On coins the two brothers are represented on horseback or standing by their horses, carrying lances and wearing egg-shaped helmets surmounted by stars. They are sometimes confused with the Kabeiroi.

Eirene (Pax). The personification of peace, Eirene is represented as a woman holding an olive-branch and caduceus, or ears of corn instead of the olive branch. Sometimes she has on her arm the infant Ploutos, god of wealth.

Eleutheria (Libertas). Personifying freedom and liberty, Eleutheria is represented as a woman seated or standing, holding a cap and sceptre, or leaning on a column and holding a wreath and sceptre (on the Alexandrian coins of the emperors Galba and Otho).

Elpis (Spes). Personifying hope, Spes usually holds a flower, and is depicted walking and slightly raising the skirt of her dress.

Eros (Cupid). The god of love, and later connected with Aphrodite, Eros is represented as a youth or boy, naked, winged, and holding a bow and arrows or a torch. Sometimes he is depicted riding on a dolphin (coins of Carteia) or driving the chariot of Hades who is carrying off Persephone. Frequently there are two Erotes, as on the coin of Aphrodisias where they are seated on the ground playing with astragali.

Eusebeia (Pietas). The personification of religious piety and civic and family duty, Eusebeia is represented either as a female figure holding a patera and sceptre or else holding an incense box in one hand and sprinkling incense on an altar with the other.

Euthenia (Abundantia). Personifying plenty, Euthenia holds ears of corn and a cornucopiae, sometimes emptying the latter. She appears on coins of Adramyteum (Mysia) and Alexandria (Egypt). In Egypt Euthenia was regarded as the consort of Nilus and invested with the attributes of the Egyptian goddess Isis, the uraeus, the Isiac knot, sistrum, etc. She is usually represented seated on a base, leaning on the androsphinx.

Gorgo or **Medusa.** A monster with a round, ugly face, snakes instead of hair, teeth of a boar and huge wings, Gorgo was said to have eyes that could transform people into stone. Killed by the hero Perseus, she gave birth to Pegasos and Chrysaor in the moment of her death. Her head is shown as a main type on some coins and also as an adornment of shields.

Hades or **Plouton.** A brother of Zeus, Hades obtained the underworld when the world was divided between the three brothers, ruling over the shades of the departed. His wife was Persephone, daughter of Demeter. He was the owner and giver of the metals in the earth, hence his name Plouton. The Greeks usually referred to him by that name rather than pronounce the dreaded name Hades which later became the name of his kingdom. On some Imperial coins of Phrygia Hades is depicted clasping the struggling Persephone round the waist, carrying her off to the underworld in a quadriga of galloping horses.

Harpocrates. The name is derived from *Har-pa-khruti* or "Horus the infant," originally a god of Lower Egypt. Horus, a son of Isis born after the murder of Osiris, succeeded after many trials in punishing the murderer, Set. He is represented on coins as a baby suckled by his mother, as a chubby infant with finger in mouth, or as a youth, usually with finger in mouth, holding a club surmounted by a hawk. He is also shown bearded, with Ammon's horn, holding sceptre and club.

Hekate. An ancient goddess who ruled over heaven, earth and sea, Hekate is often identified with Demeter, Persephone, Artemis and Kybele. Later she was recognised as an infernal deity, ruling over the souls of the departed, haunting at night tombs, cross-roads and places where murders had been committed. On coins she is shown in a long chiton, veiled and holding one or two torches. Sometimes she is on horseback or in a car drawn by lions. In another form, Hekate Triformis, she is depicted with three identical bodies with three heads, a polos on each, and the six hands holding torches, whips, wheels and serpents.

Helios (Sol). The sun-god, who crosses the sky from east to west in his chariot each day, sees and hears everything. He was later identified with Apollo. He is usually depicted nude or with chlamys, with radiate head and holding a globe, whip or torch. On some Imperial bronzes he rides in a quadriga of horses.

Hephaistos (Vulcanus). The son of Zeus and Hera, Hephaistos was god of fire and the protector of smiths and metal-workers. As he was a skilful smith himself he is represented on coins with hammer and tongs and he usually wears a conical hat or pilos. On some Imperial coins he is depicted seated on a rock or omphalos forging the shield of Achilles as described by Homer.

Hera (Juno). The sister and consort of Zeus, and the queen of heaven, Hera was the great goddess of nature, worshipped from the earliest times. She was considered to be the mother of many other gods and goddesses, and is usually represented as a majestic woman of mature age, with her hair adorned with a crown or diadem, often with a veil hanging down her back. One of her chief attributes was the peacock, her favourite bird.

Herakles (Hercules). The son of Zeus and Alkmene, Herakles was the most famous of all the heroes of antiquity; his strength, courage and wonderful exploits being the subject of numerous stories and poems all over the ancient world. His head, bust or full-length figure are amongst the most common of Greek coin types. He is often represented as a young beardless man with his head covered by the skin of the Nemean lion whom he strangled with his hands. He is also shown as a bearded, bull-necked man, usually naked, holding his club, lion's skin or bow. A club, bow, and also a bow-case, are also types referring to Herakles. His famous labours and heroic exploits are subjects of reverse types in various Greek cities during Imperial times.

Hermanubis. Derived from the Egyptian *Har-m-Anup* (Horus and Anubis), for which the Greeks substituted another compound, Hermes and Anubis, he was the jackal-headed god, guardian of other gods and god of embalming. Hermanubis is shown in the guise of a youth with modius on head accompanied by a jackal and holding a palm and cornucopiae (sometimes combined as one).

Hermes (Mercury). A son of Zeus and Maia, Hermes was the messenger of the gods, hence his herald's staff, the ribbons of which were later changed into the serpents of the caduceus. Other attributes of Hermes are the broad-brimmed travelling hat (*petasos*) adorned with wings, the golden sandals, the winged ankles, and a purse, for Hermes was patron not only of merchants but also of thieves, as well as artists, orators and travellers. He was regarded as the inventor of the lyre and plectrum, and of the syrinx. The palm-tree and tortoise were sacred to Hermes, so too were the number 4 and several kinds of fish. The caduceus adorned with a pair of wings to indicate the speed of the messenger is occasionally used as a coin type.

Hestia (Vesta). Goddess of the hearth and one of the twelve great deities, Hestia was also patroness of domestic life and giver of all domestic happiness. The public hearth of Hestia was the sacred asylum for suppliants in every city, as well as the proper place for the reception of the guests of state and foreign ambassadors. Hestia appears veiled and holding a sceptre on the coins of Maeonia (Lydia).

Homonoia (Concordia). Personifying concord and harmony, Homonoia is represented holding a patera and cornucopiae or sceptre. Sometimes used on alliance-coins of two cities.

Horus. A god of Lower Egypt and a son of Osiris and Isis. *See* Harpokrates and Hermanubis.

Hygieia (Salus). Goddess of health, and a daughter or wife of Asklepios, Hygieia is usually represented standing with her father, or alone, holding a serpent in her arms which she is feeding from a phial.

Isis. The wife of Osiris and mother of Horus, Isis was a national deity in Egypt, and during Hellenistic times became a leading goddess in the Mediterranean lands, her cult eventually extending throughout the whole Roman Empire. She is portrayed on coins in a long garment with a characteristic knot of drapery on the breast (the *nodus Isiacus*) and with the ancient Egyptian head-dress which is one of her symbols. The sistrum, a musical instrument, is another attribute. Isis Pharia, taking her name from the lighthouse (*Pharos*) of Alexandria, is represented on board ship holding a sail with both hands, sometimes also with the Pharos before her.

Kabeiroi. These non-Hellenic, probably Phrygian deities — from four to eight in number — promoted fertility and protected sailors. On coins they are represented with hammer and snake (coins of the Balearic Islands) or with rhyton (drinking horn ending in animal's head). On a coin of Caracalla of Berytus all eight of them are shown seated in a circle. Often confused with the Dioskuroi.

Kore. *See* Persephone.

Kybele. The great mother-goddess of Asia Minor, Kybele was worshipped with her youthful lover Attis, god of vegetation. She was the goddess of fertility and wild nature, and was represented on coins enthroned, with a polos or turreted crown on her head, holding a phial and resting her elbow on a tympanon, and with lions on both sides of her throne. Another type is the biga drawn by two lions, in which Kybele sits resting elbow on a tympanon. Even when her statue is shown within a temple it stands between two lions.

Medusa. *See* Gorgo.

Melqarth or **Melkart.** "Lord" of Tyre (Baal-Tsur), worshipped in Phoenicia, seems to have been originally a marine deity, as he is represented riding a sea-horse. Later he was identified with Herakles.

Mên. A Phrygian lunar divinity, Mên is represented on foot or horseback, wearing a Phrygian cap, holding a pine-cone and sceptre and with a crescent behind his shoulder to stress his lunar character. He was a healing god, a protector of tombs and a giver of oracles.

Nemesis. A fatal divinity, keeping the equilibrium in human lives, Nemesis measured out happiness and unhappiness. She was also the personification of the moral reverence for law, and hence of conscience. She is depicted with a bridle or branch of an ash tree and a wheel with a sword or scourge. The inhabitants of Smyrna worshipped two Nemeses, both of whom were daughters of Night.

Nike (Victoria). Greek goddess of victory, Nike was depicted as a woman in a long chiton, sometimes wingless (as on the coins of Terina) but more usually winged, holding wreath and palm and crowning the horses of a victorious charioteer or decorating a trophy.

Pan (Faunus). God of shepherds and flocks, Pan had horns, beard, puck nose, tail, goat's feet, was covered with hair and dwelt in grottoes. He is said to have had a terrific voice that struck terror into those who heard it. He was fond of music and is regarded, besides Hermes, as inventor of the syrinx or shepherd's pipes with which he is sometimes represented on coins (of Arcadia).

Persephone or **Kore.** Daughter of Demeter and wife of Hades (Plouton), Persephone is associated with the cult of her mother. She is usually represented with a wreath of corn on her head. *See* Demeter and Hades.

Phtha or **Ptah.** An old Egyptian god of artisans, Ptah was worshipped at Memphis and was identified with Hephaistos. He is shown holding a sceptre and tongs, clad in chiton and himation, or as a mummy, holding a sceptre. In both cases he wears a close-fitting Egyptian cap surmounted by a disk.

Plouton. *See* Hades.

Ploutos. The personification of wealth, Ploutos is represented as a child emerging from a cornucopiae. He is sometimes associated with Eirene.

Poseidon (Neptune). A brother of Zeus, Poseidon was god of earthquakes and ruler of the sea. He is usually represented holding a dolphin and a trident, or the prow ornament of a galley, and standing with one foot on a rock. A trident ornamented or entwined with dolphins appears on coins as the symbol of Poseidon

Sarapis. The name is derived from the Egyptian *Hesar-Hapi*, the deified sacred bull Apis. The cult of Sarapis arose at Memphis under the Ptolemies and the deity combined the attributes of many Hellenic gods with some characteristics of Osiris. He was represented bearded, standing or seated, with a modius on his head and a sceptre in his hand. When seated he is often accompanied by the three-headed dog Cerberos, borrowed from Hades. Sarapis was a healer of the sick, worker of miracles, superior to fate, ruler of the visible world and underworld, and god of the sun.

Thea Syria. *See* Atargatis.

Tyche (Fortuna). Personifying fortune, Tyche is represented on coins holding a rudder, sometimes with a globe and cornucopiae. She may also be shown with a wheel or holding an olive-branch or a patera. As patroness of various cities, e.g., Antioch, she wears a turreted crown and a veil.

Zeus (Jupiter). The greatest of the Olympian gods, Zeus was considered to be the father of both gods and men. He was a son of Kronos and Rhea and brother of Poseidon, Hades, Hestia, Demeter, and Hera; and he was also married to his sister Hera. He was worshipped throughout the Greek world, and in the later Hellenic age was frequently identified with local supreme gods like Ammon, Sarapis, etc. He had an immense number of epithets and surnames which were derived partly from the localities where he was worshipped and partly from his functions and powers. The eagle and oak-tree were sacred to him. His usual attributes are the sceptre, eagle, thunderbolt, and also a small figure of Nike which he holds in his hand. The Olympian Zeus sometimes wears a wreath of olive and the Dodonaean Zeus a wreath of oak leaves. He is usually represented bearded, nude or semi-nude, hurling a thunderbolt or sitting on a throne.

WEIGHT STANDARDS AND DENOMINATIONS.

We have now to consider the various weight-standards in use in the Greek world, and to find their origin it is necessary to search far back beyond the beginning of coinage. The most valuable evidence for the determination of these standards is a series of weights found by Layard in his excavations at the site of ancient Nineveh, and later added to the British Museum collections. These weights are of two shapes, some being of stone carved into the form of a duck, and others of bronze in the likeness of a lion: they are generally inscribed with two legends, one in cuneiform characters and the other in Aramaic. The purport of the legends is in every case to inform the user when the weight was made, and how many " manahs " it equals. By carefully weighing these ancient pieces and taking the appropriate averages with due allowance for damaged examples, it was discovered that the makers of these weights had two kinds of " manah," a heavy one of 15,600 grains and a light one of 7,800. Why two weights called " manah," one exactly twice the other, were in use, it is now impossible to tell, and although many theories have been put forward none seems entirely to meet every objection. Our own troy and avoirdupois systems might prove equally difficult to archaeologists of the distant future who had no access to literary records.

Having arrived at the weight of each type of " manah," a table can be drawn up, but first the ratio of value of the two precious metals must be taken into account, which was at the time of the early coinages about 1 part of gold to $13^3/_{10}$ parts of silver. As the weights described above may be taken to be those used for the weighing of gold, we must construct another system for the weighing of silver, as the two metals were, in early times, rarely weighed by the same standard. Let us take, to begin with, the heavy *mina* (to adopt the Greek name) of 15,600 grains, which was divided into 60 shekels of 260 grs. Multiplying this weight of the gold shekel by $13^3/_{10}$ to find the equivalent amount of silver, we arrive at 3,458 grains, and this is readily divisible into 15 shekels of about 230 grains. From this final figure the *Phoenician* or *Graeco-Asiatic* silver standard is assumed to have been derived, although by the time of the invention of coinage the weight of the shekel had declined. The earliest Greek staters of Phoenician weight seldom exceed 220 grs.

Now to turn to the light *mina* of 7,800 grains, divisible into 60 shekels of 130 grs. By a multiplication similar to that given above one arrives at a figure of 1729 grs. for the silver standard, producing 10 shekels of about 173 grs. each, from which the *Babylonian, Lydian and Persian* silver standard has been assumed to spring. The figures mentioned are, of course, only approximately correct.

What has been set down above is largely an abridgement of the appropriate sections of the Introduction to Barclay Head's " Historia Numorum," to which the student may be referred for more detailed study: there will be found much valuable information on the transmission of the standards to other parts of the Greek world, and on the variants occuring in different states and cities. The following table, adapted from that given in the same author's " Guide to the Principal Gold and Silver Coins of the Ancients," will be found useful, as it sets out the approximate maximum weights for the normal silver coins of each standard. Note that the stater or didrachm is generally divided into two drachms, each of which equals six obols; but a stater is not always a piece of two drachms, as for instance the coins of Corinth and her colonies which are pieces of three drachms of about 45 grains each. The Phoenician coin of 224 grains, referred to in this table as a tetradrachm, is sometimes called a didrachm, the reason being that the term *stater* was given different meanings in different places. Sometimes *stater* means " tetradrachm," sometimes " didrachm," and at Cyrene, as Head points out, even " drachm."

In the table the figures represent weights in grains.

	ATTIC	ÆGINETIC	PHOENICIAN	RHODIAN	BABYLONIC	PERSIC
1 grain = ·0648 grammes 1 gramme = 15·43 grains						
Dekadrachm	675	—	560	—	—	—
Tetradrachm	270	—	224	240	—	354
Didrachm	135	194	112	120	169	177
Drachm	67.5	97	56	60	84	88
Tetrobol	45	—	37	40	56	59
Triobol or Hemi-drachm.	33.75	48	28	30	42	44
Diobol	22.5	32	18	20	28	29
Trihemiobol	16.9	24	14	15	21	22
Obol	11.25	16	9	10	14	14

The dekadrachm is a rare denomination, the best known examples being, probably, those of Syracuse, one of which is illustrated at No. 427; a similar piece, of Carthage, is shown above. This is datable to 241-218 B.C., and belongs to a series of coins struck on a standard very slightly heavier than the Phœnician mentioned above.

In addition to the denominations set out in the table, there are, of course, still smaller pieces in some of the series, the hemiobol being the commonest. At Athens there were five divisions of the obol, as follows, the figures representing weights in grains:—

Tritemorion	$\frac{3}{4}$ obol	8.45
Hemiobol	$\frac{1}{2}$,,	5.62
Trihemitartemorion	$\frac{3}{8}$,,	4.2
Tetartemorion	$\frac{1}{4}$,,	2.8
Hemitartemorion	$\frac{1}{8}$,,	1.4

So tiny are these last four denominations that it is wonderful that any should have survived; and yet specimens exist which are quite clearly recognisable by their types.

It might be well to mention here a few of the **gold** coins on the various Greek series, with their approximate weights, for the guidance of collectors:—

Syracuse, 100-*litrae* of 403-345 B.C. .. .., 90 grs.
,, 50-*litrae* of the same period .. .. .. ,. 45 grs.
(The *litra* was a Sicilian silver coin which was in weight $\frac{1}{10}$ of the Attic didrachm or Corinthian stater, being therefore about 13.5 grs.).

Syracuse, Æ *drachm* of 317-310 B.C. .. .. 66 grs.
„ Æ *tetrobol* of the same period .. .. .. 44 grs.
Macedon: Philip II (359-336 B.C.) *stater* .. .. 133 grs.
„ Alexander the Great (336-323 B.C.), *distater* .. 266 grs.
„ *stater* of the same .. .. 133 grs.
Athens: *stater* of 430-350 B.C. .. .. 133 grs.
„ *drachm* of the same period .. .. 66 grs.
(There are three smaller denominations in gold, of 33, 22 and 11 grs. respectively).
Lydia: *stater* of 568-554 B.C. (on the Babylonic standard) .. 168 grs.
„ Similar coins on the Euboic (a lighter variant of the Attic) standard .. .. 126 grs.
Persia: *daric*, before 331 B.C. .. .. 130 grs.
„ *double daric*, after 331 B.C... .. .. 260 grs.
Egypt: Ptolemy II (285-247 B.C.) *octadrachm* .. .. .. 430 grs.
„ Æ *tetradrachm* of the same .. .. 215 grs.
Cyrene: *stater* of 431-321 B.C. .. .. 135 grs.
„ $^{1}/_{10}$ *stater* of the same period .. .. 13.5 grs.
Also some of the better-known **electrum** pieces:—
Syracuse, 100-*litrae* of 345-317 B.C. .. .. .. 112.5 grs.
„ 50-*litrae* of the same period .. .. .. 56.26 grs.
Cyzicus, *stater* of 500-480 B.C. .. .. 250 grs.
„ *sixth* or *hecte* of the same period .. .. .. 40 grs.
Lampsacus, *stater* of 6th cent. B.C. .. .. 216 grs.
„ *stater* of *c.* 500 B.C. .. .. 232 grs.
(This increase in weight suggests a change of standard, probably from the Phoenician to the Persic).
Lampsacus, *stater* of 450-412 B.C... .. .. 237 grs.
Carthage, *didrachm* of 340-242 B.C. .. .. 118 grs.
„ *drachm* of the same period .. .. 58 grs.
„ *drachm* of 218-146 B.C. .. .. 46 grs.
(The electrum coins of this last period are noticeably light in weight and poor in style).

The bronze coinage of the Greeks begins comparatively late, towards the end of the fifth century B.C., or in the early part of the fourth. It may be that some of the early Sicilian pieces were an attempt to give full value, i.e., a bronze litra should contain a silver litra's worth of the metal, but it is clear that before long bronze had sunk to token money for small change purposes. Egypt may be an exception, as the early Ptolemaic bronze coins are so large that they seem to indicate some intention on the part of the mint to keep face and intrinsic values level; but the later coins are reduced in size and must be tokens.

DATING.

We can now turn to the question of dating. Unlike the coins of our own time, comparatively few Greek coins bear a date of any kind, and were it not for literary evidences we should find it very difficult to arrange many of the different series in correct sequence. Chronological classification by style, of course, is a good general basis, because coins, of all examples of Greek art, are more amenable to stylistic arrangement, there being in every period numbers of coins whose dates can be determined with reasonable exactitude, and around which the remainder may be grouped. The seven divisions of the classification are as follows:—

I	700-480 B.C.	Period of Archaic Art.
II	480-415 B.C.	Period of Transitional Art.
III	415-336 B.C.	Period of Finest Art.
IV	336-280 B.C.	Period of Later Fine Art.
V	280-146 B.C.	Period of Decline of Art.
VI	146-27 B.C.	Period of Continued Decline in Art.
VII	27 B.C.-296 A.D.	Imperial Period.

But what we have to consider here is not a broad chronological arrangement of this kind, but whatever system or systems of dating may be exhibited by individual coins. The most usual practice in the ancient world was to date the coins of a state or city in any given year by inscribing them with the name of the magistrate or other official responsible for the mint. We refer to such dignitaries as " eponymous " when the year in which such a magistrate held office was afterwards known by his name. Readers will remember that under the Roman Republic a year was recorded as that in which a certain pair of senators were consuls. The best example of a coinage dated by magistrate's names is probably the Athenian " new style " after 186 B.C., in which each coin bears two or three personal names as well as a symbol which is taken to be the heraldic badge of the senior official.

Dating by numerals occurs on certain of the later series of Greek coins, but before dealing with this it may be well to give a table of the numerals employed:—

1	A	9	Θ	80	Π
2	B	10	I	90	Ϙ
3	Γ	20	K	100	P
4	Δ	30	Λ	200	Σ
5	С	40	M	300	T
6	S	50	N	400	Y
7	Z	60	Ξ	500	Φ
8	H	70	O	600	X

Before, however, any date expressed by these numerals can be translated into terms of " year B.C." or " year A.D.," we have to know the era in use. The ancient world had not, as we have, a single fixed point from which to reckon time forwards or backwards; but so accustomed are we to our system of dating everything so many years before the birth of Our Lord, or so many years after, that it is easy for us to forget that the Greeks made use of a number of such fixed reckoning points, each the date of some important event in the district concerned. Certain eras were purely local and date from some outstanding happening in the history of the city on whose coins they appear, but some were well-known and widely employed, such as the following:—

The Seleucid Era. Reckoned from October 1st, 312 B.C., after the victory of Seleucus and Ptolemy over Demetrius at Gaza.

The Pompeian Era. After his defeat of Tigranes in 64 B.C., Pompey the Great entered Syria, and in the winter of 64-63 fixed his headquarters at Damascus, where he stayed some months re-organising Syria as a Roman province. Amongst the cities using the Pompeian era are Antiochia ad Hippum in the Decapolis, and Dora in Phoenicia.

The Caesarian Era. This era dates from the victory of Julius Caesar over Pompey at Pharsalia, 9th August, 48 B.C.; but some of the cities of Asia Minor reckoned it as beginning earlier or later. Antiochia ad Orontem counted it from 49 B.C., as mentioned below.

The Actian Era. This era begins with the victory of Augustus over Antony at Actium in 31 B.C.

As an example of the use of these various eras, let us take the case of Antiochia ad Orontem, at one time the capital of the Seleucid empire, and for long the chief city of Asia Minor. Such of its coinage which bears any date up to 40 B.C. is dated by the Seleucid era or by the Caesarian era which began in 49. For a few years the two systems seem to run concurrently, but after 40 B.C. the Caesarian era is in sole use until the coinage of Augustus, which is dated by the Actian era. Under Tiberius, however, dating by the Caesarian era is resumed, and under Caligula we have also the regnal year of the emperor expressed in similar numerals. Subsequent issues, where dated, seem to follow the Caesarian system or to indicate the regnal year of the emperor, sometimes by mentioning the Greek equivalent of the year of tribunician power.

Mention in the previous paragraph of the emperor's regnal year being expressed on his coins brings us to the system in use at Alexandria. Here, except for the coinage of Augustus which appears to be dated according to a system inherited from the Ptolemies or to an Alexandrian era beginning in 30 B.C., every coin bore as a date the regnal year of the emperor as reckoned at Alexandria. The Alexandrian year began on 29th August (except in any year following a leap year, in which case the commencing day was 30th August) so that an emperor who began to reign in Rome in April and died the following January would have actually less than one year of power but would be credited with two regnal years at Alexandria. His coins struck before August 29th or 30th would be marked A, and those after that date marked B, the numeral preceded by the sign L.

This L is not the letter L, but an ancient Egyptian sign used in papyrus inscriptions to show that the characters which follow it are numerals. Sometimes the word ΕΤΟΥC is used instead of an L, and a further variation is provided by the numeral being, at times, written in full instead of being indicated by a sign. Thus the third regnal year of an emperor may be expressed in four different ways, viz., LΓ, ΕΤΟΥCΓ, L ΤΡΙΤΟΥ or ΕΤΟΥC ΤΡΙΤΟΥ.

BOOKS OF REFERENCE.

Bab.=BABELON, Ernest.   Traité des Monnaies Grecques et Romaines.   Paris, 1902-1932.

Bab.=BABELON, Ernest.   Les Rois de Syrie, d'Arménie et de Commagène.   Paris, 1890.

Bab.=BABELON, Ernest.   Les Perses Achéménides, les Satrapes et les Dynastes tributaires de leur Empire, Cypre et Phénicie.   Paris, 1893.

Berlin=Königliche Museen zu Berlin.   Beschreibung der Antiken Münzen.   Vol. I.   Berlin, 1888.

Blanchet=BLANCHET, A. and DIEUDONNÉ, A.   Manuel de Numismatique Française.   Vol. I.   Monnaies frappées en Gaule depuis les origines jusqu'à Hugues Capet.   Paris, 1912.

Boehringer=BOEHRINGER, Erich.   Die Münzen von Syrakus.   Berlin-Leipzig, 1929.

B.M.C.=British Museum Catalogue of Greek Coins, 29 vols.:
Italy, 1873; Sicily, 1876; Macedonia, etc., 1879; Thrace, 1877; Thessaly to Aetolia, 1883; Central Greece, 1884; Attica, Megaris, Aegina, 1888; Corinth and Colonies, 1889; Peloponnesus, 1887; Crete and Aegean Islands, 1886; Pontus, Paphlagonia, Bithynia, Bosporus, 1889; Mysia, 1892; Troas, Aeolis, Lesbos, 1894; Ionia, 1892; Caria and Islands, 1897; Lydia, 1901; Phrygia, 1906; Lycia, Pamphylia and Pisidia, 1897; Lycaonia, Isauria, Cilicia, 1900; Cyprus, 1904; Galatia, Cappadocia, Syria, 1899; Seleucid Kings of Syria, 1878; Phoenicia, 1910; Palestine, 1914; Arabia, Mesopotamia, Persia, 1922; Parthia, 1903; The Ptolemies Kings of Egypt, 1883; Alexandria and the Nomes, 1892; Cyrenaica, 1927.
British Museum Catalogue of Indian Coins—Greek and Scythic Kings, 1886.

Clerk=CLERK, M. G.   Catalogue of the Coins of the Achaean League.   London, 1895.

C.=COHEN, Henri.   Description historique des Monnaies frappées sous l'Empire Romain.   Vols. I-VIII.   2nd Edn.   Paris, 1880-1882.

Côte=Catalogue of the Sale of the Collection of Claudius Côte.   Lugano, 1929.

Du Ch.=DU CHASTEL DE LA HOWARDRIES, Count Alberic.   Syracuse.   Les Monnaies d'Argent et d'Or au point de vue artistique.   London, 1898.

Evans=EVANS, Sir Arthur.   The " Horsemen " of Tarentum (Numismatic Chronicle, 1889).

Feuardent=FEUARDENT, F.   Collections Giovanni di Demetrio.   Numismatique, Egypte Ancienne.   Vol. II.   Paris.

Forrer=FORRER, Dr. Robert.   Keltische Numismatik der Rhein- und Donaulande.   Strassburg, 1908.

Grose=GROSE, S. W.   Catalogue of the McClean Collection of Greek Coins (Fitzwilliam Museum).   Vols. I-III.   Cambridge, 1823-1929.

H.=HEISS, Aloïss.   Description Générale des Monnaies Antiques de l'Espagne.   Paris, 1870.

Hunter=Catalogue of Greek Coins in the Hunterian Collection, University of Glasgow.   By George Macdonald.   Vols. I-III.   Glasgow, 1899-1903.

I.M.C.=Catalogue of the Coins in the Indian Museum Calcutta.   Vol. I.   By Vincent A. Smith.   Oxford, 1906.

May=MAY, J. M. F.   Ainos, Its History and Coinage, 474-341 B.C.   Oxford, 1950.

Mazard=MAZARD, Jean.   Corpus Nummorum Numidiae Mauritaniaeque.   Paris, 1955.

Morgan=DE MORGAN, J.   Manuel de Numismatique Orientale.   I.   Paris, 1923-1936.

M.=MÜLLER, L.   Numismatique d'Alexandre le Grand.   Copenhagen, 1855.

Müller=MÜLLER, L.   Numismatique de l'Ancienne Afrique.   Copenhagen, 1860-1862.

Newell=NEWELL, Edward T.   The Coinage of the Eastern Seleucid Mints from Seleucus I to Antiochus III.   New York, 1935.

Noe=NOE, Sydney P.   The Coinage of Metapontum.   New York, 1927.

Petrowicz=PETROWICZ, Alexander Ritter von.   Arsaciden-Münzen.   Vienna, 1904.

P.M.C.=Catalogue of Coins in the Panjab Museum, Lahore.   Vol. I.   Indo-Greek Coins.   By R. B. Whitehead.   Oxford, 1914.

Pick=PICK, Behrendt.   Die Antiken Münzen von Dacien und Moesien.   Part I.   Berlin, 1898.   Part II=in collaboration with Kurt Regling.   Berlin, 1910.

Sambon=SAMBON, Arthur.   Les Monnaies Antiques de l'Italie.   Vol. I.   Paris, 1903.

Seltman=SELTMAN, Charles T.   The Temple Coins of Olympia (Nomisma, Berlin, 1913).

Svor.=SVORONOS, J. N.   Tresor des Monnaies d'Athènes.   Gotha, 1923.

Svor.=SVORONOS, J. N.   Numismatique de la Crète Ancienne.   Macon, 1890.

Svor.=SVORONOS, J. N.   ΤΑ ΝΟΜΙΣΜΑΤΑ ΤΟΥ ΚΡΑΤΟΥΣ ΤΩΝ ΠΤΟΛΕΜΑΙΩΝ.   Vols. I-IV.   Athens, 1904-1908.

Strack=STRACK, Max L.   Die Antiken Münzen von Thrakien.   Berlin, 1912.

T.=DE LA TOUR, Henri. Atlas de Monnaies Gauloises. Paris, 1892.

Tudeer=TUDEER, Lauri O. Th. Die Tetradrachmenprägung of Syrakus in der Periode der signierenden Künstler. Berlin, 1913.

Vlasto=VLASTO, Michel P. ΤΑΡΑΣ ΟΙΚΙΣΤΗΣ. A Contribution to Tarentine Numismatics. New York, 1922.

Zograf=ZOGRAF, A. N. Anticznyje Monety. Moscow-Leningrad, 1951.

ABBREVIATIONS.

N	=gold	laur.	=laureate
R	=silver	rad.	=radiate
AE	=copper or bronze	diad.	=diademed
Bil.	=billon	dr.	=draped
P	=potin	cuir.	=cuirassed
O. or *obv.*=obverse		stg.	=standing
R or *rev.* =reverse		adv.	=advancing
r.	=right	*R*	=rare
l.	=left	*RR*	=very rare
mon.	=monogram	*RRR*	=extremely rare
hd.	=head	*RRRR*	=of highest rarity
var.	=variety		

STATE OF PRESERVATION IN ORDER OF MERIT.

Abbreviation.	English.	French.	German.
FDC	mint state.	fleur-de-coin.	Stempelglanz.
EF	extremely fine.	superbe.	vorzüglich.
VF	very fine.	très beau.	sehr schön.
F	fine.	beau.	schön.
Fair	fair.	très bien conservé.	sehr gut erhalten.
M	mediocre.	bien conservé.	gut erhalten.
P	poor.		

Where two abbreviations are combined thus, EF/VF, the meaning is that the obverse of the coin is classed as EF but the reverse only VF.

N.B. Name in brackets after a town is either what it was known by in Roman Imperial times or more usually its present name.

SPAIN.

References are to H. Cohen—" Description historique des Monnaies frappés sous l'Empire Romain," and A. Heiss—" Description Genérale des Monnaies Antiques de l'Espagne," and the diameter of bronze coins in millimetres appears after the sign Æ in each case.

Hispania Citerior.

1 **Emporiae.** *c.* 250 B.C. Æ *drachm.* Head of Persephone r., wearing wreath of corn, ear-ring and necklace: around, three dolphins. ℞. ΕΜΠΟΡΙΤΩΝ. Pegasos flying r. *H.*, Pl. 1, 4 .. .. F £12

2 214-204 B.C. Æ 31. Female head, helmeted, r. ℞. Pegasos r.; below, Iberian legend. *H.*, Pl. 4, 38 .. .. *fair* 25/-

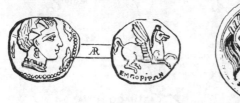

1 3

3 After 133 B.C. Æ 30. *Obv.* as preceding, countermarked DD. ℞. EMPOR. Type as preceding, countermarked DD. *H.*, Pl. 3, 56 .. .. VF/F £6

4 Æ 28. C. CAT. C. O. CAP. Q. Type as preceding. ℞. as preceding. *H.*, Pl. 3, 57
F 50/-

5 **Kissa.** 2nd-1st cent. B.C. Æ 23. Male head r. ℞. Horseman galloping r. holding palm; below, Iberian legend. *H.*, Pl. 5, 1 .. .. F/*fair* 27/6

6 **Tarraco** (Colonia Victrix Triumphalis). *Tiberius and Augustus.* Æ 23. TI. CAESAR C. V. T. Laur. head of Tiberius r. ℞. IMP. CAES. AVG. TR. POT. PON. MAX. P.P. Laur. head of Augustus r. *H.*, Pl. 8, 52; *C.* 9 .. .. F 60/-

7 **Dertosa.** *Tiberius.* Æ 24. TI. CAESAR DIVI AVG. F. AVGVSTVS. Laur. head r. ℞. M. H. I. ILERCAVONI DERT. Ship sailing to l. *H.*, Pl. 9, 1; *C.* 134 .. *fair* 37/6

8 **Celsa.** 2nd-1st Cent. B.C. Æ 28. Male head r. with three dolphins around. ℞. Horseman, holding palm, galloping r.; Iberian legend below. *H.*, Pl. 10, 2
nearly F 35/-

9 As Colonia Victrix Julia. *Augustus.* Æ 28. AVGVSTVS C. V. I. CELSA. His head r.; the whole within laurel-wreath. ℞. L. COR. TERR. M. IVN. HISP. II VIR. Bull standing r. *H.*, Pl. 11, 18; *C.* 697 .. .. *fair* 25/-

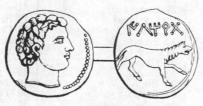

10 **Ilerda.** 2nd-1st Cent. B.C. Æ 22. Male head r. ℞. Wolf r., Iberian legend above. *H.*, Pl. 9, 16 .. .. *fair* 30/-

10A *Augustus.* Æ 25. IMP. AVGVST. DIVI F. Head r. ℞. MVN. ILERDA. Wolf r. *H.*, Pl. 10, 21 .. .. F 60/-

Hispania Citerior

1 Bilbilis
2 Caesaraugusta
3 Calagurris Julia
4 Carthago Nova
5 Cascantum
6 Castulo
7 Celsa
9 D'ertosa
10 Emporiae
12 Ercavica
13 Ilerda
14 Ilici
16 Osca
17 Rhoda
18 Saetabis
19 Saguntum

22 Segobriga
23 Tarraco
24 Turiaso
25 Valentia

Hispania Ulterior

26 Abdera
27 Carteia
28 Corduba
29 Ebura Cerealis
30 Emerita
31 Gades
32 Hispalis
33 Iliberi
34 Ilipa
35 Irippo
36 Julia Traducta

37 Malaca
38 Obulco
39 Osset
41 Ulia

Balearic Islands

42 Ebusus

Mauretania

43 Babba
44 Caesareia or Iol
45 Lix
46 Rusadir
47 Sala
48 Siga
49 Tamusida
50 Tingis
51 Zilis

11 **Osca.** 204-154 B.C. Æ *drachm.* Male head with short beard r. ℞. Horseman with lance galloping r.: below, Iberian legend. *H.*, Pl. 13, 1 .. .. VF £6

12 *Cn. Domitius Calvinus.* *c.* 39 B.C. Æ *denarius.* OSCA behind male head r. ℞. DOM . COS . ITER . IMP. Sacrificial implements. *H.*, Pl. 13, 7 .. .. .. F £6

13 **Cascantum.** *Tiberius.* Æ 28. TI . CAESAR DIVI AVG . F . AVGVSTVS. Laur. head r. ℞. MVNICIP. CASCANTVM. Bull r. *H.*, Pl. 16, 6 .. .. *fair* 27/6

14 **Calagurris Julia** (Nassica). *Tiberius.* Æ 28. IMP . CAESAR TI . AVGVS . DIVI . AVGVSTI . F. Laur. head r. ℞. L . FVL . SPARSO L . SATVRNINO II VIR. Bull standing r. *H.*, Pl. 16, 27; *C.* 116 .. .. F 52/6

15 **Erala.** 2nd-1st Cent. B.C. Æ 28. Type as No. 11. *H.*, Pl. 17, 1 .. *fair* 25/-

16 **Ercavica.** *Augustus.* Æ 28. AVGVSTVS DIVI F. His laur. hd. r. ℞. MVN. above bull standing r.; ERCAVICA in ex. *H.*, Pl. 17, 4; *C.* 706 .. .. .. *fair* 27/6

17 **Segea.** 2nd-1st Cent. B.C. Æ 25. Type as No. 11. *H.*, Pl. 18, 3 .. F 45/-

18 **Bilbilis.** *Caligula.* Æ 28. C . CAESAR AVG . GERMANICVS IMP. His laur. head r. ℞. C . CORN . REFEC . M . HELV . FRONT . MVN . AVG . BILBIL. Wreath with II VIR within. *H.*, Pl. 20 ,23; *C.* 36 .. .. *fair* 32/6

19 **Caesaraugusta.** *Tiberius.* Æ 28. TI . CAESAR DIVI AVGVSTI F . AVGVSTVS. Laur. head r. ℞. M . CATO L . VETTIACVS II . VIR . C . C . A. Priest l. ploughing with a yoke of oxen. *H.*, Pl. 25, 34; *C.* 102 .. .. *fair* 27/6

20 **Turiaso.** 2nd-1st Cent. B.C. Æ *drachm.* Type as No. 11. *H.*, Pl. 22, 3
good Γ 85/-

21 *Augustus and Livia.* Æ 28. SILBIS. Head of Livia r. ℞. TVRIASO. Augustus on horseback l. *H.*, Pl. 22, 11; *C.* — .. .. *fair* 45/-

22 **Damania.** 204-154 B.C. Æ 24. Young male head r. between X and dolphin. ℞. Horseman with lance in rest galloping r.: below, Iberian legend. *H.*, Pl. 27, 2 F 45/-

23 **Saguntum.** 1st Cent. B.C. Æ 16. Scallop shell. ℞. Dolphin r.; Iberian legend below. *H.*, Pl. 27, 5 .. .. *fair* 17/6

24 **Valentia.** *c.* 138 B.C. Æ 28. T . AHI . T . F . L . TRINI . L . F . Q. Head of Roma r. ℞. VALENTIA beneath cornucopiae and thunderbolt in saltire. *H.*, Pl. 28, 3 *fair* 35/-

25 **Segobriga** (Colonia Victoria Julia). 204-154 B.C. Æ 25. Young male head between palm and dolphin; below, M. ℞. Similar to No. 11. *H.*, Pl. 34, 4 .. F 45/-

24   30

27 **Carthago Nova.** *Augustus.* Æ 27. AVGVSTVS DIVI F. Laur. head r. ℞. C . VAR. RVF. SEX. IVL. POL. II. VIR. Q. Sacrificial implements. *H.*, Pl. 35, 1 .. *fair* 25/-

28 Æ 19. V I N K. Tetrastyle temple; around, magistrate's names. ℞. Quadriga galloping r. *H.*, Pl. 36, 23 .. .. *fair* 25/-

30 *Caligula and Caesonia.* Æ 28. C. CAESAR. AVG. GERMANIC. IMP. P. M. TR. P. COS. Laur. head of Caligula r. ℞. CN. ATEL. FLAC. CN. POM. FLAC. II. VIR. Q. V. I. N. C. Bust of Caesonia r., between SAL AVG. *H.*, Pl. 36, 35 .. .. *fair* £7/10/-

31 *Tiberius, Nero and Drusus.* Æ 27. TI . CAESAR DIVI AVGVSTI . F. AVGVSTVS . P . M . Bare head of Tiberius l. ℞. NERO ET DRVSVS CAESARES QVINQ . C . V . I . N . C. Bare heads of the two Caesars face to face. *H.*, Pl. 36, 28 .. .. .. F 80/-

32 **Ilici** (Colonia Julia Ilici Augusta). *Augustus.* Æ 21. AVGVSTVS DIVI F. before his laur. head r. ℞. Q . PAPIR . CAR . Q . TER . MONT . II VIR . Q . Tetrastyle temple with IVNONI across frieze; C. I. IL. A across field. *H.*, Pl. 37, 1; *C.* 715 .. .. *fair* 25/-

33 *Tiberius.* Æ 27. TI . CAESAR . DIVI . AVG . F . AVGVSTVS P . M. His bare head l. ℞. M . IVLIVS SETTAL . L . SESTI . CELER . II . VIR. Altar inscribed SAL . / AVG .; in field C. I. I. A. *H.*,.Pl. 37,.7 .C .141 .. .. *nice dark patina, good* VF £15

34 **Saetabis.** 214-204 B.C. Æ 25. Young male head r.: behind, club. ℞. Horseman galloping r.: below, Iberian legend. *H.*, Pl. 38 .. .. *fair* 22/6

35 **Segisa.** 204-154 B.C. Æ 23. Young male head between two dolphins. ℞. Similar to preceding. *H.*, Pl. 38, 7 .. .. F 35/–

36 **Castulo.** 204-154 B.C. Æ 33. Young male head r. ℞. Sphinx r., wearing apex: in field, star: in ex., Iberian legend. *H.*, Pl. 39, 1 .. .. .. F 50/–

37 2nd-1st Cent. B.C. Æ 27. L. QVL. F. Q. ISC. F. Male head l. ℞. Europa (or Artemis Tauropolos) on bull galloping r.: in ex., M.C.F. *H.*, Pl. 40 .. .. R, F 60/–

38 1st Cent. B.C. Æ 21. Hd. l. ℞. Bull r., crescent above; Iberian legend in ex. *H.*, Pl. 39, 12 .. .. *fair* 22/6

Hispania Ulterior.

39 **Corduba** (Colonia Patricia). 1st Cent. B.C. Æ 18. Head of Venus r.; behind, three pellets. ℞. Cupid standing l.: in field, l., three pellets. *H.*, Pl. 41, 2 .. *fair* 21/–

40 *Augustus.* Æ 32. PERMISSV CAESARIS AVGVSTI, his bare head l. ℞. COLONIA PATRICIA. Legionary eagle between two standards. *H.*, Pl. 42, 4; *C.* 604 .. .. *fair* 27/6

41 Æ 24. PERM . CAES . AVG. Head l. ℞. COLONIA PATRICIA in wreath. *H.*, Pl. 42, 6; *C.* 607 .. .. *fair*/F 30/–

42   45

42 **Obulco.** 2nd Cent. B.C. Æ 32. OBVLCO. Female head r.: all within wreath. ℞. Plough and ear of corn: below, Iberian legend in two lines. *H.*, Pl. 42, 2 .. *fair* 30/–

43 Æ 27. OBVLCO. Female head r. ℞. Iberian legend in two lines, between plough and ear of corn. *H.*, Pl. 43, 8 .. .. *fair* 22/6

44 Æ 19. OBVLCO. Male head (? Apollo) r. ℞. NIC. Bull r.: above, crescent. *H.*, Pl. 44, 29 .. .. *fair* 20/–

45 **Abdera.** 2nd-1st Cent. B.C. Æ 25. Punic legend between two tunny-fish. ℞. Tetrastyle temple. *H.*, Pl. 45, 7 .. .. R, *fair* 27/6

46 **Malaca.** 2nd-1st Cent. B.C. Æ 24. Head of Hephaistos r., wearing pointed cap, pincers behind. ℞. Head of Helios, facing. *H.*, Pl. 45, 2 .. .. *fair* 20/–

46A Æ 21. Similar, but flat cap. ℞. Star within wreath. *H.*, Pl. 45, 6 .. *fair* 20/–

47 **Irippo.** 2nd Cent. B.C. Æ 20. IRIPPO. Young male head r. ℞. Female figure seated l., holding cornucopiae. *H.*, Pl. 46, 2 .. .. *fair* 22/6

48 **Ebura Cerealis.** 2nd-1st Cent. B.C. Æ 26. Male head r. ℞. Triskelis with face in centre; Iberian legend below. *H.*, Pl. 47, 3 .. .. *fair* 30/–

49

49 **Ulia.** 2nd Cent. B.C. Æ 31. Rude laur. head of Apollo r. ℞. VLIA within oblong frame. *H.*, Pl. 48, 2 .. .. *fair* 27/6

50 **Iliberi.** 2nd-1st Cent. B.C. ℞ *drachm.* Male head r. ℞. Horseman galloping l. leading spare horse, Iberian legend in ex. *H.*, Pl. 48, 1 .. .. VF £7/10/-

51 Æ 24. Similar, but no spare horse; horseman holding couched lance and buckler. *H.*, Pl. 48, 10 .. .. F/*fair* 30/-

50   52

52 **Carteia.** 2nd-1st Cent. B.C. Æ 18. CARTEIA. Female head, turreted, r.: behind, trident. ℞. IIII VIR EX D. D. Winged genius riding on dolphin r. *H.*, Pl. 49, 23
F 35/-

53 Æ 17. CARTEIA. Dolphin and trident. ℞. IIII . VIR D . D. Rudder. *H.*, Pl. 49, 24
F 30/-

54 **Julia Traducta.** *Augustus.* Æ 24. PERM. CAES. AVG. Head l. ℞. IVLIA TRAD in wreath. *H.*, Pl. 50, 2 .. .. *fair* 22/6

55 **Gades.** 2nd-1st Cent. B.C. Æ 26. Head of young Herakles l.; behind, club. ℞. Punic legend: two tunny fish l. *H.*, Pl. 51, 5 .. .. F 45/-

56 **Ilipa.** 2nd Cent. B.C. Æ 32. ILIPENSE. Fish r.; above, crescent. ℞. Ear of barley. *H.*, Pl. 56, 3 .. .. F 65/-

56   59

57 **Romula.** *Augustus and Livia.* Æ 31. PERM . DIVI AVG . COL . ROM. His radiate head r.; star above; thunderbolt in front. ℞. IVLIA AVGVSTA GENETRIX ORBIS. Her head l. on globe, crescent above. *H.*, Pl. 59, 2; *Cohen* 3 .. .. F £6/10/-

58 **Hispalis.** *Tiberius, Drusus and Germanicus.* Æ 28. PERM . DIVI . AVG . COL . ROM. Laur. head r. ℞. DRVSVS CAESAR GERMANICVS CAESAR: their two heads facing each other. *H.*, Pl. 59, 3 .. .. F 80/-

59 **Osset.** *Augustus.* Æ 24. OSSET. His bare hd. r. ℞. Male figure standing l. holding bunch of grapes. *H.*, 59, 4 .. .. *fair* 25/-

60 **Emerita** (Colonia Augusta). *Augustus.* Æ 25. CAESAR AVGVST. TRIB . POTEST. His bare head r. ℞. P . CARISIVS / LEG . / AVGVSTI. *H.*, Pl. 60, 10 .. .. F 45/-

61 Æ 24. DIVVS AVGVSTVS . PATER. His rad. head l.; thunderbolt in front. ℞. COL . AVGVSTA EMERITA. City gate. *H.*, Pl. 61, 25 .. .. *fair* 25/-

62 *Tiberius.* Æ 26. TI . CAESAR AVGVSTVS PON . MAX . IMP. Laur. head l. ℞. COL . AVGVSTA EMERITA. City gate. *H.*, Pl. 62, 37 .. .. *fair* 30/-

63 **BALEARIC ISLANDS, Ebusus** (Iviza). 3rd Cent. B.C. Æ 21. Squatting Kabeiros facing, holding hammer and serpent; on l., palm. ℞. Phoenician legend in two lines. *H.*, Pl. 63, 3 .. .. R, F £6

GAUL

Tribes		
1 Elusates	16 Redones	32 Eburones	47 Bituriges Cubi
2 Bituriges Vivisci	17 Abrincatui	33 Aduatuci	48 Arverni
3 Nitobriges	18 Unelli	34 Treveri	49 Ruteni
4 Cadurci	19 Baïocasses	35 Parisii	50 Helvetii
5 Petrocorii	20 Turones	36 Bellovaci	51 Allobroges
6 Santones	21 Carnutes	37 Suessiones and	52 Volcae Tectosages
7 Lemovices	22 Aulerci Eburovices	Meldi	
8 Pictones	23 Lexovii	38 Remi	Towns
9 Namnetes	24 Veliocasses	39 Mediomatrici	60 Antipolis
10 Andes	25 Caletes	40 Leuci	61 Avenio
11 Aulerci Cenomani	26 Ambiani	41 Lingones	62 Cabellio
12 Aulerci Diablintes	27 Morini	42 Senones	63 Glanum
13 Osismii	28 Atrebates	43 Rauraci	64 Lugdunum
14 Veneti	29 Veromandui	44 Sequani	65 Massalia
15 Coriosolites	30 Menapii	45 Ambarri	66 Nemausus
	31 Nervii	46 Aedui	67 Vienna

64 **Auriol Find.** 520-470 B.C. Æ *obol.* Ram's head l. R. "Mill-sail" incuse.
T. 387 .. .. VF £16

65 **Massalia** (Marseilles). *After* 400 B.C. Æ *obol.* Young head l. R. MA in spokes of wheel.
T. 689 .. .. VF £5

66 400-200 B.C. Æ *drachm.* Head of Artemis r. R. MAΣΣA. Lion prowling r. T. 791
VF £12/10/–

67 *After* 200 B.C. Æ *drachm.* Head of Artemis r., bow and quiver at shoulder. R.
Blundered legend: lion r. T. 851 .. .. VF £7/10/–

68 — Similar, later style, barbarous. T. 1418 .. .. VF £5

69 200-49 B.C. Æ 24. Head of Apollo l. R. MAΣΣAΛIHTΩN. Bull rushing r. T. 1481
F 60/–

70 Æ 21. Helmeted head of Athena r. R. MAΣΣA. Tripod-lebes. T. 1912 *fair* 20/–

71 Æ 20. Similar, but legend MA. T. 1914 .. .. *fair* 17/6

Coinages of the Gaulish Tribes.

As the denominations of the undermentioned coins are uncertain, the diameter in millimetres is given in each case, even with the silver pieces. Coins marked " P." are of potin, and all in this metal are cast, not struck. Most were probably struck in the first century B.C. References are to De la Tour's " Atlas de Monnaies Gauloises," Forrer's " Keltische Numismatik," and Blanchet's " Manuel de Numismatique Française," Vol. I.

72 **SOUTH-WESTERN GAUL. The Elusates.** Æ 19 (*drachm* ?). Vestiges of head
r. R. Degraded Pegasos l. *Forrer* 533 .. .. .. *good* VF £8/10/–

73 **WESTERN GAUL. The Santones.** Æ 14. ARIVOS. Helmeted head l. R.
SANTONOS. Horse prancing r. T. 4525 .. .. F 50/–

74 **AREMORICA. The Baïocasses.** *Billon* 22. Helmeted head r. R. As last, but
traces of driver above; boar r. beneath. T. 6978 .. .. .. *fair*/F 75/–

75 **The Osismii.** *Bil.* 23. Head r., elaborately stylised; boar above; three human heads
round the head. R. Quadruped with human head l.; two human heads above, boar
r. and eagle below. T. 6555 .. .. *good* F/F £7/10/–

76 **NORTH-WESTERN GAUL: The Carnutes.** Æ 16. Head r. R. Two horses
galloping r. T. 5986 .. .. F 75/–

77 Æ 16. Head r. R. Dog r. sitting on horse prancing r.; triskelis beneath. T. 6017
VF £7/10/–

78 Æ 17. Head r. (Herakles in lion's skin). R. Eagle flying r. T. 6108 *good* F 60/–

79 **NORTHERN GAUL. The Aduatuci.** Æ 15. Swastica with wavy arms; around,
circles enclosing pellets. R. AVAVCIA. Horse l. T. 8885 .. .. *fair* 45/–

80 **The Caletes.** Æ 13. CVCINATIO. Helmeted hd. r. R. VLATO. Horse advancing
r. T. 7203 .. .. VF/F 85/–

81 Æ 15. ATEVLA. Bust of Nike l. R. VLATOS. Bull r. T. 7191 .. .. F 60/–

82 **The Treveri.** Æ *stater.* VOCARAN. Portions of head, showing eye. R. Horse l.,
VOCARAN above, double wreath below. T. 8823 .. .. F/VF £37/10/–

83 Æ 19. Diad. young male head r. R. GERMANVS INDVTILLI. Bull running l.
Blanchet (*legends*) 177; T. 9248 (*Leuci*) .. .. *fair* 35/–

84 **NORTH-EASTERN GAUL. The Bellovaci.** *P.* 19. Barbarous head r. ℞. Grotesque eye l. *T.* 7905 .. .. F 42/6

85 Æ 16. Female head l. ℞. Small and large eagles, wings outspread, l. *T.* 8000
good F 50/-

86 **The Leuci.** *P.* 22. Barbarous head l. ℞. Barbarous boar l., lily beneath. *Forrer* 48
F 50/-

87 *P.* 20. Head l. with diadem and distinct locks. ℞. Boar l.; circle enclosing pellet beneath. *F.* 46 .. .. F 42/6

88 **The Lingones.** *P.* 20. Bucranium, ornaments around. ℞. Bear r. *T.* 8351
F 60/-

89 **The Remi.** *N stater.* Angular lines representing portion of laur. hd. with an eye; above, three radiate pellets, perhaps representing a crown. ℞. Horse with triple tail l., pellet within wreath above and below. *Cf. Forrer* 460 *good* VF/*good* F £30

90 *P.* 20. Warrior with flying pig-tail advancing r., holding torque and spear. ℞. Bear r. devouring prey. *Blanchet*, Fig. 115; *T.* 8124 (*Catalauni*) .. .. .. F 65/-

91 Æ 17. REMOS behind young male head l., ANTISIOS before. ℞. Lion bounding l.; beneath, dolphin l. *T.* 8054 .. .. F 45/-

92 Æ 15. REMO. Three young male busts jugate l. ℞. REMO below biga galloping l. driven by winged figure. *T.* 8040 .. .. F 75/-

93 **The Senones.** *P.* 17. Head r. ℞. Horse l.; in field, three large pellets. *T.* 7417
fair 32/6

94 *P.* 17. Grotesque head l. ℞. Horse l. *T.* 7434 .. .. F 65/-

94A Æ 16. Head r. ℞. IIILLO l. in front of tree; five-pointed star above. *T.* 7508
F 45/-

95 **CENTRAL AND EASTERN GAUL. The Aedui.** Æ 14. ANORBO. Helmeted head r. ℞. Horse prancing r.; BN below. *T.* 4972 .. .. .. VF £5

96 Æ 13. Types l. and more barbarous; ΚΑΛ – ΕΔ on *rev*. *Forrer* 188 .. F 45/-

97 Æ 18. TVRONOS. Head l., ear of corn behind. ℞. CANTORIX. Horse galloping l.; in front, five-pointed star; above, S; below, curved sword. *T.* 7005 .. .. *fair* 70/-

98 **The Sequani.** Sequanoiotuos. Æ 15. Head l., curls of hair indicated by annulets enclosing pellets. ℞. SEQVANOIOTVOS (legend seldom complete). Boar l. *T.* 5351
good F/F £5

99 Togirix. Æ 14. TOGIRIX. Barbarous head l. ℞. TOGIR. Horse galloping l.; below, serpent. *T.* 5550 .. .. F 45/-; VF 85/-

100 110

100 *P.* 17. TOG. Helmeted head r. ℞. TOG. Lion springing r. *T.* 5629 .. F 60/-

101 Docirix, Samulati f. Æ 14. Q DOCI. Helmeted head l. ℞. Q DOCI SAM F. Horse galloping l. *T.* 5405 .. .. F 75/-

102 **THE RHONE VALLEY. League against Ariovistus and the Helvetii.** Æ 13. BRI. Helmeted head r. ℞. BRI. Horseman with lance galloping r. *T.* 5803
fair 40/-

103 Æ 16. DVRNACOS. Helmeted head r. ℞. AVSCRO. Type as preceding. *T.* 5762
F 75/-

104 Æ 19. BRICO. Helmeted head r. ℞. COMA. Type as preceding. *T.* 5815
VF £6

105 Æ 17. Types as preceding, but MOR on *obv*. and CAL on *rev*. *T.* 5916 .. VF £7

106 **The Rauraci.** *P.* 20. Head, laur., l. ℞. Grotesque horse l. *T.* 5390 *fair* 50/-

Roman Colonies of Gaul.

109 **Antipolis** (Antibes). Lepidus, B.C. 44-42. Æ 14. Female head r., wreath behind, ΙΣΔΗΜ before. ℞. ΑΝΤΙΠ ΛΕΠ. Nike standing r. placing wreath on trophy. *T.* 2179
fair 80/–

110 **Avenio** (Avignon). Æ *denarius.* Laur. head of Apollo l. ℞. ΑΟΥΕ above boar at bay l., crescent below. *T.* 2513 .. .. F £5

111 **Cabellio.** Æ 15. COL before bearded male head r. wearing crested helmet. ℞. CABE before female head r. *T.* 2563 .. .. F £5

112 **Lugdunum** (Lyons). Æ *dupondius.* IMP DIVI F. Heads of Julius Caesar and Augustus (?) back to back. ℞. Prow of galley; above, uncertain object in circle. *T.* 4660
fair £5

113 **Nemausus** (Nimes). Æ *as.* IMP DIVI F. Heads of Augustus and Agrippa back to back. ℞. COL NEM. Crocodile chained to palm-tree: in field, wreath and palm branches. *T.* 2806; *C.* 7. (Worth very much more with leg attached as illustration) .. VF/F £6

114 **Vienna.** Æ *dupondius.* DIVI IVLI/IMP CAESAR DIVI F. Heads of Julius Caesar and Augustus back to back. ℞. C. I. V. Prow of galley with superstructure. *T.* 2943; *C.* 7 .. .. F £10

BRITANNIA.

For the Celtic coins of Britain, many of which are derived from Greek and Gaulish proto-types, see Seaby's *Standard Catalogue of British Coins,* nos. 1-202 (Price 25/–).

ITALY

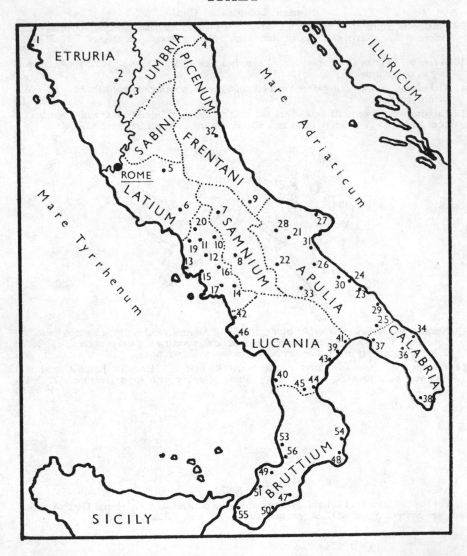

ETRURIA.

115 **Populonia.** 450-350 B.C. Æ *didrachm.* Gorgon's head facing; below x · x. ℞. Plain. *Sambon* 42. **Plate I** .. .. *nearly* VF £35

117 — Similar, but *rev.* two caducei. *Sambon* 53 .. .. *RR, good* F/F £50

118 **Chiana Valley.** 3rd Cent. B.C. Æ 19. Negro's head r. ℞. Elephant r., with bell on neck. *Sambon* 145 .. .. *fair* 40/–

119 **Etruria in genere.** 350-280 B.C. Æ *uncia.* Wheel of six spokes. ℞. Double axe. *B.M.C.* 5 .. .. *fair* £5

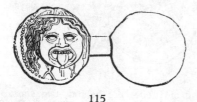

115   121

UMBRIA.

120 **Tuder** (Todi). 300-200 B.C. Æ 19. Head of Silenus r., crowned with ivy. ℞. TVTERE (retrograde). Eagle l. *B.M.C.* 1; *Sambon* 157 .. .. .. F 75/–

PICENUM.

121 **Ancona.** 290-268 B.C. Æ 21. Hd. of Aphrodite r. ℞. ΑΓΚΩΝ. Bent arm holding palm, two stars above. *Sambon* 159 .. .. F £7/10/–

LATIUM.

122 **Alba Fucens.** 303-268 B.C. Æ 14 (18 grs.). Head of Hermes. ℞. ALBA. Winged griffin flying r. *Sambon* 160 .. .. *fair* 80/–

123 **Aquinum.** 268-217 B.C. Æ 20. Head of Athena l. ℞. AQVINO before cock l. *Sam.* 167 .. .. F 75/–

123   125

SAMNIUM.

124 **Aesernia** (Isernia). *After* 268 B.C. Æ 21. VOLCANOM. Head of Hephaistos l., wearing conical cap wreathed with laurel: behind, pincers. ℞. Jupiter in galloping biga r. *B.M.C.* 4; *Sambon* 189 .. .. R, F £6

125 **Beneventum.** *After* 268 B.C. Æ 20. BENVENTOD. Laur. head of Apollo l. ℞. ΠΡΟΠΟΜ. Free horse prancing r. *Sam.* 193 .. .. F 75/–

FRENTANI.

126 **Larinum.** Late 3rd Cent. B.C. Æ 19 *sextans.* Veiled head of Dione r. ℞. Dolphin r.: above, v: below, LADINOD and two pellets. *B.M.C.* 9; *Sambon* 207 VF/F £5

CAMPANIA.

127 **Allifae.** 400-350 B.C. Æ *litra.* ALLIBA. Laur. head of Apollo l. ℞. Skylla r., two swans, etc. *Sam.* 824 .. .. F £6

128 **Cales** (Calvi). 334-268 B.C. Æ *didrachm.* Helmeted head of Athena r. Ŗ. CALENO.
Nike in biga galloping l. *Sambon* 914 ..   ..   VF/F £35

129 Æ 22. CALENO. Head of Apollo, laur., l. Ŗ. Man-headed bull, lyre above. *Sam.*
942   ..   ..   *fair* 20/-

130 *After* 268 B.C. Æ 20. Head of Athena l., wearing crested Corinthian helmet. Ŗ.
CALENO. Cock r.: in field, star. *B.M.C.* 26; *Sambon* 916   ..   ..   ..   F 40/-

128   131

131 **Capua.** 268-218 B.C. Æ 24 *sextans.* Head of Jupiter r. : behind, two stars. Ŗ.
Two soldiers; on l., two stars ; Oscan legend in ex. *B.M.C.* 6 ; *Sambon* 1030   F 85/-

132 **Cumae.** 480-421 B.C. Æ *didrachm.* Head of Cumaean Sibyl r., wearing diadem,
hair rolled. Ŗ. KVMAION. Mussel-shell and grain of corn. *Sambon* 281
                                                                      good F £24

132A — As last but head of finer style. Ŗ. KVMAION. Skylla swimming r., mussel-shell
below. *Sambon* 276   ..   ..   *fair, RR* £45

133 **Hyria.** 400-335 B.C. Æ *didrachm.* Head of Athena l., wearing helmet wreathed
with olive. Ŗ. YPINAI. Man-headed bull walking l. *Sambon* 780   ..   F £15

132A   137A

134 **Neapolis** (Naples). 370-340 B.C. Æ *didrachm.* Head of nymph r., wearing diadem and ear-
ring; around, four dolphins. Ŗ. NEOΠOΛITΩN in ex.: man-headed bull walking r.,
crowned by flying Victory: below bull, OYIA. *B.M.C.* 90; *Sambon* 458   *good* F £10

135 340-300 B.C. Æ *didrachm.* *Obv.* Similar, but without dolphins: bunch of grapes
behind head. Ŗ. As preceding, but below bull ΔI ΘE, and NEOΠOΛITHΣ in ex. *Sambon*
440   ..   ..   *nearly* VF £14

136 — As preceding, with small figure of Artemis behind head, and XAPI beneath; MY mon.
below bull. *B.M.C.* 80. **Plate I**   ..   ..   *nearly.* VF/VF £21

137 300-280 B.C. As preceding, but types to l., with EY behind head of nymph and ΛOY
below bull. *B.M.C.* 63; *Sambon* 483   ..   ..   VF/F £13/10/-

137A 280-241 B.C. Another as last, but hair less waved, oinochoe behind hd. of nymph.
Ŗ. Similar but bull r., BI below. *Sambon* 497(a)   ..   ..   EF £50

138 240-220 B.C. Æ 16. Head of Apollo, laureate, r. Ŗ. Forepart of man-
headed bull r., star on shoulder. *B.M.C.* 141; *Sambon* 564   ..   ..   R, VF/F 85/-

139 Æ 19. NEOΠOΛITΩN. Head of Apollo, laur., l. Ŗ. Man-headed bull r., crowned
by flying Victory: below bull, monogram IΣ: in ex., IΣ. *B.M.C.* 225; *Cf. Sambon* 652
                                                                      good F 42/-

140 Æ 16 *hemilitron.* Laur. head of Apollo r. Ŗ. NEOΠOΛITΩN. Tripod. *B.M.C.* 198;
Sambon 705   ..   ..   F 25/-

141 Æ 20 *litron.* Laur. head of Apollo l. Ŗ. NEOΠOΛITΩN. Omphalos and lyre. *Sambon*
740   ..   ..   *fair* 21/-

142 Æ 14. Head of Artemis r., quiver at shoulder. Ŗ. NEOΠOΛITΩN. Cornucopiae.
Sambon 742   ..   ..   F 22/6

143 **Nola.** 360-325 B.C. Æ *didrachm.* Female head r., wearing diadem, ear-ring and necklace. R. ΝΩΛΑΙΩΝ. Man-headed bull walking r., crowned by Nike flying r. *Sambon* 802 .. .. F £30

143A — Head of Athena r. wearing Athenian helmet bound with olive-wreath upon which is perched an owl. R. As last but without Nike, Æ below bull. *Sambon* 811

nearly VF £35

143A   144

144 **Nuceria Alfaterna.** *After* 308 B.C. Æ *didrachm.* Young male head l., with ram's horn and diadem; Oscan legend. R. Youth standing l., holding horse by rein, sceptre in l. hand. *Sambon* 1006 .. .. *nearly* VF £40

145 **Phistelia.** 380-350 B.C. Æ *obol.* Young male head facing. R. Oscan legend: corn-grain between mussel and dolphin. *B.M.C.* 4; *Sambon* 836 .. VF £7/10/–

146 — *Obv.* Similar. R. Lion l.; above, star. *Sambon* 845 F/good F 75/

147 **Suessa Aurunca** (Sessa). 313-268 B.C. Æ *didrachm.* Head of Apollo, laur., r. R. SVESANO. Youth on horse walking l., holding palm and leading second horse. *Sambon* 852 .. .. F £20

147A 268-240 B.C. Æ 20. Head of Athena l. R. Cock advancing r., star behind. *Sambon* 873 .. .. *fair* 22/6

147   148

148 **Teanum Sidicinum.** Æ *didrachm.* Head of young Herakles r., wearing lion's skin. R. Nike driving triga l., Oscan legend in ex. *Sambon* 978 .. .. *fair, R* £10

149 Æ 20. Head of Athena l., wearing crested Corinthian helmet. R. TIANO. Cock r.: in field, star. *B.M.C.* 16; *Sambon* 1004 .. .. *fair* 22/6; F/VF 65/–

149A Æ 20. Laur. head of Apollo l. R. Man-headed bull r., Nike flying above, legend in local characters in ex. *Sambon* 1002 .. .. VF/F 65/–

APULIA.

150 **Arpi.** 3rd Cent. B.C. Æ *didrachm.* ΑΡΠΑΝΩΙΝ. Head of Persephone l. R. Horse prancing l., star above, ΔΑΙΟΥ and helmet below. *Grose* 394 *fair, RR* £12/10/–

151 Æ 21. ΠΥΛΛΟ. Bull rushing r. R. ΑΡΠΑΝΟΥ. Horse prancing r. *B.M.C.* 9

good F 45/–

151A Æ 21. ΔΑΙΟΥ. Laur. hd. of Zeus l. R. ΑΡΠΑΝΩΝ. Calydonian boar r., spear-head above. *B.M.C.* 4 .. .. F/*fair* 35/–

151B **Asculum.** 3rd Cent. B.C. Æ 19. Head of young Herakles l. ℞. ΑΥCΚΛΑ. Nike standing r. ..   .. *fair* 27/6

152 **Barium.** *c.* 200 B.C. Æ 18 *sextans.* Laur. head of Zeus r., two eight-pointed stars behind. ℞. ΒΑΡΙΝΩΝ. Eros r. on prow of galley, dolphin r. below. *B.M.C.* 2
                                                     fair 30/-

153 **Butuntum** (Bitonto). 3rd Cent. B.C. Æ 15. Owl l. ℞. ΒΥΤΟΝΤΙΝΩΝ above and below thunderbolt. *Grose 417*   ..   ..   *fair* 30/-

154 **Caelia.** 268-200 B.C. Æ 19 *sextans.* Head of Athena r., wearing crested Corinthian helmet; above, two pellets. ℞. ΚΑΙΛΙΝΩΝ. Trophy. *B.M.C.* 3 ..   F/VF 65/-

155 Æ 13 *uncia.* *Obv.* as previous. ℞. ΚΑΙ. Warrior (? Ares) standing l., holding branch. *B.M.C.* 8   ..   ..   F 35/-

156 **Canusium.** *About* 300 B.C. Æ *obol* (7.5 grs.). Amphora between flower and vase. ℞. ΚΑ. Lyre. *B.M.C.* 2   ..   ..   F £5

157 Third Cent. B.C. Æ 21. Young male head l. ℞. ΚΑΝΥCΙΝΩΝ below horseman galloping r. carrying couched lance. *B.M.C.* 4   ..   ..   ..   F/*fair* 27/6

158 **Hyrium** (Rodi). 3rd Cent. B.C. Æ 14. Head of Athena r. ℞. ΥΡΙΑ ΤΙΝΩΝ above and below rudder over dolphin. *B.M.C.* 1 ..   ..   *fair* 20/-

159 **Luceria.** 250-217 B.C. Æ 25 *quincunx.* Helmeted head of Athena r.; above, five pellets. ℞. ΛΟVCΕΡΙ between spikes of wheel. *B.M.C.* 54   ..   *fair*/F 60/-

160 **Neapolis.** *After* 300 B.C. Æ 20. Head of Dionysos r. ℞. ΝΕΑΠ below bunch of grapes. *Grose 449*   ..   ..   *fair* 35/-

161 **Rubi.** 3rd Cent. B.C. Æ *diobol.* Head of Athena r. ℞. ΡΥ. Ear of corn. *B.M.C.* 1
                                                       F, R £7/10/-

162 Æ 16. Head of Athena r. ℞. ΡΥΒΑCΤΕΙΝΩΝ. Owl r., head facing, standing on olive branch. *B.M.C.* 10   ..   ..   F/*fair* 32/6

162   163

163 **Salapia.** 3rd Cent. B.C. Æ 22. ΣΑΛΑΠΙΝΩΝ retrograde. Laur. head of Zeus l. ℞. ΠΥΛΛΟΥ. Boar r., at bay: trident above. *B.M.C.* 1   ..   ..   ..   *fair* 35/-

164 **Teate** (Chieti). 250-200 B.C. Æ 28 *quincunx.* Head of Athena r. ℞. ΤΙΑΤΙ. Owl standing facing: in ex., five pellets. *B.M.C.* 3   ..   ..   ..   R, *good* F/F £10

165 Æ *triens.* Head of Herakles r. ℞. ΤΙΑΤΙ. Wolf r., club above. *Garrucci 92, 13 variety*   ..   ..   R, F £8

166 **Venusia** (Venosa). 268-217 B.C. Æ 28 *quincunx*. Laur. head of Zeus l., five pellets behind. ℞. VE mon. before eagle l. on thunderbolt. *B.M.C.* 22 F £7/10/-

166 168

CALABRIA.

167 **Brundisium** (Brindisi). 245-217 B.C. Æ 24 *uncia*. Laur. head of Poseidon r., long trident behind neck, pellet below. ℞. BRVN below Taras on dolphin l. holding Nike and cornucopiae. *B.M.C.* 3 .. .. VF/F 85/-

168 200-89 B.C. Æ 20 *semis*. Head of Poseidon r., M.BIT before. ℞. BRVN. Taras, holding Nike and lyre, on dolphin l., S behind. *B.M.C.* 14 .. nearly F 35/-

169 **Graxa.** 200-89 B.C. Æ 16. Head of Zeus r., : behind. ℞. ΓΡΑΚΡΗ. Two eagles on fulmen; to r, : *B.M.C. Italy,* p. 221, 3 .. .. *fair* 35/-

170 **Hyria** or **Orra** (Oria). 217-89 B.C. Æ 16 *quincunx*. Bust of Aphrodite r. ℞. ORRA. Eros r., playing lyre; behind, five pellets. *B.M.C.* 6 .. .. .. F 75/-

171 **Tarentum** (Taranto). *Before* 510 B.C. Æ *litra*. Scallop shell. ℞. Wheel of four spokes. *Cf. B.M.C.* 56 .. .. F 80/-

172 510-473 B.C. Æ *stater*. ΤΑΡΑΣ. Taras seated on dolphin l., arms extended, cockleshell beneath. ℞. ΤΑΡΑΣ above hippocamp with curled wing. *Côte* 31
good F/VF £60

173 Æ *litra*. Scallop shell. ℞. Female head r. within shallow incuse. *Côte* 44
good F £5/10/-

174 473-460 B.C. Æ *didrachm*. ΤΑΡΑΣ (retrograde). Taras on dolphin r., arms extended, cockle-shell beneath. ℞. ΤΑΡΑΣ (retrograde). Male figure seated on stool, holding distaff. *Vlasto* 14a .. .. *fair* £21

174A 443-400 B.C., *didrachm*. ΤΑΡΑΝ-ΤΙΝΩΝ. Phalantos helmeted, seated on dolphin l., holding acrostolium, round shield and two javelins; below, tunny l. ℞. Male figure seated on diphros l., holding kantharos and staff. *Vlasto* 46. **Plate I**
RRRR, VF/almost EF £175

175 420-350 B.C. Æ *litra*. Cockle-shell. ℞. Dolphin r., thunderbolt below. *B.M.C.* 396 .. .. good F 90/-

176 344-334 B.C. Æ *didrachm*. Naked youth r. on horse; below, boy extracting stone from raised l. forefoot; to r., Φ. ℞. ΤΑΡΑΣ. Taras l. astride dolphin, holding kantharos and circular shield and trident, E and waves below. *Evans*, iv, C.3 .. VF £30

177 334-302 B.C. Æ *didrachm*. Naked rider on prancing horse r., spearing downward, ΣΑ below horse. ℞. ΤΑΡΑΣ. Taras l. on dolphin, holds small dolphin and distaff; ivy leaf in field to r., ΦΙ below. *Ev.* v, B.1 .. .. VF/F £10

178 — As before, but Taras holds kantharos and trident, dolphin below. *Ev.* v, B.11
good F £7/10/-

179 — As before, but Taras holds bow and three arrows. *Ev.* v, B.17 .. .. VF £14

179A — Diad. female hd. l. ℞. Boy on horseback r., crowning his horse: in field, ΤΑ: beneath horse, dolphin. *Côte* 288. **Plate I** .. .. VF/good VF, *neat style* £25

180 Æ *diobol*. Hd. of Athena r. ℞. Herakles kneeling r. strangling lion. and holding club. *Côte* 256 .. .. good F 80/-

181 Æ *obol*. Kantharos; five pellets around. ℞. Kantharos, κ in field to l. *Côte* 260
fair/F 35/-

182 302-281 B.C. Æ *didr*. As No. 177, but ℞. ΤΑΡΑΣ. Taras l. on dolphin, l. hand extended holding dolphin. *Ev.* vi, D.3 .. .. R, VF £18

183 — Boy on galloping horse l., holding buckler. ℞. ΤΑΡΑΣ. Taras, on dolphin l., holding corn-spike; spear-head below. *Ev.* vi, E.2 .. .. .. R, VF £20

184 **Tarentum.** 302-281 B.C. Æ *drachm.* Head of Athena r.; on helmet, Skylla r. hurling stone. ℞. TAP. Owl r., IOP and club before. *B.M.C.* 308 .. .. F/VF £8

185 281-272 B.C. Æ *didrachm.* Naked rider on prancing horse r., carrying circular shield and two short spears aiming downwards with another, ΓY to l., ΣΩΣT / PATOΣ below. ℞. TAPAΣ ΠOΛY. Taras on dolphin l., holding Nike crowning him, and cornucopiae, thunderbolt in field. *Ev.* vii, A.2 .. .. *nearly* VF £9

186 — As before. EY to l., ΦIN TYΛOΣ below, and Taras holds Nike and trident, prow below. *Ev.* vii, A.4 .. .. *good* VF £16

187 — Naked youth, holding wreath, on horse pacing r.: in field IΩ NEYMH. ℞. Taras, holding helmet, seated l. on dolphin: below, TAPAΣ: in field, two stars. *Evans* vii, C.2 VF £14

188 — The Dioskuri galloping l. ℞. Taras, holding small figure of Nike l. in his r. hand, and round shield and two javelins in his l., seated l. on dolphin; below, representation of waves: in field, TAPAS and ΓY. *Evans* vii, D.1. **Plate I** .. *RR*, VF £30

189 — Helmeted horseman galloping l., with two javelins and large round shield decorated with star: in field IΩ and AΠOΛΛΩ. ℞. Taras, holding bunch of grapes and distaff, seated l. on dolphin: in field, ANΘ. *Evans* vii, F.1 .. .. .. VF £12

190 — Youth on horse standing r. crowning himself, IΩ to l.; IAΛO and Ionic capital and neck of column below horse. ℞. As before but acrostolium in place of grapes. *Ev.* vii, G.1 .. .. VF £13/10/-

191 Æ *drachm.* Head of Athena r., wearing crested helmet decorated with Skylla. ℞. Owl standing r., head facing, on olive branch: in field, OΛYMΠIΣ. *B.M.C.* 315 VF £10

192 Æ *diobol.* Head of Athena l. ℞. Herakles l., r. knee on back of lion standing l., brandishing club in r. hand and twisting lion's tail with l. *Côte* 443 .. F 65/-

193 272-235 B.C. Æ *didrachm.* Youth on horseback l., crowning horse which lifts off foreleg. NK monogram above, ΦIΛOKPA below. ℞. TAPAS AΠOΛ. Taras on dolphin l., holding kantharos and long trident. *Ev.* xiii, A.6 .. .. .. *good* F £8

194 — As before, but ΣY above, ΛYKI / NOΣ below and Taras brandishes trident, owl in field. *Ev.* viii, A.9 .. .. VF £10

195 — As before, but ΔI above, ΦIΛΩ / TAΣ below, and Taras holds kantharos and distaff; in field, cock l. *Ev.* viii, A.11 .. .. VF £12

196 — As before, but horse to r., AΓAΘ – A / PXOΣ below. Taras holds kantharos and cornucopiae; in field lighted torch. *Ev.* viii, B.1 .. .. VF £13/10/-

197 — Naked horseman galloping r., striking with lance and holding shield and two javelins: in field l., ΔI: below horse, APIΣTO / KΛHΣ. ℞. Taras, holding kantharos and trident, seated on dolphin l.: in field r., female head l.: below dolphin, TAP. *Types as illustration, but different legends and symbol. Evans* viii, D.1 .. .. .. VF £14

198 — Naked youth on horse standing r.: below, ΦIΛHM / HNOΣ. ℞. Taras, holding tripod and trident, seated l. on dolphin: in field, r., bucranium: below, TAPAΣ. *Evans* viii, E.1 R, F/VF £12

199 — Rider wearing crested helmet and cuirass on horse standing r., holding spear and circular shield; ῘHPA / K ΛHTOΣ below. ℞. Taras as before, holding flower and cornucopiae; E and thymiaterion behind. *Ev.* viii, G.1 .. .. VF £12

200 Æ *diobol.* Kantharos with rosette above and four pellets around. ℞. Kantharos with caduceus to l. and pellets around. *B.M.C.* 438 .. .. .. VF £5

201 Æ *obol.* Horse's head r. ℞. Similar. *B.M.C.* 420 .. .. *good* F 75/-

202 *After* 281 B.C. Æ *diobol.* Helmeted head of Athena r. ℞. Herakles kneeling r., strangling lion .. .. *fair* 30/-

203 — Similar: above lion, grasshopper l. *B.M.C.* 343 .. .. .. *good* F 75/-

204 Æ *diobol.* Similar, but Herakles standing r., TAPAN above lion. *B.M.C.* 361
VF/EF £6

205 235-228 B.C. Æ *didrachm.* Naked rider on prancing horse r., holding palm, AP mon. above to l., ΑΡΙΣΤΙΠΠΟΣ below. ℞. Taras l. on dolphin crowned with wreath holding kantharos; TAPAC below, M in field. *Ev.* ix, E.1. **Plate I** .. *RR, good* VF £27/10/-

206 212-209 B.C. Æ *hemiobol.* (4 grs.). Scallop-shell. ℞. Dolphin r. *B.M.C.* 396 VF £5

207 3rd Cent. B.C. Æ 13. Scallop-shell. ℞. TAPAN. Taras on dolphin r., holding kantharos and cornucopiae. *B.M.C.* 479 .. .. F/*fair* 30/-

208 Æ 12. Scallop-shell. ℞. TA. Two dolphins r. *B.M.C.* 485 .. VF/F 60/-

209 **Uxentum** (Ugento). *c.* 89 B.C. and later. Æ 17 *semis.* Head of Athena r., spear-head before. ℞. OIAN. Herakles standing with club, cornucopiae and lion's skin; Nike flies above crowning him; S in field. *Grose* 801 .. .. R, *fair* 37/6

209   211A

LUCANIA.

210 **The Lucani.** Æ 27. Head of young Herakles r. in lion's skin. ℞. ΛΥΚΙΑΝΩΝ. Bellona r. striding forward with shield and spear. *B.M.C.* 5 .. R, *fair* 50/-

211 **Heraclea** (Policoro). 432-380 B.C. Æ *diobol.* Similar. ℞. HE. Lion running r. *B.M.C.* 1 VF £6/10/-

211A 380-330 Æ *didrachm.* Head of Athena r., in crested Athenian helmet adorned with Skylla hurling stone, ΔK before. ℞. ⊦ΗΡΑΚΛΗΙΩΝ. Herakles standing r., strangling lion, club behind, owl between legs. *B.M.C.* 28 .. .. F/*good* F, RR £50

212 345-281 B.C. Æ *didrachm.* Head of Athena r., wearing crested Corinthian helmet decorated with Skylla: behind, K. ℞. ΗΡΑΚΛΗΙΩΝ. Herakles standing facing, holding club, lion-skin, bow and arrow: in field, l., one-handled vase and AΘA. *B.M.C.* 35 *nearly* VF £25

213 380-281 B.C. Æ *diobol.* Head of Athena r., hippocamp on helmet. ℞. HPA. Herakles r. strangling lion. *B.M.C.* 19 .. .. VF 85/-

214 330-228 B.C. Æ 14. Head of Athena r. ℞. ⊦HPA ΚΛΕΙΩΝ. Herakles standing l. *B.M.C.* 58 .. .. *fair* 25/-

215 **Laus** (Laino). 500-450 B.C. Æ *didrachm.* ΖΑΛ above man-headed bull l. looking back. ℞. ΖΑΛ above man-headed bull r. *B.M.C.* 3 .. .. F £60

216 400-350 B.C. Æ 15. Bust of Demeter facing. ℞. Two crows passing one another, l. and r.: above, M. *B.M.C.* 14 .. .. *fair* 50/-

217 **Metapontum.** 550-480 B.C. Æ *stater* (125 grs.) of archaic style. META. Ear of barley: border of dots between lines. ℞. Same type incuse: border of radiating lines. *B.M.C.* 11. **Plate I** .. .. EF £50

218 — METAΠ retrograde. Ear of barley; elevated border of dots between two plain lines. ℞. Similar incuse; border of rays. *B.M.C.* 13 .. *good* F/VF £25

219 — META. Similar, smaller module, with cable border enclosing dots on raised bands on *obv.* ℞. Same type incuse, border of somewhat closer lines. *B.M.C.* 17 VF £18

220 Æ *sixth-stater* (18 grs.). MET. Ear of barley: border of dots on raised band. ℞. Bucranium incuse: border of radiating lines. *B.M.C.* 40 .. .. *nearly* VF £8

221 400-350 B.C. Æ *stater.* Female head (? Homonoia) l., diademed. ℞. META. Ear of barley: in field, r., praying mantis. *Cf. B.M.C.* 61; *Noe " Coinage of Metapontum,"* No. 398 .. .. RR, F £75

222 — Head of Hygeia, wearing double fillet and ear-ring, r.: on truncation of neck ⊦ΥΓΙΕΙΑ. ℞. MET. Ear of barley with leaf l.: in field, l., T. *B.M.C.* 63 .. *good* F £35

222A — Head of Apollo Karneios r., with ram's ear and horn. ℞. ME TA, ear of barley with leaf to l. *Noe* 336. **Plate I** .. .. RR, EF £280

222B **Metapontum.** 400-350 B.C. Æ *stater.* Head of Demeter veiled r.; in front, cross-headed torch. ℞. ΜΕΤΑ ΠΟΝΤ. Ear of barley. *B.M.C.* 146; *Noe* 323   *RR*, F   £100

223 Æ *sixth-stater* (19 grs.). Young male head, with ram's horn, r. ℞. Similar type to preceding. *Cf. B.M.C.* 156 ..   .. *fair* £7/10/-

224 — Helmeted head of Athena r. ℞. As preceding. *B.M.C.* 162 ..   .. F £5

225 350-330 B.C. Æ *distater* (*plated*). Head of Leukippos, r., bearded, wearing Corinthian helmet decorated with Nike in quadriga, etc.: behind head, ΑΠΗ and forepart of lion r. ℞. ΜΕΤΑΠΟΝΤΙΝΩΝ. Ear of barley with leaf l.: in field, l., club and ΑΜΙ. *B.M.C.* 75 ..   .. *RRR*, VF/F   £100

226 — Æ *stater.* Very similar but helmet plain. ΛΕΥΚΙ[ΠΠΟΣ] above, dog behind. ℞. ΜΕΤΑ. Ear of barley, leaf on r.; above which, dove; below, ΑΜΙ. *B.M.C.* 79
good F   £32/10/-

227 — — Head of Demeter r., bound with wreath of barley with ears of corn and veil. ℞. ΜΕΤΑ to r. of ear of barley with leaf on l., on which, mouse; below leaf, Φ. *B.M.C.* 122
F £25

228 350-300 B.C. Æ 24. Female head r. ℞. ΜΕ. Ear of barley r. *B.M.C.* 167
F 52/6

229 Æ 14. Bust of Helios facing. ℞. ΜΕ. Three barley-corns. *B.M.C.* 183   F 35/-

230 330-300 B.C. Æ *stater.* Head of nymph r., hair rolled. ℞. ΜΕΤΑ. Ear of barley with leaf r.; in field r., ΙΩ. *B.M.C.* 85 ..   .. F £11

231 — Head of Persephone r. wreathed with barley. ℞. ΜΕΤΑ. Ear of barley with leaf r., plough above leaf; beneath, ΜΑΝ. *B.M.C.* 96 ..   .. *nearly* VF £20

232 — Head of Persephone three-quarter r. ℞. ΜΕΤΑ. Ear of barley with leaf to r, bucranium above, ΑΘΑ beneath. *B.M.C.* 117. **Plate I**   .. F/VF £36

233 212-207 B.C. Æ *drachm.* Head of Athena r. ℞. Ear of barley, club to l. *B.M.C.* 149
F £7/10/-

234 Æ *diobol.* Head of Athena r. ℞. Ear of barley, cornucopiae to r. *B.M.C.* 163
F 65/-

235 **Poseidonia** (Pesto). 550-480 B.C. Æ *stater* of archaic style. ΜΟΠ. Poseidon adv. r., hair in formal curls, wearing chlamys with pointed ends falling over both shoulders: he brandishes ornamental trident in r. hand and extends l. arm: dotted cable border. ℞. ΜΟΠ. Similar figure l., incuse, but trident plain and chlamys shown passing round back. *B.M.C.* 1 ..   .. *RR*, VF £150

236 — Similar, but trident is plain and chlamys has square ends: *rev.* does not show trident. (115 grs.). *B.M.C.* 5-6 ..   .. *RR*, VF £125

237 Æ *half-stater or drachm* (55 grs.). ΠΟΜΕΣ. Type as preceding, double border of dots. ℞. Same legend retrograde, and same type incuse. *Cf. B.M.C.* 19   *RR*, VF £65

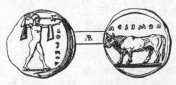

239 480-400 B.C. Æ *stater* (lumpy fabric). ΠΟΜΕΙΔ. Type as before but less archaic. ℞. ΠΟΜΕSDAN retrograde above bull l., all within shallow incuse. *B.M.C.* 33/32
nearly VF/F £25

240 Æ *sixth.* ΠΟΜ retrograde. Poseidon r. ℞. ΠΟΜ retrograde above bull l., in ex. barley corn. *B.M.C.* 47 ..   .. F £8

241 Æ 13. ΠΟΣΕΙ Poseidon   ℞. ΡΟΣΕΙ. Bull butting r. *B.M.C.* 71   .. F 40/-

242 **Paestum** (The Lucanians who captured Poseidonia corrupted the name to Paestum). 300-268 B.C. Æ 20. Head of Poseidon r. ℞. ΠΑΙΣΤΑΝΟ. Eros l. riding on dolphin. *B.M.C.* 2 .. .. F/*fair* 40/–

243 268-89 B.C. Æ 16 *triens*. Head of Dionysos r.: behind, four pellets. ℞. ΠΑΙΣ. Cornucopiae. *B.M.C.* 8 .. .. F 30/–

244 Æ 15 *quadrans*. Head of Poseidon r.: behind, three pellets. ℞. ΠΑΙΣ. Dolphin r.; above, three pellets: below, laurel branch. *B.M.C.* 16 .. .. .. VF 65/–

245 Æ 18 *sextans*. Head of Persephone r. ℞. ΠΑΙΣ. Forepart of boar r.: below, two pellets. *B.M.C.* 21 .. .. 4 40/–

246 Æ 12 *uncia*. Head of Artemis r. ℞. ΠΑΙΣ. Ear of corn: in field, l., pellet. *B.M.C.* 29 F 25/–

247 *After* 89 B.C. Æ 17 *semis*. Head of Poseidon r.: behind, s and trident. ℞. CN . TĒY. Prow r. *B.M.C.* 37 .. .. *fair* 25/–

248 Æ 15 *semis*. ΠΑΕ. Head of Pallas, r.: behind, s. ℞. L.F.AP/L.S.AT. Clasped hands *B.M.C.* 51 .. .. *fair* 18/6

249 — ΠΑΕQVIS. Side view of temple with six columns. ℞. CN · COR · M · TVC · PATR within wreath. *B.M.C.* 60 .. .. F 35/–

250 Æ 19. Two figures working at anvil. ℞. Scales: in ex., ΠΑΕ. *B.M.C.* 76 *fair* 25/–

251 *Tiberius*. Æ 17 *sextans*. His head r.; in front, lituus. ℞. C . LOLLI M. Woman (Livia ?) seated r. *B.M.C.* 78 .. .. F 40/–

252 **Siris and Pyxus.** 560-510 B.C. Æ *stater*. MSPSNOM retrograde. Bull standing l. looking back. ℞. ΠVΧΘΕΜ. Same type incuse. *B.M.C.* 1 *RR*, VF £300

253 **Sybaris.** 550-510 B.C. Æ *stater*. Bull standing l., looking back: in ex., VM: borders of dots on band. ℞. Same, incuse and reversed. *B.M.C.* 1. **Plate I** *good* F £30

254 — Similar, but ΥΜ above bull. *B.M.C.* 5 .. .. VF £50

255 Æ *third*. As before but ΥΜ in ex. *B.M.C.* 9 .. .. *fair* £5

256 Æ *sixth*. Bull l., head turned back, VM in ex. ℞. Diota incuse. *B.M.C.* 15 VF £8

257 453-448. Æ *sixth*. Poseidon advancing r. ℞. VM above bull r. *B.M.C.* 23 F £8

258 *c.* 445 B.C. Æ *third*. Head of Athena r. ℞. ΣΥΒΑΡΙ above bull r., head lowered, fish in ex. *B.M.C.* 32 .. .. F/*fair* 85/–

259 Æ *sixth*. Similar. ℞. ΣΥΒΑ. Bull r. looking back. *B.M.C.* 33 *good* F/F £7/10/–

260 **Thurium.** 440-420 B.C. Æ *stater*. Head of Athena r., helmet wreathed with olive. ℞. ΘΟΥΡΙΩΝ above bull butting r., tunny fish in ex. *B.M.C.* 2. **Plate I** VF £50

261 Æ *sixth*. Similar. ℞. ΘΟΥΡΙ, similar, but bull l. *Grose* 1230 *good* F 90/–

262 400-350 B.C. Æ *distater*. Type as preceding, but helmet decorated with Skylla: on flap, griffin. ℞. ΘΟΥΡΙΩΝ. Bull butting r.: in ex., tunny-fish r. *B.M.C.* 26

RR, F/VF £120

263 — As preceding, somewhat later in style: Skylla hurling stone, ΣΑΝ behind head. ℞. As preceding, with ΕΥΦΑ above bull; in ex., two tunny-fish. *B.M.C.* 38

RR, VF £200

264 Æ *stater*. Obv. as preceding, but Skylla holding trident. ℞. ΘΟΥΡΙΩΝ. Bull butting r.: in ex., fish. *B.M.C.* 57 .. .. VF £35

264A — Similar but Skylla just raises her hand, and the whole piece is of the finest style. *Cf. B.M.C.* 29. **Plate I** .. .. VF £125

265 Æ *sixth-stater*. Types as preceding, but ΗΡΑ above bull. *B.M.C.* 110 .. F 75/–

266 Æ 16. Types similar to preceding: above bull, Η. *B.M.C.* 132 .. .. *fair* 22/6

267 **Velia.** *c.* 540-500. Æ *drachm.* Forefront of lion r., devouring prey. ℞. Incuse quartered square. *Grose,* 1395

irregular flan, EF/VF £40; EF *and beautifully struck, RR* £65

267A — Æ *obol.* As before .. .. F £6/10/-

267B 500-400 B.C. Æ *didrachm.* B above lion crouching r. ℞. VEΛH below archaic female head r. *B.M.C.* 2 .. .. *fair* £10

268 450-400 B.C. Æ *drachm.* Female head r., hair bound with fillet and turned up behind. ℞. YEΛH. Owl r. on olive-branch: in field, Δ. *B.M.C.* 9 .. *R,* VF/*good* F £25

269 400-268 B.C. Æ *didrachm.* Head of Athena l., wearing crested Athenian helmet adorned with griffin; Φ on flap of helmet, monogram AP behind. ℞. YEΛHTΩN. Lion walking r.: above, caduceus. *B.M.C.* 105 .. .. *good* F £12

270 — *Obv.* Type similar to preceding, but A above helmet and IE behind in incuse square. ℞. Lion springing l. on stag. *B.M.C.* 111 .. .. *good* F £14

271 — Head of Athena l., wearing Phrygian helmet decorated with female centaur: behind, monogram ꓗE. ℞. YEΛHTΩN. Lion l., devouring prey: above, A: beneath, monogram ꓗE. *B.M.C.* 74 .. .. *nearly* VF/*good* F £30

272 *After* 350 B.C. Æ 14. Head of Herakles r. in lion's skin. ℞. YEΛH. Owl l. *B.M.C.* 119 .. .. F/*fair* 21/-

273 Æ 12. Head of Poseidon r. ℞. YEΛH. Owl facing, wings spread. *B.M.C.* 123 F 25/-

271					274

BRUTTIUM.

274 **The Bruttii.** 282-203 B.C. Æ *didrachm.* Busts of the Dioskuri r., wearing chlamydes and laur. pilei; above, two stars; behind, cornucopiae and Γ. ℞. BPETTIΩN in ex. The Dioskuri on horseback r.; below, knotted staff. *B.M.C.* 8 *RRR,* VF £400

274A Æ *octobol.* Bust of winged Nike, diademed, r. ℞. BPETTIΩN. Pan standing facing, crowning himself, spear in l. hand. *B.M.C.* 16 .. .. .. EF £25

275 Æ 26. Head of Ares l., wearing crested Corinthian helmet decorated with griffin: below head, thunderbolt. ℞. BPETTIΩN. Bellona, helmeted, running r., holding shield with both hands and spear under l. arm: in field, r., torch. *B.M.C.* 47

green patina, F 45/-; VF 90/-

276 Æ 26 *sextans.* *Obv.* as preceding, but corn-ear below head and two pellets behind. ℞. BPETTIΩN. Nike l., crowning trophy: in field, cornucopiae. *B.M.C.* 57 F 45/-

277 — — Laur. head of Zeus r. ℞. BPETTIΩN. Naked warrior advancing r.; in front, bucranium. *B.M.C.* 71 .. .. VF £5

277A — — Similar, but *rev.* type, eagle l. on thunderbolt. *B.M.C.* 86 .. *nearly* F 35/-

278 Æ 18. NIKA. Head of Nike l. ℞. BPETTIΩN. Zeus advancing r., with thunderbolt and sceptre: in field, star and cornucopiae. *B.M.C.* 98 .. .. VF/F 50/-

279 **Caulonia.** 550-480 B.C. Æ *stater* of archaic style. KAVL. Naked archaic male figure, r. arm raised and holding branch, l. arm extended and bearing small figure running r.: in field, r., stag r., looking back. ℞. Same type incuse, but small figure not shown. *B.M.C.* 8. **Plate I** .. .. *RR,* VF £80

279A **Caulonia.** As preceding, but *rev.* has small figure in relief on outstretched arm of large incuse figure. *B.M.C.* 1 .. .. *RR*, VF £90

280 — As preceding, smaller and cruder fabric, with *obv.* legend KAVLO retrograde, and no small figure on *rev.* *B.M.C.* 15 .. .. *R*, F £25

281 480-388 B.C. Æ *stater.* KAVL retrograde. Type similar to preceding. Ŗ. KAVL retro. Stag standing r.: in field, r., sapling growing: linear border. *B.M.C.* 18
R, good F £22

282 Æ *third.* Similar figure. Ŗ. ΚΑΥΛΟ. Stag r. *B.M.C.* 38 var. .. *fair*/F £5/10/-

283 Æ *sixth-stater* (15.5 grs.). Types as preceding. *B.M.C.* 45 .. .. *fair* 45/-

284 **Croton** (Cotrona). 550-480 B.C. Æ *stater* of archaic style. ϘΡΟ. Tripod-lebes with three handles and legs ending in lion's feet: cable border. Ŗ. Same type incuse. *B.M.C.* 1
RR, VF £75

285 — Similar, smaller module and cruder style: in *obv.* field, l., crane r. *B.M.C.* 18. **Plate I** .. .. *nearly* VF £20

286 — Similar, thick fabric and tripod more elaborate: crane r. in field l. *B.M.C.* 26
good F £16

287 — Similar, with both sides in relief. *B.M.C.* 46 .. .. F £13

287A — Similar, but no crane. Ŗ. Eagle flying r., design sunken. *B.M.C.* 35
F/*good* F £13

288 480-420 B.C. Æ *stater.* Eagle standing l., head r., on stag's head. Ŗ. ϘΡΟ. Tripod-lebes: in field, l., ivy-leaf. *B.M.C.* 68. **Plate II** .. .. .. *good* VF £75

289 Æ *sixth.* *Obv.* as *rev.* of preceding. Ŗ. Pegasus flying l., with curled wing: below, Ϙ. *B.M.C.* 52 .. .. F £8/10/-

290 420-390 B.C. Æ *stater.* Eagle standing l. on olive-branch. Ŗ. ΚΡΟ. Tripod-lebes: in field, r., Δ. *B.M.C.* 80 .. .. F £15

291 Æ *stater.* Head of Hera Lakinia almost facing, wearing necklace and stephanos, hair flowing. Ŗ. ΚΡΟΤΩΝΙΑΤΑΝ. Herakles reclining l. on rock covered with lion-skin, holding wine-cup in r. hand and resting on l. elbow: in field, bow, club, small M and large Δ: to l., tripod. *B.M.C.* 92 .. .. *pleasing style, RRR, good* F £60

292 370-330 B.C. Æ *stater.* Head of Apollo, laur., r., with long hair. Ŗ. ΚΡΟΤ. Tripod-lebes: in field, r., laurel branch. *B.M.C.* 100 .. .. .. VF/*good* VF £120

293 Æ 16. Head of young Herakles r. in lion's skin. Ŗ. Crab, KPO below. *B.M.C.* 114
F 45/-

291   294

294 **Hipponium** (Bivona). 330-325 B.C. Æ 19. ΔΕΟΣ. Laur. head of Zeus r. Ŗ. ΕΙΠΩΝΙΕΩΝ. Amphora. *B.M.C.* 14 .. .. *fair* 40/-

295 **Vibo Valentia.** (new name for Hipponium after it received a Roman garrison in 272 B.C.). 192-89 B.C. Æ 20 *semis.* Head of Hera r., s behind neck. Ŗ. VALENTIA. Double cornucopiae. *B.M.C.* 9 .. .. *good* F 45/-

296 Æ 18 *triens.* Head of Athena r., four pellets behind. Ŗ. VALENTIA. Owl and four pellets. *B.M.C.* 20 .. .. *nearly* F 30/-

297 Æ 16 *quadrans.* Hd. of Herakles, three pellets behind. Ŗ. VALENTIA. Two clubs, their handles joined together; in field, star and three pellets. *B.M.C.* 27 *good* F 35/-

298 **Locri Epizephyrii.** 332-326 B.C. Æ *stater.* Head of Zeus, laureate, r.: behind, thunderbolt. Ŗ. ΛΟΚΡΩΝ. Eagle l., with wing spread, devouring supine hare. *B.M.C.* 10 .. .. *nearly* VF £20

299 350-300 B.C. Æ *stater* of Corinthian type. Pegasos flying l.: below, thunderbolt. Ŗ. ΛΟΚΡΩΝ. Helmeted head of Athena l. *B.M.C.* (*Corinth*) 9. **Plate II** .. VF £18

300 300-280 B.C. Æ *stater.* Eagle on hare r., ΛΟ below. Ŗ. ΛΟΚΡΩΝ above thunderbolt, ΛΟ below. *Grose* 1806 .. .. *good* F/F £17/10/-

300A **Locri.** 280-268 B.C. *Æ stater.* Struck when the Locrians were under the influence of Rome. Head of Zeus l., NE mon. below. ℞. ΛΟΚΡΩΝ in ex. Roma seated r. being crowned by Locri stg. l., PΩMA on l., ΠΙΣΤΙΣ on r. *B.M.C.* 15..   *fine style*, VF, *RRR* £200

301 300-268 B.C. Æ 23. ΔΙΟΣ. Head of Zeus l. ℞. ΛΟΚΡΟΝ. Winged thunderbolt. *B.M.C.* 24 ..   ..   F 40/-

302 Æ 29. Female head (? Persephone) r. ℞. ΛΟΚΡΩΝ. Eagle, wings closed, standing l. on thunderbolt. *B.M.C.* 31 ..   ..   F 50/-

303 Æ 20. Helmeted head of Athena l.: above, EY. ℞. ΛΟΚΡΩΝ. Eagle, wings open, standing on thunderbolt: in field, star. *B.M.C.* 38 ..   ..   ..   F/*fair* 35/-

304 Æ 19. Busts of the Dioskuri r. ℞. ΛΟΚΡΩΝ. Zeus seated l. *B.M.C.* 40   *fair* 22/6

305 **Mesma** (colony of Locri). *After* 350 B.C. *Æ stater* of Corinthian type. Pegasos flying l. ℞. Head of Athena l., M above. *B.M.C. (Corinth)* 2; *Grose* 1836   F £25

306 **Mystia and Hyporon.** *c.* 300 B.C. Æ 19. Laur. head of Apollo r. ℞. Υ Ρ / Π Ω either side of tripod lebes, MY below. *Grose* 1840 ..   ..   *R, fair* 45/-

307 **Nuceria.** 350-270 B.C. Æ 20. Head of Apollo, laur., r.: below, corn-ear. ℞. ΝΟΥΚΡΙΝΩΝ. Horse standing l.: below, pentagram. *B.M.C.* 1 ..   ..   F 60/-

307   309A

308 **Petelia** (Strongoli). 280-216 B.C. Æ 20. Head of Demeter r., veiled and wearing wreath of barley. ℞. ΠΕΤΗΛΙΝΩΝ. Zeus facing, striding l., holding thunderbolt and sceptre. *B.M.C.* 5 ..   ..   F 45/-

309 **Rhegium.** 494-480 B.C. *Æ drachm.* Lion's scalp facing. ℞. RECION reversed. Calf's head l. *B.M.C.* 1 ..   ..   *good* F £40

309A 466-415 B.C. *Æ tetradrachm.* Lion's scalp facing. ℞. RECINOS. Male figure seated l., on stool, holding sceptre; all within olive wreath. *B.M.C.* 8 ..   VF £200

310 *Æ drachm.* Similar. *B.M.C.* 16 ..   ..   *nearly* F/F £10

310A *Æ obol.* *Obv.* as before. ℞. REGI in olive wreath. *B.M.C.* 22   F   £8/10/-

311 415-387 B.C. *Æ tetradrachm.* Lion's scalp facing. ℞. PHΓINOΣ. Head of Apollo r.; olive-leaf behind. *B.M.C.* 23. **Plate II** ..   ..   F £135

312 *Æ obol.* *Obv.* As preceding. ℞. P H within spray of olive. *B.M.C.* 30   VF £8/10/-

313 350-270 B.C. Æ 19. Lion's scalp facing. ℞. Head of Apollo, laur. r.: behind, dolphin. *B.M.C.* 66 ..   ..   VF 90/-

314 270-203 B.C. Æ 22. Head of Apollo, laur., l., hair long: behind, lyre tuning-key. ℞. PHΓINΩN. Tripod-lebes. *B.M.C.* 75 ..   ..   VF 90/-

315 203-89 B.C. Æ 27 *pentonkion*. Janiform female head. ℞. ΡΗΓΙΝΩΝ. Asklepios
     seated l., holding serpent-staff: in field, l., Π.   *B.M.C.* 89   ..   ..   .. VF £10

316 — Similar, with tripod in l. of *rev.* field.   *B.M.C.* 92   ..   ..   .. F 75/-

317 Æ 25 *tetras*. Jugate heads of Apollo and Artemis r. ℞. ΡΗΓΙΝΩΝ. Tripod: in
     field, r., four pellets. *B.M.C.* 97   ..   .. VF £6

318 Æ 15 *tetras*. Jugate busts of the Dioskuri, wearing laureate caps. ℞. ΡΗΓΙΝΩΝ.
     Young Asklepios standing l., holding bird and serpent-staff: in field, l., ΙΙΙΙ. *B.M.C.* 110
                                                                                       VF/F 55/-

319 **Terina.** 440-400 B.C. Æ *stater*. ΤΕΡΙΝ. Head of nymph r., hair in knot on crown
     of head. ℞. ΤΕΡΙΝΑΙΟΝ. Nike, winged, seated l. on stool, with ball on back of r.
     hand. *B.M.C.* 13 ..   .. *R, nearly* VF/VF £55

320 — ΤΕΡΙΝΑΙΟΝ. Head of nymph r., wearing sphendone decorated with maeander pattern,
     hair in knot in crown. ℞. Nike seated l. on square cippus, r. hand resting on upright
     caduceus. *B.M.C.* 18. **Plate II**   ..   ..   *RRR, good* VF/*almost* EF £200

321 — *Obv.* Similar to previous. ℞. Nike standing l., bending forward, r. foot on rock,
     r. arm resting on knee and holding caduceus, handle downwards: in field, Π *B.M.C.* 22
                                                          obverse off-centre, fair/F £25

321A — ΤΕΡΙΝΑΙΟΝ. Head of nymph r., richly ornate with curly hair. ℞. Nike on square
     cippus l., receiving alighting dove on r. hand. *B.M.C.* 41
                                                       very pleasing, R, nearly VF £120

322 *After* 400 B.C. Æ *third*. Head of nymph r., ΤΕΡ behind. ℞. Nike seated l. on cippus
     holding bird. *B.M.C.* 32   ..   .. F £6/10/-

323 Æ *sixth*. Female head l., wearing ampyx. ℞. Nike seated l. on cippus. *B.M.C.* 34
                                                                                       F £5

324 — Female head r. ℞. Nike seated l. on capital of Ionic column, holding branch.
     B.M.C. 39 ..   .. F/*fair* 60/-

326 Æ 15. Female head r. ℞. ΤΕΡΙ. Nike seated l. on cippus. *B.M.C.* 61 *fair* 25/-

SICILY

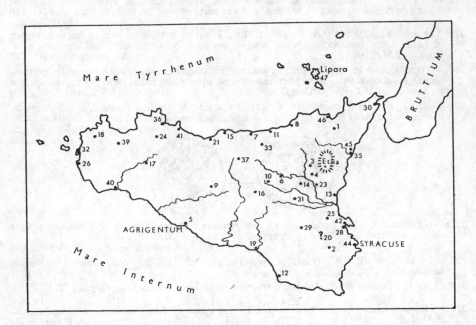

1 Abacaenum	15 Cephaloedium	31 Morgantina
2 Acrae	16 Enna	32 Motya
3 Adranum	17 Entella	33 Mytistratus
4 Aetna	18 Eryx	35 Naxus
5 Agrigentum	19 Gela	36 Panormus
6 Agyrium	20 Herbessus	37 Petra
7 Alaesa	21 Himera	39 Segesta
8 Aluntium	23 Hybla Magna	40 Selinus
9 Amestratus	24 Iaetia	41 Solus
10 Assorus	25 Leontini	42 Stiela
11 Calacte	26 Lilybaeum	44 Syracuse
12 Camarina	28 Megara	45 Tauromenium
13 Catana	29 Menaenum	46 Tyndaris
14 Centuripae	30 Zancle-Messana	47 Lipara

327 **Abacaenum** (Tripi). 450-400 B.C. Æ *litra*. Laur. head of Zeus r. ℞ ABA in ex., ΝΙΑΧ above boar standing r.; in front, acorn. *B.M.C.* 2 .. .. .. VF £18

327A **Acrae** (Palazzuolo-Acreide). *After* B.C. 210. Æ 22. Head of Persephone. ℞. ΑΚΡΑΙΩΝ. Demeter standing l. with torch and sceptre. *B.M.C.* 1 .. .. .. F £6

327 328

328 **Adranum** (Aderno). *After* 345 B.C. Æ 33. ΑΠΟΛ. Head of Apollo, laur., l. ℞. Lyre of seven strings. *B.M.C.* 1 .. .. .. *RR, overstruck on coin of Syracuse*, F £8

329 **Aetna.** *After* 210 B.C. Æ 20 *trias*. Rad. head of Apollo r. ℞. ΑΙΤΝΑΙΩΝ. Warrior standing l: in field l., three pellets. *B.M.C.* 1 .. .. F £5

330 **Agrigentum.** 550-472 B.C. Æ *didrachm*. ΑΚΡΑCΑΝΤΟΣ retrograde. Eagle standing l., wings closed. ℞. Crab. *B.M.C.* 7 .. .. .. *almost* VF £45

331 — Similar, of smaller and thicker fabric. *Obv.* legend ΑΚRΑCΑΝ. *B.M.C.* 23. **Plate II** VF £40

332 — Similar, with eagle to r. *B.M.C.* 19 .. .. F £20

333 472-415 B.C. Æ *tetradrachm*. *Obv.* ΑΚRΑCΑΝΤΟΣ. Eagle l. ℞. Crab. *B.M.C.* 37 RR, VF/EF £50

334 Æ *litra*. ΑΚRΑ. Eagle standing l. on Corinthian capital. ℞. Crab: below, rose. *Cf. B.M.C.* 48 .. .. VF £7/10/–

335 Æ *trias* of tooth-shaped or conical form, 20 × 16 mm. Eagle's head on each of the two smaller sides; crab on wider side; three pellets on base .. .. *RRR, fair* £20

336 Æ *hexas*. Similar, 18 × 12. On one side, eagle's head l.; on the other, uncertain type; with two pellets on base .. .. *RRR*, F £25

337 Æ *uncia* of somewhat ellipsoid form, 19 × 11 × 5 mm. On one side, eagle's head l.; on the other, crab's claw .. .. *RRR*, F £20

(*The above three pieces are referred to in B.M.C., pp. 23-24 as being, perhaps, coin-weights rather than coins*).

338 413-406 B.C. Æ *tetradrachm*. ΑΚRΑΓΑΝΤΙΝΟΝ. Eagle standing l. with spread wings and lowered head on dead hare lying on rock, on which corn grain and scallop shell. ℞. Crab between scallop and conch; below, large fish (gurnard). *B.M.C.* 59 *RRR*, F £300

338A Æ *hemidrachm*. Eagle r., with spread wings, on hare: in field, l., barley-corn. ℞. ΑΚRΑ. Crab: below, sea-monster with fish in its jaws. *B.M.C.* 63 *fair* £5

339 — Similar, with *obv.* type 1. ℞. Crab: below, fish r. *B.M.C.* 68 F £10

340 Æ 25 *hemilitron*. ΑΚRΑ. Eagle standing r., wings spread, on fish. ℞. Crab with eel in l. claw: below, conch-shell and octopus: around, six pellets. *B.M.C.* 86 F 60/–

341 Æ 21 *trias*. Eagle r., wings spread, preying on hare. ℞. Crab: below, three pellets and cray fish l. *B.M.C.* 102 .. .. *fair* 25/–

342 Agrigentum.   340-287 B.C.   Æ *hemidrachm.*   Horse cantering r.   ℞.   Crab.
B.M.C. 75   R, F   £20

343 Phintias, tyrant 287-279 B.C.   Æ 21.   Head of Artemis l.   ℞.   ΒΑΣΙΛΕΟΣ ΦΙΝΤΙΑ.
Boar l.   *B.M.C.* 138   ..   ..   F/*fair* 55/-

344 279-241 B.C.   Æ 21.   Head of Apollo, laur., r.   ℞.   Two eagles l. preying on hare.
B.M.C. 140   ..   ..   F 50/-

345 241-210 B.C.   Æ 20.   ΒΩCΙΟC.   Head of Persephone r.   ℞.   ΑΚΡΑΓΑΝ ΤΙΝΩΝ.
Asklepios facing, head l., r. hand extended.   *B.M.C.* 153   ..   ..   F/*fair* 55/-

346 Agyrium (Agira).   345-300 B.C.   Æ 27.   Hd. of young Herakles or Iolaös r. wearing
lion's skin.   ℞.   ΑΓΥΡΙΝΑΙΩΝ.   Leopard r. devouring hare.   *B.M.C.* 6   *nearly* VF   £15

346A *After* 241 B.C.   Æ 25.   ΕΠΙ CΩΝΑΤΡΟΥ.   Laur. head of Zeus r.   ℞.   ΑΓΥΡΙΝΑΙΩΝ.
Male figure standing l., Nike flies to crown him.   *B.M.C.* 12   ..   R, *fair* 60/-

347 **Alaesa** (Tusa).   *c.* 340 B.C.   Æ 21.   Horse prancing l.: in ex., ΚΑΙΝΟΝ.   ℞.   Griffin galloping l.   *B.M.C.* 6   ..   ..   F 50/-

347A Æ 30.   ΑΡΧΑΓΕΤΑΣ.   Laur. hd. of Apollo l.   ℞.   ΣΥΜΜΑΧΙΚΟΝ.   Lighted pine-torch
between two stalks of barley.   *B.M.C.* p. 28, 1   ..   ..   F £5

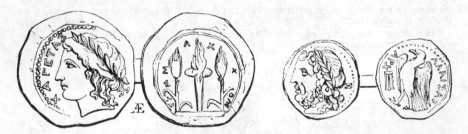

347A   348A

348 275-212 B.C.   Æ 20.   Laur. head of Apollo r.   ℞.   ΑΛΑΙΣΑΣ.   Apollo standing l.,
leaning on lyre and holding wreath.   *B.M.C.* 7   ..   ..   ..   F/*fair* 50/-

348A Æ 20.   Laur. hd. of Zeus l.   ℞.   ΑΛΑΙΣΑΕ ΑΡΧ.   Eagle standing l., tripod before.
B.M.C. 3   ..   ..   *fair* 30/-

349 **Aluntium.**   250-210 B.C.   Æ 17.   Young male head, wearing Phrygian helmet, l.
℞.   ΑΛΟΝ - - -.   Man-headed bull standing l., water streaming from mouth.   *B.M.C.*
4   ..   ..   R, *fair* 75/-

349A Æ 25.   Laur. hd. of bearded Herakles r.   ℞.   ΑΛΟΝΤΙΝΩΝ.   Eagle standing r. on
carcase.   *B.M.C.* 2   ..   ..   F 75/-

350 **Amestratus** (Mistretta).   *c.* 241 B.C.   Æ 17.   Head of young Dionysos r.   ℞.   ΑΜΗΣ-
ΤΡΑΤΙΝΩΝ ΛΕΥ.   Horseman galloping l.   *B.M.C.* 1   ..   ..   ..   R, F   £5

349A 351

351 **Assorus.** *After* 210 B.C. Æ 22. ASSORV. Laur. head of Apollo r. ℞. CRYSAS.
River-god Chrysas standing l. *B.M.C.* 1 .. .. *R, fair* 45/-

352 **Calacte** (Caronia). 241-210 B.C. Æ 20. Head of Athena r. ℞. ΚΑΛΑΚΤΙΝΩΝ. Owl r. on
amphora. *B.M.C.* 1 .. .. *fair* 35/-

353 **Camarina.** 495-485 B.C. Æ *litra.* ΚΑΜΑΡΙΝΑΙΟΝ. Athena standing l., with spear
and shield. ℞. Nike flying l.: at her feet, swan l.: all within olive-wreath. *B.M.C.* 3
good F £8/10/-

352 354

354 461-405 B.C. Æ *tetradrachm.* Same legend: Head of young Herakles l., wearing
lion-skin. ℞. Quadriga galloping r., driven by Athena wearing helmet and crowned
by flying Nike: in ex., barley-corn. *B.M.C.* 15 .. .. .. *RR,* F £120

355 413-405 B.C. Æ 15 *trias.* Head of Athena l. ℞. ΚΑΜΑ. Owl l., head facing, lizard
in claw; three pellets in ex. *B.M.C.* 39 .. .. *fair* 30/-

356 **Catana.** 461-415 B.C. Æ *tetradrachm.* Slow quadriga r.: above, Nike flying r.,
crowning horses. ℞. ΚΑΤΑΝΑΙΟΝ. Head of Apollo, laur., r. *B.M.C.* 22 F £50

356A — by Heracleidas. Facing hd. of Apollo; to r. ΗΡΑΚΛΕΙΔΑΣ. ℞. ΚΑΤΑΝΑΙΩΝ in ex.
Quadriga to l., Nike above; also in ex., fish. *B.M.C.* 32
VF/F *but has been corroded and cleaned* £1750

357 3rd-2nd Cent. B.C. Æ 17 *hexas.* Laur. head of Apollo. ℞. ΚΑΤΑΝΑΙΩΝ. Isis
standing r. holding bird; to r., ΙΙ. *B.M.C.* 65 .. .. F 40/-

358 Æ 20. ΚΑΤΑΝΑΙΩΝ. Head of Zeus Ammon r. ℞. Dikaiosyne standing l. holding
scales and cornucopiae: in field, three monograms. *B.M.C.* 85 .. *R,* F 65/-

359 Æ 22. Janiform head of Sarapis: in field, three monograms. ℞. ΚΑΤΑΝΑΙΩΝ.
Persephone standing l., holding corn-ears and torch. *B.M.C.* 91 .. *R,* F 60/-

360 **Centuripae** (Centorbi). *After* 241 B.C. Æ 26 *dekonkion*. Head of Zeus, laur. r. ℞. KENT-
OPIΠINΩN. Winged thunderbolt: beneath, Δ. *B.M.C.* 3 .. .. .. F 50/-

361 Æ 24 *hemilitron*. Head of Apollo r. ℞. KENTOPIΠINΩN. Lyre between six pellets.
B.M.C. 7 .. .. F 45/-

362 Æ 17 *hexas*. Bust of Persephone r.: behind, ear of barley. ℞. KENTOPIΠINΩN.
Plough r., on which, bird r.: behind, two pellets. *B.M.C.* 12 .. .. F 37/6

363 **Cephaloedium** (Cefalu). 254-210 B.C. Æ 21. Laur. head of Herakles r. ℞.
KEΦA. Club between lion's skin and quiver with bow and arrows. *B.M.C.* 3 R, F 75/-

363   365A

364 **Enna** (Castrogiovanni). Under Roman rule. Æ 22. MVN HENNAE. Head of Artemis r.
℞. M . CESTIVS L . MVNATIVS II VIR. Male figure standing l. *B.M.C.* 11.. F 90/-

365 **Entella**. *c.* 450 B.C. Æ *litra*. ENTEΛΛINΩN above and below man-headed bull r. ℞.
Female sacrificing. *Grose* 2229 .. .. R, F £27/10/-

365A *c.* 340 B.C. Æ 20. ENTEΛΛ. Hd. of Persephone r. ℞. KAMΠANΩN. Pegasos flying l.
B.M.C. 4. Struck by Campanian mercenaries .. .. F 85/-

366 **Eryx**. Before 480 B.C. Æ *drachm*. ERVKINON retrograde. Eagle standing r. on Ionic
column. ℞. Crab, Ꮿ below. *B.M.C.* 1 .. .. RR, F £50

366A 415-400 B.C. Æ *litra*. EPYKINON. Aphrodite seated l. on throne: before
her, winged Eros flying r., holding garland. ℞. Hound r.; above, star; in front, floral
ornament. *B.M.C.* 13 .. .. R, F £17/10/-

366   367   368

367 **Gela**. Before 466 B.C. Æ *tetradrachm* (264.5 grs.). CEΛAΣ. Forepart of man-
headed bull r., swimming, r. fore-leg bent. ℞. Quadriga r., horses walking, charioteer
holding goad and reins: beyond horses, Ionic column (meta). *B.M.C.* 11
                                                   R, F/good F £35

368 Æ *didrachm*. *Obv.* Similar to preceding. ℞. Helmeted horseman cantering r.,
brandishing spear. *B.M.C.* 19 .. .. R, VF £22/10/-

369 Æ *litra*. Bridled horse r., wreath above. ℞. CEΛΛ above forepart of man-headed bull swimming r. *B.M.C.* 32 .. .. VF/F £11

370 466-415 B.C. Æ *tetradrachm*. Quadriga, with charioteer, walking slowly r. ℞. CEΛΑΣ, as last but of later or better style. *B.M.C.* 43 .. .. .. VF £50

371 Æ *litra*. Horseman galloping l. ℞. As last. *B.M.C.* 52 .. .. F/*fair* £8/10/-

372 After 241 B.C. Æ 20. Head of river-god Gelas r. ℞. ΓΕΛΩΙΩΝ. Warrior slaughtering ram r. *B.M.C.* 83.. .. .. F/*fair* 47/6

373 **Herbessus.** *c.* 340 B.C. Æ 29. ΕΡΒΗΣΣΙΝΩΝ. Head of nymph Sikelia r. ℞. Head of man-headed bull r. *Grose* 2282 .. .. *R, fair* £5

374 **Himera** (Termini). *Before* 480 B.C. Æ *drachm*. Cock advancing r. ℞. Square device, consisting of eight triangles, four incuse and four in relief, arranged mill-sail fashion, within incuse border of dots. *B.M.C.* 5 .. .. *RR,* F/VF £40

375 Æ *obol*. Similar types to preceding. *B.M.C.* 10 .. .. *fair* 65/-

376 482-472 B.C. Æ *didrachm*. ΗΙΜΕΡΑ. Cock l. ℞. Crab in circular incuse, annulet on shell. *B.M.C.* 24. **Plate II** .. .. *good* F £25

376A 472-413 B.C. Æ *tetradrachm*. ΙΜΕΡΑΙΟΝ retrograde in ex. Quadriga of horses walking slowly, Nike flies above to crown charioteer. ℞. The nymph Himera standing facing, head l., sacrificing with patera over altar; on r., Seilenos bathing in water from fountain in shape of lion's head; barley-corn above nymph's r. arm. *B.M.C.* 33
RR, F £100

376A   378

376B Æ 28 *hemilitron*. Gorgon-head facing. ℞. Six pellets. *Grose* 2304 *R,* F £10

377 **Hipana** *c.* 450 B.C. Æ *litra*. Eagle l. ℞. Cockle-shell beneath dolphin. *Pozzi* 461
RRR, EF £50

378 **Hybla Magna** (Paternò). 275-212 B.C. Æ 19. Female head r., wearing polos and veil. ℞. ΥΒΛΑΣ ΜΕΓΑΛΑΣ. Female standing l., panther or dog leaping up in front. *B.M.C.* 1 .. .. *fair* 45/-

378A **Iaetia** (Iato). *After* 241 B.C. Æ 23. ΙΑΙΤΙΝΩΝ. Head of Herakles r. ℞ Gorgon's head in centre of triskeles: between the legs, three ears of barley. *B.M.C.* 2
R, fair 60/-

379 **Leontini.** 500-466 B.C. Æ *tetradrachm*. ΛΕΟΝΤΙΝΟΝ. Quadriga r., with male charioteer; Nike flying r. above. ℞. Lion's head r. with open mouth, surrounded by four barley-corns. *B.M.C.* 4 .. .. *nearly* VF/VF £75

380 Æ *obol*. Lion's scalp facing, crudely represented. ℞. ΛΕΟΝ. Barley-corn. *B.M.C.* 21 .. .. *R,* F £12

381 Æ *tetradrachm* struck after the Carthaginian defeat in 479 B.C. Quadriga r., horses walking; above, Nike flies l., crowning young charioteer; in ex., lion running r. ℞. ΛΕΟΝΤΙΝΟΝ. Somewhat archaic laur. head of Apollo r. of superb style; around, three bay leaves; beneath, lion running r. *B.M.C.* 10.. .. *RRRR,* EF £4000

382 **Leontini.** 466-422 B.C. Æ *tetradrachm*. Head of Apollo r., wearing laurel-wreath with three rows of leaves, hair rolled behind. ℞. LEONTINON. Lion's head r., mouth open; around, four barley-corns. *B.M.C. 34* .. .. *RR, fine style*, VF/EF £110

383 Æ *litra*. LEON. Lion's head r. ℞. River-god standing l., holding patera and laurel-branch: before him, altar; behind, barley-corn. *B.M.C. 47* .. *R, nearly* VF/F £18

384 *After* 210 B.C. Æ 22. Head of Demeter facing: in field, l., plough. ℞. ΛΕΟΝ. River-god seated r. on rock, holding cornucopiae and branch. *B.M.C. 62* *R,* F 50/-

385 **Lilybaeum.** *After* 241 B.C. Æ 22. Laur. head of Apollo r. ℞. ΛΙΛΥΒΑΙΙΤΑΝ either side of lyre. *B.M.C. 2* .. .. F 45/-

385 386

385A **Longane.** 466-413 B.C. Æ *litra*. ΛΟΓΓΑΝΙΟΝ retrograde. Head of young Herakles r. ℞. Head of young river-god with short horns. *B.M.C. 1* *RRR,* F £35

385B **Megara.** 4th cent B.C. Æ *litra*. Female head. ℞. ΜΕΓΑ. Man-headed bull. *Head,* p. 151 .. .. *RRR,* F £30

386 **Menaenum.** *After* 210 B.C. Æ 17. Laur. bust of Zeus Sarapis r. ℞. ΜΕΝΑΙΝΩΝ above and below biga galloping r., driven by Nike, Π below horses. *B.M.C. 9* F 32/6

387 **Zankle-Messana.** *Before* 493 B.C. Æ *drachm* (81 grs.). DANKLE. Sickle-shaped representation of the harbour of Zankle, within which, dolphin r. ℞. Incuse square divided into nine compartments, those at the corners divided by diagonal lines radiating from the central square; within the latter, scallop shell. *B.M.C. 4* *RR,* VF £80

388 490-461 B.C. Æ *tetradrachm* (264 grs.). MEZZENION. Hare running r. ℞. Biga of mules walking r., driven by bearded charioteer holding reins and goad: in ex., olive-leaf r. *B.M.C. 11.* **Plate II** .. .. *RR,* F £30

389 — MEZZANION. Hare running r.; below, spray of olive. ℞. As preceding, but with Victory flying r. crowning mules. *Cf. B.M.C. 19* .. .. .. *RR,* F/VF £40

390 461-396 B.C. Æ *tetradrachm*. As before but dolphin r. below hare. ℞. Biga as before but driven l. by Messana, who is crowned by Nike flying r.; in ex., two dolphins meeting .. .. VF £80

391 Æ *litra*. Hare running r., ivy-leaf below. ℞. ΜΕΣ within olive-wreath. *B.M.C. 60* F £6

392 420-396 B.C. Æ 24. Female head l. ℞. Biga of mules r., driven by female figure holding long palm and reins. *B.M.C. 67* .. .. F 50/-

393 357-288 B.C. Æ 25. ΠΕΛΩΡΙΑΣ. Head of Pelorias l., wearing wreath of corn: in field, l., two dolphins. ℞. ΜΕΣΣΑΝΙΩΝ. Warrior advancing l., with spear and shield. *B.M.C. 81* .. .. F 75/-

394 Æ 19. ΠΟΣΕΙΔΑΝ. Laur. head of Poseidon l. ℞. ΜΕΣΣΑΝΙΩΝ. Ornamented trident head between two dolphins. *B.M.C. 75* .. .. F 40/-

390 398

395 The Mamertini (The name taken by the Oscan mercenaries who seized Messana). 282-210 B.C. Æ 27. ΑΡΕΟΣ. Laur. head of Ares r. ℞. ΜΑΜΕΡΤΙΝΩΝ. Eagle, with wings open, standing l. on thunderbolt: in field, l., Φ. *B.M.C.* 4 .. .. F 55/-

396 *After* 210 B.C. Æ 27 *pentonkion.* Head of Zeus r. ℞. Legend as preceding: helmeted warrior advancing r., with spear and shield: in field, r., Π. *B.M.C.* 25 35/-

397 — Head of Ares l. ℞. Legend as preceding: horseman standing l., holding spear, beside horse: in field, l., Π. *B.M.C.* 32 .. .. .. *fair* 20/-; VF 85/-

398 Morgantina. *c.* 340 B.C. Æ 26. ΜΟΡΓΑΝΤΙΝΩΝ. Head of Athena r., owl behind. ℞. Lion r. tearing stag's head; in ex., ΑΒ mon. *B.M.C.* 9 .. .. *R, fair* 45/-

399 Motya. 480-413 B.C. Æ *didrachm.* ΜΟΤΥΑΙΟΝ retrograde. Head of nymph r. ℞. Dog standing r., small plant below. *B.M.C.* 4 .. .. *RRR,* F £50

399A Mytistratus (Marianopoli) *c.* 340 B.C. Æ 28 *hemilitron.* Head of Hephaestos in conical cap. ℞. ΥΜ in midst of six pellets, all in wreath. Overstruck of coin of Syracuse. *B.M.C.* 1 .. .. *RR, fair* 85/-

399B Nacona. Before 400 B.C. Æ 19 *trias.* ΝΑΚΟΝΑΙΟΝ. Head of nymph r. ℞. Seilinos seated sideways on ass walking l.: in field, three pellets. *B.M.C.* 1 *RR, fair* 60/-

399   400

400 Naxus. 413-404 B.C. Æ *tetradrachm.* Hd. of bearded Dlony os r., hair in luxuriant curls, bound with broad band adorned with ivy-wreath. ℞. ΝΑΞΙΟΝ, bearded Seilinos, naked, with long tail and pointed ear, seated on ground from which vine springs, he holds kanthasos and thyros. *B.M.C.* 18 .. .. *RRR,* VF £600

400A Æ *hemidrachm.* ΑΣΣΙΝΟΣ. Horned head of young river-god Assinos l. ℞. ΝΑΞΙΩΝ. Silenos seated facing, head l., holding wine-cup. *B.M.C.* 23.. .. *RR,* F £18

401 Panormus (Palermo). *After c.* 409 B.C. Æ *tetradrachm.* Victorious quadriga l., horses prancing; above, Nike crowning charioteer; beneath, ΖΙΖ in Punic script between two dolphins. ℞. Hd. of Persephone l. surrounded by four dolphins. Copied from a Syracusan dekadrachm by Euainetos. *B.M.C.,* p. 248, 11 .. .. .. EF £250

402 254-100 B.C. Æ 26. Helmeted bust of Athena r. ℞. ΠΑΝΟΡΜΙΤΑΝ. Female figure standing l., holding patera and cornucopiae. *B.M.C.* 10 .. .. .. *fair* 20/-

402A Æ 24. ΠΑΝΟΡΜΙΤΑΝ. Type as preceding. ℞. Triquetra of legs: in centre, Gorgon-head: between the legs, ears of barley. *B.M.C.* 11 .. .. .. *R, fair/F* 52/6

403 Under Roman Rule: Man. Acilius, quaestor. Æ 22, *as.* Head of Janus: above, I. ℞. M̄N ACILI Q in wreath. *B.M.C.,* p. 126 1, ... *R, fair* 30/-

404 Æ 24. Head of Zeus r. ℞. M̄N. ACILI. Eagle standing facing on thunderbolt. *B.M.C.* 2 .. ..R, F 60/-

405 Æ 16. SEPT · EIBA · D · HVIR, triquetra of legs, with Gorgon-head in centre. ℞. L SEIO PROCOS D D. *B.M.C.* 13 .. .. *R, fair* 30/-

406 Imperial Times. Æ 18. Square altar. ℞. D D. Round edifice with battlements. *B.M.C.* 22 .. .. *fair* 22/6

406A Petra (Petralia). *After* 241 B.C. Æ 19. Head of Herakles r. ℞. ΠΕΤΡΓ€ΙΝΩΝ. Female figure l., resting against column. *B.M.C.* 1 .. .. .. *R, fair* 50/-

406B Piacus. 415-400 B.C. Æ *hemilitron.* ΠΙΑΚΙΝ, mark of value, six pellets between the letters. Head of young river-god with horns and olive-wreath l. ℞. Dog r. seizing fawn by the throat. *B.M C.* 1 .. .. *RRR, fair* £35

407 **Segesta** (Sestri). 461-415 B.C. Æ *didrachm.* ΣΕCΕΣΤΑ IIB retrograde. Head of Segesta l., hair waved and turned up under diadem. ℞. Hound l.; above, murex. *B.M.C.* 7
R, good F £40

408 *Before* 409 B.C. Æ 20 *tetras.* Head of Segesta r., hair bound with broad diadem. ℞. Hound r., four annulets in field. *B.M.C.* 49 .. .. *R, fair* 50/-

409 **Selinus.** 480-466 B.C. Æ *didrachm.* Selinon-leaf. ℞. Incuse square divided into twelve triangles, the alternate ones deeper, all radiating from central pellet. *B.M.C.* 7
R, good F/VF £25

407   410

410 466-415 B.C. Æ *tetradrachm.* River-god Selinos standing l., sacrificing with patera at altar and holding laurel-branch: in foreground, cock r.; in field r., selinon-leaf and figure of bull l. on pedestal: on the latter, Α incuse. ℞. Quadriga walking r., driven by Artemis: on her r., stands Apollo, drawing bow. *B.M.C.* 30 .. .. .. *RR,* VF £100

411 Æ *litra.* Female figure seated l. on rock, r. hand extended and touching snake which advances towards her: above, selinon-leaf. ℞. ΣΕΛΙΝΟΕΣ. Man-headed bull r.: in ex., fish. *B.M.C.* 40 .. .. *RR,* F/VF £11

412 **Solus** (later Soluntum). *After* 241 B.C. Æ 17. Laur. head of Poseidon r., trident over shoulder. ℞. COΛONTINON retrograde. Warrior advancing l. *B.M.C.* 6
fair 35/-

412A **Stiela.** 450-415 B.C. Æ *hemidrachm.* Young male head l.: before, branch. ℞.ΣΤΑ. Forepart of man-headed bull l. *B.M.C.* 2 .. .. *RRR,* F £40

413 **Syracuse.** 530-510 B.C. Æ *tetradrachm.* ΣVRA above walking quadriga r., driven by male charioteer. ℞. Small female head l., in centre of quadripartite square. *B.M.C.* 1
VF £500

413A 510-485 B.C. Æ *didrachm.* Horseman r., leading second horse. ℞. Female head r., hair indicated by dots, bound with diadem and hanging down untied on neck, three dolphins around *Boehringer* 53 .. .. *good* F £50

414 485-479 B.C. Æ *tetradrachm.* ΣΥΡΑΚΟΣΙΟΝ. Female head r., wearing necklace, hair confined by diadem of pearls and falling in formal tress on neck: around, four dolphins. ℞. Quadriga r., driven by bearded charioteer, horses walking: above, Nike flying r., crowning horses. *Du Ch.* 6 .. .. VF/*good* F £75

414A — Similar, but with larger head with hair turned up under diadem, over which the ends fall. *Du Ch.* 17. **Plate II** .. .. *R, good* F/F £50

415 Æ *litra.* ΣΥRΑ. *Obv.* type similar but without dolphins. ℞. Sepia (cuttle-fish). *B.M.C.* 49 .. .. *nearly* VF £6

416 Æ *obol. Obv.* type similar. ℞. Wheel of four spokes. *B.M.C.* 55 .. F 75/-

417 478-467 B.C. Æ *tetradrachm.* ΣΥΡΑΚΟΣΙΟΝ. Female head r., wearing ear-ring and necklace, hair turned up under diadem of large pearls: around, four dolphins. ℞. Similar to No. 414, but both wings of Nike showing. *Du Ch.* 19 .. .. VF £85

418 466-412 B.C. Similar, with larger head, hair bound by thin fillet and in roll behind. ℞. Similar. *Boehringer* 515. **Plate II** .. .. VF £120

419 — Similar, with legend ΣΥΡΑΚΟΣΙΟΝ and large head, hair bound by broad diadem and showing in delta-shaped lock above it at back. *Cf. Du Ch.* 41 .. *R,* VF/F £75

420 — Similar, smaller head with short curling hair and *rev.* has quadriga to l., and sea-monster in ex. *Du Ch.* 43 .. .. *RR, fair* £40

421 — Similar, somewhat larger head with hair gathered in tuft on top of head, and Nike on *rev.* flying to r. to crown charioteer: horses prancing. *Du Ch.* 45 VF £125

421A — Another, hair in saccos with border ornament of key and zig-zag pattern. *Boehr.* 642
RRR, VF £165

422 Æ 15. ΣΥΡΑ. Female head l. ℞. Sepia. *B.M.C.* 248 .. .. .. F 40/-

423 412-406 B.C. Æ *tetradrachm by Eukleides.* ΣΥΡΑΚΟΣΙΩΝ. Female head l., wearing large ear-ring and necklace, hair in broad diadem with tresses flying. R. Quadriga galloping l.; above, Nike flying r. crowning charioteer: in ex., dolphin l.   *Tudeer* 89
RR, VF/F £150

424 412-406 B.C. Æ *tetradrachm by Euainetos and Eumenes.* ΣΥΡΑΚΟΣΙΩΝ. Head of Arethusa l., ΕΥΜΕΝΟΥ; below, four dolphins around. R. Quadriga galloping r.; above, Nike carrying wreath and label, bearing signature ΕΥΑΙΝ / ΕΤΟ; in ex., two dolphins meeting. *Tudeer* 43 ..   ..   F £60

425 413-400. Æ 10, *piece of twenty litrae.* ΣΥΡ. Head of Herakles l. R. ΣΥΡΑ in quarters of quadripartite incuse square; in centre, female head of archaic style. *B.M.C.* 133
about EF £65

426 Æ 15, *piece of one hundred litrae.* ΣΥΡΑΚΟΣΙΩΝ. Female head l. of the finest style. R. ΣΥΡΑΚΟΣΙΩΝ. Herakles kneeling r., strangling lion. *B.M.C.* 169 .. RR, EF £1000

427 Æ *dekadrachm by Kimon.* Female head l. as illustration, surrounded by four dolphins, on the lower one ΚΙΜΩΝ. R. Quadriga three-quarters l. at the gallop, Nike flies r. above crowning youthful charioteer; in ex., cuirass between two greaves and crested helmet, ΑΘΛΑ below ..   ..   VF £1800

427A 406-400 B.C. Æ *dekadrachm of the Euainetos type.* Head of Persephone l., wearing wreath of corn, car-ring of three drops, and necklace: around, four dolphins; behind head, scallop-shell; above, in very small letters, ΣΥΡΑΚΟΣΙΟΝ. R. Quadriga galloping l., driver holding long goad in r. hand; above, Nike flying r. to crown him; in ex., panoply of arms. *Du Ch.* 144. **Plate II** ..   .. good F £650

428 412-345 B.C. Æ 16. ΣΥΡΑ. Female head l. R. Star of sixteen rays in middle of incuse quadripartite square. *B.M.C.* 241   ..   ..   F 32/6

429 Æ 30, *litra.* ΣΥΡΑ. Head of Athena l. R. Star between two dolphins. *B.M.C.* 287
F 50/-

430 Æ 20, *trias.* Similar. R. Hippocamp l. *B.M.C.* 290   ..   ..   ..   F 32/6

431 357-353 B.C. Electrum 16, *piece of fifty litrae.* Laur. head of Apollo l.: behind, star. R. ΣΥΡΑΚΟΣΙΟΝ. Tripod-lebes. *B.M.C.* 258. **Plate II.**   ..   ..   .. VF £50.

432 345-317 B.C. (time of Timoleon). Æ 12, *thirty litrae.* ΖΕΥΣ ΕΛΕΥΘΕΡΙΟΣ. Laur. head of Zeus Eleutherios l., of very good style. R. ΣΥΡΑΚΟΣΙΟΝ. Pegasos flying l., A before chest; three pellets (= mark of value = 3 Corinthian *staters* or 30 silver *litrae*) below belly. **Plate II** ..   ..   RRR, good F £75

433 Æ Corinthian *stater.* Pegasos flying l. R. ΣΥΡΑΚΟΣΙΟΝ. Head of Athena r. *B.M.C.* 1
VF £20

434 Æ 20. ΣΥΡΑΚΟΣΙΩΝ. Head of Persephone l., wearing wreath of corn. R. Pegasos l.; below, Σ. *B.M.C.* 309 ..   .. VF 60/-

435 Æ 27. ΖΕΥΣ ΕΛΕΥΘΕΡΙΟΣ. Head of Zeus Eleutherios l. R. Horse prancing l. *B.M.C.* 311   ..   ..   F 35/-

436 Æ 24. *Obv.* Similar, but head r. R. ΣΥΡΑΚΟΣΙΩΝ. Thunderbolt upright : in field r., eagle r. *B.M.C.* 313 ..   .. good F/F 45/-

437

441

437 Æ 17. ΣΥΡΑΚΟΣΙΩΝ. Laur. head of Apollo l. R. Pegasos flying l. *B.M.C.* 321
good F/F 40/-

438 **Syracuse.** Agathokles (317-289 B.C.). Æ *tetradrachm* of 1st coinage, 317-310 B.C.
Head of Persephone l., wearing necklace, ear-ring and wreath of corn; around, three
dolphins; below head, ΦΙ. ℞. Quadriga galloping l.: above, triquetra of legs: in ex.,
ΣΥΡΑΚΟΣΙΩΝ and monogram ΑΝ. *B.M.C.* 352 .. .. VF £75

439 Æ *tetradrachm* of 2nd coinage, probably struck in Africa. ΚΟΡΑΣ. Head of Persephone
r. with wreath of corn. ℞. ΑΓΑΘΟΚΛΕΙΟΣ. Nike standing r., erecting trophy; triquetra
of legs in field l. *Du Ch.* 101; *B.M.C.* 381 .. .. .. *nearly* VF/F £32

439A Ν 80 *litrae* of 3rd coinage, 306-289 B.C. Head of Athena r, wearing crested helmet
decorated with griffin. ℞. ΑΓΑΘΟΚΛΕΙΟΣ ΒΑΣΙΛΕΟΣ. Winged thunderbolt; Φ below.
B.M.C. 418. **Plate III** .. .. *RR, good* EF £300

440 Æ Corinthian *stater.* Head of Athena r. ℞. ΣΥΡΑΚΟΣΙΩΝ. Pegasos flying l.; below,
triskeles. *B.M.C.* 8 .. .. *good* F £12

441 Æ 22. ΣΥΡΑΚΟΣΙΩΝ. Head of Apollo, laur., l. ℞. Bull l.: above and below, a dolphin.
B.M.C. 358. *Illustrated on p.* 57 .. .. *good* F 50/-

442 Æ 22. ΣΟΤΕΙΡΑ. Bust of Artemis r. ℞. ΑΓΑΘΟΚΛΕΟΣ ΒΑΣΙΛΕΟΣ. Winged thunderbolt. *B.M.C.* 422 .. .. *nearly* VF 60/-

443 Hiketas (287-278 B.C.). Æ 21. ΣΥΡΑΚΟΣΙΩΝ. Head of Persephone l. ℞. Biga
galloping r. *B.M.C.* 441 .. .. *nearly* VF/F 60/-

444 Æ 23. ΔΙΟΣ ΕΛΛΑΝΙΟΥ. Head of Zeus Hellenios l. ℞. ΣΥΡΑΚΟΣΙΩΝ. Eagle, wings
spread, standing l. on thunderbolt. *B.M.C.* 468 .. .. .. F/VF 60/-

445 Pyrrhus (278-275 B.C.). Æ 22. Head of young Herakles l. ℞. ΣΥΡΑΚΟΣΙΩΝ. Athena
Promachos standing r. *B.M.C.* 503 .. ..F 45/-

443   447

446 Hieron II (274-216 B.C.). Æ *four-litrae.* Head of Gelon, diademed, l. ℞. ΣΥΡΑ-
ΚΟΣΙΟΙ ΓΕΛΩΝΟΣ. Eagle, with closed wings, standing r. on thunderbolt between ΒΑ
and Κ. *B.M.C.* 536 .. .. *RR,* VF £35

447 Æ 16-*litrae* with name of Queen Philistis. Head of Philistis l., diademed and veiled.
℞. ΒΑΣΙΛΙΣΣΑΣ ΦΙΛΙΣΤΙΔΟΣ. Slow quadriga r., driven by Nike: in front, Α.
B.M.C. 554 .. .. *good style,* EF £85

448 Æ 27. Head of Hieron, diademed, l. ℞. ΙΕΡΩΝΟΣ (in ex.). Helmeted horseman
galloping r., with spear: below, ΜΙ. *B.M.C.* 587 .. .. .. F/VF 55/-

449 Æ 22. Head of Poseidon l. ℞. ΙΕΡΩΝΟΣ. Ornamental trident between two dolphins.
Cf. B.M.C. 598 .. .. *good* F 40/-

450 Æ 20. Similar, smaller module. *Cf. B.M.C.* 612 .. .. F 25/-

451 Æ 20. Head of Persephone l., wearing wreath of corn. ℞. ΙΕ (in ex.). Bull butting
l.: above, club and Ι; in ex., ΙΕ. *B.M.C.* 620 .. .. VF/*good* F £5

451   452

452 Hieronymus (216-215 B.C.). Æ 10 *litrae.* His diad. hd. l., Κ behind. ℞. ΒΑΣΙΛΕΟΣ/ΜΙ
above thunderbolt, ΙΕΡΩΝΥΜΟΥ below. *B.M.C.* 641 .. .. .. EF £60

452A Æ 22. Somewhat similar. *B.M.C.* 645-8 .. .. .. • *fair* 22/6

453 Democracy.   215-212 B.C.   Æ 23, *piece of eight litrae*.   Head of Athena l.   ℞.   ΣΥΡΑΚΟ-
ΣΙΩΝ above thunderbolt; ΣΥΑΛ below.   *B.M.C.* 657 ..   .. VF £35

454 Under Roman rule, *after* 212 B.C.   Æ 20.   Head of Sarapis r.   ℞.   ΣΥΡΑΚΟΣΙΩΝ.
Isis standing l., holding sistrum and sceptre.   *B.M.C.* 701 ..   ..   *R, fair* 27/6

455 Æ 24.   Laur. head of Zeus r.   ℞.   ΣΥΡΑΚΟΣΙΩΝ.   Nike in biga r.   *B.M.C.* 691
F 35/–

456 Æ 15.   Laur. head of Apollo l.   ℞.   ΣΥΡΑΚΟΣΙΩΝ.   Long torch.   *B.M.C.* 713   F 25/–

457 **Tauromenium.**   358-275 B.C.   Æ 18.   ΑΡΧΑΓΕΤΑΣ.   Head of Apollo l.   ℞.   ΤΑΥ-
POMENITAN.   Forepart of butting bull l.   *B.M.C.* 25   ..   ..   *fair* 20/–

458 Æ 20.   Similar, but *rev.* type tripod   *B.M.C.* 29   ..   ..   ..   F 45/–

459

459 275-210 B.C.   Æ *piece of four litrae*.   Laur. head of Apollo l.   ℞.   As last   VF £30

460 Æ 20.   Similar type.   *B.M.C.* 46   ..   .. F 37/6

461 Æ 16.   Helmeted head of Athena r.   ℞.   Legend as preceding: Pegasos r.   *B.M.C.*
45 ..   ..   *fair*/F 22/6

462 **Tyndaris.**   254-210 B.C.   Æ 16.   Female head r., veiled.   ℞.   ΤΥΝΔΑΡΙΤΑΝ.   Caps
of the Dioskuri.   *B.M.C.* 17   ..   ..   F 60/–

463 **ISLANDS OF SICILY : Lipara.**   350-300 B.C.   Æ 21, *hemilitron*.   Young Hephaistos
seated l., holding hammer and kantharos.   ℞.   ΛΙΠΑΡΑΙΟΝ around six pellets.   *B.M.C.*
36 ..   ..   *R, fair* 75/–

464 **Sardinia.**   3rd Cent. B.C.   Æ 20.   Head of Persephone l.   ℞.   Three ears of corn;
crescent above.   *Grose* 3064   ..   ..   F/*fair* 55/–

465 *Before* 146 B.C.   Æ 18.   Head of Persephone l.   ℞.   Cow r., star above.   *Grose* 3065
nearly VF   £5

466 61-59 B.C.   Æ 22.   M · ATIVS BALBVS · PR.   Young male head l.   ℞.   SARD · PATER.   Head
of Sardus Pater r. wearing plumed headdress.   *B.M.C.* 1   ..   ..   ..   F 65/–

461   469

467 **Siculo-Punic Coinage.**   *About* 400 B.C.   Æ *tetradrachm* (attributed to *Heraclea
Minoa*).   Head of Persephone l., wearing wreath of corn, ear-ring and necklace; around
three dolphins.   ℞.   Quadriga galloping l.: above, Nike flying r., crowning driver.
B.M.C. 5   ..   ..   *R, good* F   £70

468 410-310 B.C.   Æ *tetradrachm*.   Head of young Herakles r., wearing lion-skin.   ℞.
Horse's head l.: behind, palm-tree: below, Punic legend.   **Plate III**   *good* VF   £70

469 — Head of Persephone l., surrounded by four dolphins, scallop-shell below chin.   ℞.
As last.   *B.M.C.* 12 *var.* ..   ..   *good* VF   £150

470 — Head of Persephone r.: in front, thymiaterion.   ℞.   Horse advancing l., crowned
by Nike flying r.; palm in background; caduceus in front.   *Cf. Müller* 28; *Lockett coll.*
1042   ..   ..   *good* VF   £100

471 Æ 16.   Head of Persephone l.   ℞.   Horse prancing r.   *B.M.C.* 1   ..   F 30/–

472 Æ 20.   *Obv.*   Similar to preceding, but of coarse style.   ℞.   Horse's head r.   F 37/6

473 Æ 19.   Palm-tree with fruit.   ℞.   As preceding   ..   ..   ..   *fair* 15/–

474 Æ 16.   As last.   ℞.   Pegasos flying l.   *Grose* 3049 ..   ..   ..   *good* F 37/6

Macedon	17 Amphipolis	33 Madytus	49 Pautalia
1 Neapolis	18 Tragilus	34 Sestus	50 Philippopolis
2 Eion	19 Philippi	35 Hephaestia,	51 Serdica
3 Lete	20 Pydna	*Lemnos*	52 Topirus
4 Aegae	21 Pella	36 Myrina, *Lemnos*	53 Trajanopolis
5 Therma	22 Thessalonica	37 Bisanthe	
6 Orthagoreia		38 Byzantium	*Moesia Superior*
7 Acanthus	*Thrace*	39 Perinthus	54 Viminacium
8 Uranopolis	23 Abdera	40 Selymbria	
9 Terone	24 Aenus	41 Anchialus	*Moesia Inferior*
10 Olynthus	25 Maroneia	42 Mesembria	55 Callatis
11 Aphytis	26 Aegospotami	43 Apollonia Pontica	56 Dionysopolis
12 Scione	28 Cardia	45 Augusta Trajana	57 Istrus
13 Mende	30 Crithote	46 Bizya	58 Marcianopolis
14 Potidaea	31 Elaeus	47 Deultum	59 Nicopolis ad Istrum
16 Aeneia	32 Lysimachia	48 Hadrianopolis	60 Odessus
			61 Tomis

MACEDON.

475 **PANGAEAN DISTRICT : Orrescii.** 500-480 B.C. Æ *stater.* ΩRΗΣΚΙΩΝ retrograde. Centaur kneeling r., carrying in his arms nymph clad in long chiton. ℞. Quadripartite incuse square. *B.M.C.* 5   *RRR, nearly* VF £140

476 **Neapolis** (Kavala). 500-411 B.C. Æ *stater.* Gorgon-head. ℞. Quadrilateral incuse square of mill-sail or swastika pattern. *B.M.C.* 7. **Plate III** ..   .. *RR,* VF £100

477 411-350 B.C. Æ *drachm.* Gorgon's head facing. ℞. ΝΕΠΟ. Head of Nike r., wearing olive-wreath. *B.M.C.* 14   ..   ..   VF £30

478 Æ *hemidrachm.* Similar. *B.M.C.* 25 ..   .. F £7

479 **Eion.** 500-437 B.C. Æ *trihemiobol.* Goose r., with head turned back; above, lizard l.; below, N. ℞. Incuse square. *B.M.C.* 20 ..   ..   VF £15

480 **EMATHIAN DISTRICT : Lete.** *Before* 500 B.C. Æ *stater.* Naked satyr with horse's feet, r., seizing by the wrist a nymph l.; in field, six pellets. ℞. Incuse square, diagonally divided. *B.M.C.* 1 ..   ..   *RR,* VF £120

481 Æ *trihemiobol.* Naked satyr squatting r.: in field, pellet. ℞. As preceding. *B.M.C.* 12 ..   .. *R, good* F £24

482 500-480 B.C. Æ *trihemiobol.* Naked satyr, with horse's feet and tail, kneeling r. ℞. Incuse square of swastika pattern. *B.M.C.* 29   ..   ..   .. *R,* VF £20

483 **Aegae.** 500-480 B.C. Æ *stater.* Goat kneeling r., looking back: above, ΛΑ. ℞. Quadripartite incuse square. *B.M.C.* 2..   ..   ..   ..   *RRR,* F £280

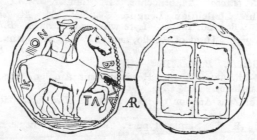

484 **BISALTIAN DISTRICT : The Bisaltae.** 500-480 B.C. Æ *octadrachm.* Naked warrior r., standing beside horse. ℞. Quadripartite incuse square, the quarters granulated. *B.M.C.* 1 ..   ..   *RR,* F £300

484A — Æ *drachm.* Similar. *Grose* 3103 ..   .. *RR,* F £50

484B Mosses, unknown king *c.* 500-480 B.C. Æ *drachm.* Similar. ℞. ΜΟΣΣΕΩ and raised square within incuse square. *Grose* 3106   ..   ..   .. *RRR,* F £75

485 **Therma.** *About* 480 B.C. Æ *tetradrachm.* Pegasos, with curled wing, walking l. ℞. Incuse square, divided diagonally, surface granulated. *Cf. B.M.C.* 4, *uncertain of* *Macedon* ..   .. *RRR, fair* £75

486 **CHALCIDIAN DISTRICT : Orthagoreia.** 400-350 B.C. Æ 13. Head of Apollo, laur., r. ℞. ΟΡΘΑΓΟΡΕΩΝ. Helmet with cheek-pieces, facing. *B.M.C.* 6   F 65/-

487 **Acanthus.** 500-424 B.C. Æ *hemidrachm.* Forepart of lion r., devouring prey; above, acanthus flower. ℞. Quadripartite incuse square, the quarters granulated. *Bab.,* Pl. liv, 19 ..   ..   VF £30

488   494

488 424-400 B.C. Æ *tetradrachm.* Lion r. springing upon bull l., ΑΛΕΞΙΣ in ex. ℞. ΑΚΑΝΘΙΟΝ around quadripartite linear square, the whole within incuse square. *B.M.C.* 25   *RRR*, VF £360

488A Æ *tetrobol.* Forepart of bull kneeling l., head turned back; above, Π and swastika. ℞. Quadripartite incuse square, surface granulated. *B.M.C.* 33   *good* F £12

489 *After* 400 B.C. Æ 15. Helmeted head of Athena r. ℞. ΑΚΑΝ in the four quarters of a wheel. *B.M.C.* 42 ..   ..   F 50/-

490 **Uranopolis.** *About* 300 B.C. Æ 16. Star of eight rays. ℞. ΟΥΡΑΝΙΔΩΝ ΠΟΛΕΩΣ. Aphrodite Urania seated on globe, holding sceptre. *B.M.C.* 2   ..   F/*fair* 60/-

491 Æ 13. Star and crescent. ℞. As preceding. *B.M.C.* 5 ..   ..   F 70/-

492 **Terone.** 500-480 B.C. Æ *tetradrachm.* ΤΕ. Amphora. ℞. Quadripartite incuse square. *Not in B.M.C.* ..   ..   *RRR*, F £120

493 480-424 B.C. Æ *tetrobol.* ΤΕ. oenochoe. ℞. Similar. *B.M.C.* 8   *good* F £15

494 **Olynthus. The Chalcidian League.** 392-358 B.C. Æ *tetradrachm.* Head of Apollo, laur., l. ℞. ΧΑΛΚΙΔΕΩΝ. Lyre with seven strings. *B.M.C.* 5   VF £200

495 Æ *tetrobol* (33 grs.). Head of Apollo, laur., l. ℞. ΧΑΛΚΙΔΕΩΝ. Lyre: all in incuse square. *B.M.C.* 13 ..   ..   *RR*, *good* F/VF £25

496 Æ 20. Very similar. *B.M.C.* 31 ..   ..   F 50/-

497 **Aphytis.** 424-358 B.C. Æ 18. Head of Zeus Ammon, three-quarter face l. ℞. ΑΦΥΤΑΙΩΝ. Kantharos. *B.M.C.* 1   ..   ..   ..   *RR*, F £5

498 Æ 16. Head of Zeus Ammon r. ℞. ΑΦΥΤΑΙ. Two eagles face to face. *B.M.C.* 3   *nearly* VF/F £5

499 *After* 168 B.C. Æ 21. Similar type r. ℞. ΑΦΥΤΑΙ. Eagle r. *B.M.C.* 4   *fair*/F 40/-

500 **Scione.** 450-424 B.C. Æ 18. Youthful male head r. ℞. ΣΚΙΩ below helmet. *B.M.C.* 3 ..   ..   *RR*, *fair* 60/-

501 **Mende.** 500-450 B.C. Æ *hemiobol.* Ass's head r. ℞. Incuse square containing five triangular depressions. *Cf. B.M.C.* 3 ..   ..   ..   *RR*, F £21

502 450-424 B.C. Æ *tetradrachm.* Seilenos reclining l. on back of ass walking r.; he holds kantharos in r. hand; crow in front, dog between legs of the ass. ℞. ΜΕΝΔΑΙΟΝ around quadripartite linear square, in which, vine with five bunches of grapes; all in shallow incuse square. *B.M.C.* 4 ..   ..   *RR*, VF/F £200

503 Æ *tetrobol.* Seilenos standing r. behind ass, which he pulls back by the ears. ℞. Legend as preceding: crow r. *B.M.C.* 5   ..   ..   ..   *RR*, F £35

504 Æ *diobol.* Ass standing r. ℞. Kantharos in incuse square. *Gaebler* 28   *R*, F £25

505 Æ *hemiobol.* Forepart of ass r. ℞. As preceding. *B.M.C.* 7   *R*, F £10

506 424-358 B.C. Æ *tetrobol.* *Obv.* Type as 502; below ass, M. ℞. ΜΕΝΔΑΙΗ. Amphora; all in double linear square. *B.M.C.* 8 ..   ..   *R*, F £20

507 **Potidaea.** 500-429 B.C. Æ *diobol.* Naked horseman r., on forepart of prancing horse. ℞. Female head of archaic style in incuse square. *B.M.C.* 9 *R, fair* £12

508 **Cassandreia.** *Nero.* Æ 23. NEPO CLAVΔ . CAESAR AVC . CERM . PM . TRP. His head l. ℞. COL . IVL . AVG . CASSENDREN. Head of Zeus Ammon l. *Grose* 3195
RR, M 50/–

509 **The Bottice.** 392-379 B.C. Æ 16. Laur. head of Apollo r. ℞. BOTTIAIΩN. Lyre. *B.M.C.* 3 .. .. *R,* F 70/–

510 **Dicaea.** 500-450 B.C. Æ *tetrobol.* Cock r. ℞. Sepia in shallow incuse square. *Gaebler* 7. .. .. *RRR,* F/*fair* £45

511 **Aeneia.** 500-424 B.C. Æ *tetrobol.* Head of Aeneas (the legendary founder of the city), helmeted, r. ℞. Incuse of swastika pattern. *B.M.C.* 1 *RR,* VF/F £100

512 **STRYMONIAN DISTRICT. Amphipolis.** 424-358 B.C. Æ *tetradrachm.* Head of Apollo, three-quarter face to r. ℞. AMΦIΠOΛITEΩN within linear square around race-torch; in field to l., cicada; all in incuse square. *B.M.C.* 3 .. *RRR,* VF £2500

512A Æ *drachm.* Similar but without symbol. *B.M.C.* 7 .. .. .. F £75

513 Æ 13. Head of Apollo, laur., r. ℞. AMΦI. Race-torch; all in linear square. *B.M.C.* 12 .. .. F/VF 50/–

514 *After* 148 B.C. Æ 23. Head of Medusa, winged, facing. ℞. AMΦIΠOΛEITΩN. Athena Nikephoros standing l. *B.M.C.* 44 .. .. F 50/–

515 Æ 19. Head of Poseidon r. ℞. AMΦIΠOΛITΩN. Horse trotting r. *B.M.C.* 46
good F/*fair* 35/–

516 Æ 14. Head of Artemis r. ℞. AMΦIΠOΛITΩN. Ear of corn. *B.M.C.* 53
F/*fair* 30/–

517 Under Roman rule: *Augustus.* Æ 23. KAICAP ΘEOY YIOC. His bare head r. ℞. AMΦIΠOΛEITΩN. Artemis Tauropolos seated on bull galloping r. *B.M.C.* 73
nearly F/F 75/–

518 *Elagabalus.* Æ 21. AV . K . M . AVP . ANTΩNINOC . C. His laur. bust r. ℞. AMΦIΠOΛEITΩN. Tyche seated l. *B.M.C.* 131 .. .. F 60/–

519 **Tragilus.** 400-350 B.C. Æ 15. Head of Hermes r., wearing petasos. ℞. TPAIΛION. Rose: in field, r., bunch of grapes. *B.M.C.* 13 .. .. F 45/–

520 **Philippi.** 358-340 B.C. Æ 17. Head of young Herakles r. ℞. ΦIΛIΠΠΩN. Tripod. *B.M.C.* 14 .. .. F 45/–

521 *Augustus.* Æ 18. VIC AVG. Statue of Nike l. ℞. COHOR PRAE PHIL. Three military standards. *B.M.C.* 23 .. .. F 37/6

522 **BOTTIAEAN DISTRICT. Pydna.** 364-358 B.C. Æ 15. Female head r. ℞. ΠYΔNAIΩN. Owl l. *B.M.C.* 4 *R, fair* 32/6

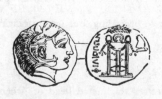

520   523

523 **KINGS OF MACEDON: Alexander I.** 498-454 B.C. Æ *tetradrachm.* Horse standing r.; behind, horseman with two spears. ℞. AΛEΞANΔPO around quadripartite linear square; all within incuse square. *B.M.C.* 2 .. .. .. *RR,* F £150

523A **Alexander I.** Æ *light tetrobol.* Horse advancing r. ℞. Helmet within linear square. *B.M.C.,* p. 159, 5 .. .. *RR, good* F £18

524 **Perdiccas II.** 454-413 B.C. Æ *heavy tetrobol.* Horseman r., wearing kausia and carrying two spears. ℞. Forepart of lion r., both forefeet visible, in shallow incuse square. *B.M.C.,* p. 161, 21 .. .. *RR, nearly* VF £30

525 **Archelaus I.** 413-399 B.C. Æ *stater.* Young male head, wearing taenia, r. ℞. ΑΡΧΕΛΑΟ. Horse walking r.: all in shallow incuse square. *B.M.C.* 3   *RR,* F £60

525A **Amyntas II.** 392-390. Æ *stater.* Similar but ΑΜΥΝΤΑ. *B.M.C.* 1
RRR, F £85

525A   526

526 **Pausanias.** 390-389 B.C. Æ *stater.* Similar but ΠΑΥΣΑΝΙΑ. *B.M.C.* 2
RR, F £60

527 **Amyntas III.** First reign, 389-383 B.C. Æ *stater.* Head of bearded Herakles, wearing lion-skin, r. ℞. ΑΜΥΝΤΑ. Horse standing r. *B.M.C.* 3. **Plate III**   *R,* VF £75

528 Second reign, 381-369 B.C. Æ 16. Head of young Herakles r. ℞. ΑΜΥΝΤΑ. Eagle r., devouring serpent. *B.M.C.* 17 .. .. *R,* F 60/–

528A **Perdiccas III.** 364-359. Æ 21. Similar. ℞. ΠΕΡΔΙΚ ΚΑ. Lion r. holding in its jaws a broken javelin. *B.M.C.* 2 .. .. *RR, fair* 60/–

529   531A

529 **Philip II.** 359-336 B.C. N *stater.* Head of Apollo, laur., r. ℞. ΦΙΛΙΠΠΟΥ. Chariot, with charioteer driving two horses r. **Plate III** .. .. F £40; VF £85

530 N *quarter-stater.* Head of Herakles r. ℞. Bow above club, lion's head above, ΦΙΛΙΠΠΟΥ below. M. 167 .. .. *R, nearly* VF £30

531 Æ *tetradrachm.* Head of Zeus, laur., r. ℞. ΦΙΛΙΠΠΟΥ. Bearded Macedonian horseman l., wearing kausia and raising r. hand: below horse, bow and forepart of Pegasos
VF £60

531A — *Obv.* Similar. ℞. ΦΙΛΙΠΠΟΥ. Naked youth on horseback r., carrying palm-branch. **Plate III** .. .. VF £30; EF £75

532 Æ *tetrobol.* Head of Apollo, laur., r. ℞. Similar to preceding, but horse prancing
good F £8

533 Æ 18. Types as preceding .. .. F 40/–

534 Æ 18. Similar to preceding, but types l. .. .. F 50/–

535 Æ 10. Head of young Herakles r. ℞. Club .. .. F 40/–

536 **Alexander III (the Great).** 336-323 B.C. N *distater.* Helmeted head of Athena r. ℞. ΑΛΕΞΑΝΔΡΟΥ. Winged Nike standing l., holding wreath and standard   VF £250

537 N *stater.* Similar types. **Plate III** .. .. F £30; *good* VF £75

538 N *quarter-stater.* Similar. ℞. Thunderbolt, bow, ΑΛΕΞΑΝ, club and ΔΡΟΥ
R, nearly VF £35

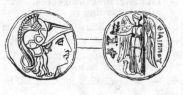

539   549

539 Æ *tetradrachm.* Head of young Herakles r., wearing lion-skin. ℞. ΑΛΕΞΑΝΔΡΟΥ to r. of Zeus seated l. on throne without back holding eagle and sceptre. (There are various letters or symbols in the field or under the chair indicating the mint, these are legion)
from F £7; VF £15; EF £30

540 — As before but with ΒΑΣΙΛΕΩΣ below. **Plate III** ..   VF £17/10/–; EF £40

541 — As No. 539, but countermarked with an anchor (for the Seleucid kings of Syria) on reverse ..   ..   F £17/10/–

542 Æ *didrachm.* Type as No. 539   ..   ..   ..   *RR, good* F £30

543 Æ *drachm.* Similar types   ..   ..   *nearly* VF/F 55/–; *good* VF £5

544 Æ *hemidrachm.* Similar types   ..   ..   R, F 80/–

545 Æ *obol.* Similar types ..   ,,   ..   *fair* 45/–

546 Æ 15. Head of young Herakles, wearing lion-skin, r. ℞. ΑΛΕΞΑΝΔΡΟΥ. Eagle r., head l.   ..   ..   F 50/–

547 Æ 18. *Obv.* as preceding. ℞. ΑΛΕΞΑΝΔΡΟΥ between club and bow in bow-case.
F 35/–; *nearly* VF 65/–

548 Æ 16. Head of Apollo, laur., r. ℞. Legend as preceding: horse prancing r., thunderbolt below ..   ..   F 37/6

549 **Philip III.** 323-316 B.C. *N stater.* Type as Alexander the Great but legend ΦΙΛΙΠΠΟΥ
F £40

550 Æ *tetradrachm.* Type as Alexander but ΦΙΛΙΠΠΟΥ (sometimes with ΒΑΣΙΛΕΩΣ as well)
nearly VF/F £10; VF £20

551 Æ *drachm.* Similar type   ..   ..   F 50/–; VF £5

552 Æ *hemidrachm.* Similar type   ..   ..   R, F £5

553 **Cassander.** 316-297 B.C. Æ 18. Head of Apollo, laur., r. ℞. ΒΑΣΙΛΕΩΣ ΚΑΣΣΑΝΔΡΟΥ. Tripod   ..   ..   F 45/–

554 Æ 18. Head of young Herakles, wearing lion-skin, r. ℞. Legend as preceding: boy on horse r.: in field, Λ and star   ..   ..   F 40/–

555 Æ 16. *Obv.* as preceding. ℞. Legend as preceding: lion l.   ..   ..   F 45/–

556 Æ 17. *Struck by his general Eupolemus.* 314-313 B.C. Three Macedonian shields. ℞. ΕΥΠΟΛΕΜΟΥ. Sword with scabbard and belt   ..   ..   R, F £5

557 **Demetrius Poliorcetes.** 306-283 B.C. Æ *tetradrachm.* Prow of galley l., on which Nike standing l. blowing trumpet. ℞. ΒΑΣΙΛΕΩΣ ΔΗΜΗΤΡΙΟΥ. Poseidon standing l., chlamys over extended l. arm, wielding trident in r. hand: in field, l. and r., monograms
RR, VF £275

558 Æ *drachm.* Similar types. **Plate III** ..   ..   R, *good* F £35

559 Æ *tetradrachm.* Head of Demetrius r. ℞. ΒΑΣΙΛΕΩΣ ΔΗΜΗΤΡΙΟΥ. Poseidon standing l., r. foot on rock, l. hand holding trident upright: in field, l. and r., monogram
VF £75

560 **Demetrius Poliorcetes.** Æ 19. Laur. head of Zeus r. ℞. Legend as before. Athena standing r.   *R, fair* 50/-

561 Æ 17. Similar. ℞. BA above prow of ship, mon. below ..   ..   *R, fair* 45/-

562 Æ 15. Head of Athena r. ℞. As last   ..   ..   F 40/-

563 **Interval.** 286-277 B.C. Æ 16. Macedonian shield; in centre, thunderbolt. ℞. BA. Macedonian helmet with crest ..   ..   F 30/-; F/VF 50/-

564 — Similar, with gorgon-head in centre of shield and caduceus in *rev.* field l.   *R, VF/EF* £5

565 Æ 19. Head of young Herakles, wearing lion-skin, r. ℞. ΒΑΣΙΛΕΩΣ. Bow in case, club and race-torch ..   ..   F 30/-

566 **Antigonus Gonatas.** 277-239 B.C. Æ *tetradrachm.* Head of Poseidon r., with flowing locks bound with marine plant. ℞. Prow of galley inscr. ΒΑΣΙΛΕΩΣ ΑΝΤΙΓΟΝΟΥ, upon which Apollo seated l. holding bow in r. hand: in ex., monogram   *RR, nearly* VF/F £75

567 Æ *tetradrachm.* Macedonian shield, in centre of which head of Pan, horned, l., with pedum on shoulder. ℞. ΒΑΣΙΛΕΩΣ ΑΝΤΙΓΟΝΟΥ. Athena Alkis standing l., wearing helmet and aegis, holding shield and thunderbolt: in field, l., Macedonian helmet with crest and cheek-pieces: in field, r., ΚΤ. **Plate III** ..   ..   ..   VF £40

567A Æ *drachm.* Laur. head of Zeus r. ℞. As last ..   ..   ..   *RR*, F £35

568 **Antigonus Gonatas** or **Doson.** 277-220 B.C. Æ 18. Helmeted head of Athena r. ℞. BA and monogram ΑΝΤΙ. Pan r., erecting a trophy ..   ..   F 37/6

569 Æ 18. Macedonian shield, and monogram ΑΝΤΙ in centre. ℞. ΒΑΣ. Macedonian helmet ..   ..   F 37/6

570 Æ 16. Young head of Herakles, wearing lion-skin, r. ℞. Horse and rider: BA and monogram ΑΝΤΙ ..   ..   F 37/6

571 **Demetrius II.** 239-229 B.C. Æ 16. Macedonian shield with monogram in centre. ℞. ΒΑΣΙ. Helmet ..   ..   F 45/-

571A Æ 16. Similar, but star on helmet. ℞. ΒΑΣΙΛΕΩΣ ΔΗΜΗΤΡΙΟΥ. Helmet   *R, fair* 35/-

572 **Philip V.** 220-179 B.C. Æ *tetradrachm.* His head r. ℞. ΒΑΣΙΛΕΩΣ ΦΙΛΙΠΠΟΥ. Athena Alkis l. as on No. 567 ..   ..   *RRR*, F £175

573 Æ *tetradrachm.* Macedonian shield; in centre, head of hero Perseus l. ℞. Legend as before but above and below club; all in oak-wreath ..   ..   *RR*, F £100

573A Æ *didrachm.* His head r. ℞. as last ..   ..   *RR*, F £40

573B Æ *drachm.* Similar type to preceding ..   .. *R*, F £16

573C Æ *hemidrachm.* Similar ..   .. *R*, F £12

574 Æ 23. Head of Helios, radiate, r. ℞. ΒΑΣΙΛΕΩΣ ΦΙΛΙΠΠΟΥ. Thunderbolt F 50/–

575 Æ 22. Head of bearded Herakles r. ℞. Similar legend, above and below, harpa
F 50/–

576 Æ 21. Young head of Herakles, wearing lion-skin, r. ℞. Β Α Φ. Two goats kneeling
r. .. .. *R, fair* 32/6

577 Æ 19. Head of Poseidon r. ℞. ΒΑΦ. Athena Alkis r. fighting .. F 45/–

578 Æ 16. Head of hero Perseus, r. ℞. ΒΑΣΙΛΕΩΣ ΦΙΛΦΠΠΟΥ. Horse r. .. F 55/–

579 Autonomous issues under Philip V, *c.* 185-178 B.C. *Æ tetrobol.* Macedonian shield,
with MA KE and club, in centre. ℞. Macedonian helmet between three monograms
and thunderbolt. *B.M.C.* 12 .. .. VF £9

580 *Æ tetrobol.* Head of Maenad r. ℞. ΜΑΚΕΔΟΝΩΝ. Prow of galley r. *B.M.C.* 26
VF £7

581 Æ 20. Laur. head of Apollo r. ℞. Similar legend. Tripod. *B.M.C.* 37 F 40/–

582 **Perseus.** 178-168 B.C. *Æ tetradrachm.* Head of king Perseus, diademed, r. ℞.
ΒΑΣΙΛΕΩΣ ΠΕΡΣΕΩΣ. Eagle, wings open, on thunderbolt r.: all in oak-wreath EF £100

583 Æ 18. *Obv.* as No. 578. ℞. ΠΕΡ in monogram: eagle on thunderbolt .. F 45/–

584 **Adaeus.** *c.* 200 B.C. (?). Æ 18. Head of Apollo r. ℞. ΑΔΑΙΟΥ. Tripod lebes
fair 40/–

585 Æ 18. Head of Herakles. ℞. ΑΔΑΙΟΥ above club.. .. .. .. F 65/–

586 **KINGDOM OF PAEONIA : Patraus.** 340-315 B.C. *Æ tetradrachm* (190 grs.). Head
of Apollo, laur., r. ℞. ΠΑΤΡΑΟΥ. Horseman r., spearing prostrate enemy. *Cf.*
B.M.C. 5 .. .. *R, somewhat barbarous style,* VF/F £30

587 **Audoleon.** 315-286 B.C. *Æ drachm.* Helmeted head of Athena, facing. ℞.
ΑΥΔΟΛΕΟΝΤΟΣ. Horse r. *B.M.C.* 13 .. .. *R, fair* £5

588 **MACEDON UNDER THE ROMANS.** 158-146 B.C. First Region. *Æ tetradrachm.*
Macedonian shield, with diademed bust of Artemis, r., in centre. ℞. ΜΑΚΕΔΟΝΩΝ
ΠΡΩΤΗΣ. Club r.; above, monogram; all within oak-wreath: to l., dolphin. *B.M.C.* 1
VF/F £15

589 — Similar, with N beneath, and thunderbolt to l. *B.M.C.* 4 .. F/VF £12

590 — Similar, with three monograms. *B.M.C.* 7.. .. .. .. VF £20

591 Fourth Region. Æ 21. Laur. hd. of Zeus r. ℞. ΜΑΚΕΔΟΝΩΝ ΤΕΤΑΡΤΗΣ above and
below club, two monograms. *B.M.C.* 49 .. .. F 50/–

592 **Macedon a Roman Province.** *After* 146 B.C. Aesillas, *quaestor*, 93-92 B.C. Æ *tetradrachm.* ΜΑΚΕΔΟΝΩΝ. Head of Alexander the Great r., with flowing hair and horn of Ammon; before, mon. Ɽ. AESILLAS Q. Club between money-chest and quaestor's chair, all within wreath. *B.M.C.* 81 var. **Plate III**
nearly EF/nearly VF £35

593 Æ 20. Head of Roma, helmeted, r. Ɽ. ΜΑΚΕΔΟΝΩΝ ΤΑΜΙΟΥ ΓΑΙΟΥ ΠΟΠΛΙΛΙΟΥ in wreath. *B.M.C.* 74 .. .. *R, fair* 35/-

594 *Domitian.* Æ 24. ΑΥΤΟ ΚΑΙΣΑΡ ΔΟΜΙΤΙΑΝΥΣ ΣΕΒ. His laur. head r. Ɽ. ΚΟΙΝΟΝ ΜΑΚΕΔΟΝΩΝ. Macedonian shield. *Gaebler* 252 .. .. F 60/-

595 Third Century A.D. Æ 26. ΑΛΕΞΑΝΔΡΟΥ. Helmeted head of Alexander r. Ɽ. ΚΟΙΝΟΝ ΜΑΚΕΔΟΝΩΝ ΝΕΩΚΟΡ. Two temples, between which, pillar surmounted by statue. *B.M.C.* 127 *var.* .. .. *R, fair/F* 65/-

596 Æ 27. *Obv.* Similar, without helmet. Ɽ. Legend similar: Alexander galloping r. *B.M.C.* 124 *var.* .. .. F 80/-

597 Æ 26. *Obv.* Similar to preceding. Ɽ. Legend similar: Alexander r., taming Bucephalus. *Cf. B.M.C.* 135/6 .. .. *R, F* £6

598 **Bottiaea** (district around Pella) 185-168 B.C. Æ 16. Macedonian shield. Ɽ. Macedonian helmet l. *Gaebler* 30 .. .. F 40/-

599 Gaius Publilius. 148-146 B.C. Æ 20. Head of Athena r. Ɽ. Bull feeding r. *B.M.C.* 76 .. .. F 50/-

600 **Pella.** 168-146 B.C. Æ 20. Head of Pan, r. Ɽ. ΠΕΛΛΗΣ. Athena Alkis r., with spear and shield, between two monograms. *B.M.C.* 8 .. .. .. F 45/-

601 Æ 14. Head of Apollo, laur., r. Ɽ. ΠΕΛΛΗΣ. Tripod. *B.M.C.* 15 .. *fair* 21/-

602 Imperial Times: *Julia Mamaea.* Æ 25. Bust r. Ɽ. COL IVL AVG PELLA. Pan seated l. on rock, holding pedum: in field, l., syrinx. *B.M.C.* 39 .. .. *fair* 50/-

603 *Gordian III.* Æ 25. Bust r. Ɽ. As previous. *B.M.C.* 42 .. .. F £5

604 **Thessalonica** (Salonica). 2nd Cent. B.C. Æ 20. Head of young Dionysos r. Ɽ. ΘΕΣΣΑΛΟΝΙΚΗΣ. Goat r. *B.M.C.* 10/16 .. .. F 40/-

605 Æ 18. Head of Poseidon wearing taenia; trident at shoulder. Ɽ. ΘΕΣΣΑΛΟΝΙ. Prow r. *B.M.C.* 22 .. .. F 45/-

605A Æ 19. Imperial Times. ΟΜΟΝΟΙΑ. Head of Homonoia, veiled, r. Ɽ. ΘΕΣΣΑΛΟΝ. Horse r.; below ΡΩΜ. *B.M.C.* 43 .. .. F 50/-

606 Æ 20. ΘΕΣΣΑΛΟΝΙΚΕΩΝ. Bust of Tyche r. Ɽ. ΚΑΒΕΙΡΟΣ. Kabeiros standing l., holding rhyton and hammer. *B.M.C.* 47 .. .. *fair* 30/-

607 *Vespasian.* Æ 23. ΑΥΤΟΚΡΑΤΩΡ ΚΑΙΣΑΡ ΟΥΕΣΠΑΣΙΑΝ. Laur. bust l. Ɽ. ΘΕΣΣΑΛΟΝΙΚΕΩΝ in wreath. *B.M.C.—* .. .. F 85/-

608 *Julia Donna.* Æ 22. ΙΟΥΛΙΑ ΔΟΜΝΑ CE. Bust r. Ɽ. Legend as preceding, Kabeiros as No. 606 but in distyle temple. *B.M.C.* 94 .. .. F/*fair* 75/-

609 *Elagabalus.* Æ 24. Greek legend, radiate bust r. Ɽ. Legend as preceding: Nike standing l., holding Kabeiros and palm. *B.M.C.* 103.. .. .. *fair/F* 45/-

610 *Severus Alexander.* Æ 24. Greek legend, laur. bust r. Ɽ. Legend as preceding: Kabeiros r. between two anvils. *B.M.C.—* .. .. *fair* 55/-

611 *Maximus.* *Obv.* Similar. Ɽ. Same legend; Nike advancing l. *B.M.C.* 115
F 85/-

612 *Gordian III.* Æ 25. *Obv.* Similar. Ɽ. ΘΕΣΣΑ ΛΟΝΙΚΕΩΝ ΝΕΩΚΟΡ. Apollo l. *B.M.C.* 126 .. .. *fair* 35/-

THRACE.

For map see page 60.

SOUTHERN COAST OF THRACE.

613 **Abdera.** 478-450 B.C. Æ *tetradrachm.* Griffin springing l., owl l. above. ℞. ΕΠΙ Δ / ΕΟ / ΝΥ / ΔΟΣ around quadripartite linear square with granulated quarters. *Strack* 45
RR, F £140

613A   627

613A — ΚΑΛΛΙΔΑΜΑΣ. Griffin with curved wing seated l. on fish. ℞. ΑΒΔΗΡΙΤΕΩΝ around quartered square; all within incuse square. *Strack* 61 .. .. *RR*, EF/F £750

614 425-400 B.C. Æ *hemidrachm.* Griffin l.; ΑΒΔ to r. below wing. ℞. ΕΠΙ ΦΙΛΑ / ΙΟ. Hermes standing r. within incuse square. *Strack* 125 .. .. *nearly* F £10

615 400-390 B.C. Æ *drachm.* ΕΠΙ / Χ / ΑΡΜ / Ο. Griffin l. ℞. ΑΒΔ / ΗΡΙ / ΤΕΩΝ around linear square in which laur. head of Apollo l. *Strack* 144 .. .. F £15

616 390-352 B.C. Æ *stater* or *tetradrachm.* ΑΒΔΗ / ΡΙΤΕΩΝ. Griffin recumbent r. ℞. ΕΠΙ ΔΗ / ΜΗΤΡΙΟΥ. Laur. head of Apollo r. *B.M.C.* 66. **Plate III** *nearly* VF/F £90

617 — Similar. ℞. As last, but ΕΠΙ ΔΙΟ / ΝΥΣΑΔΟΣ. *B.M.C.* 68 .. .. VF £150

618 Æ *drachm.* As before, but griffin l. and magistrate's name on *rev.* ΕΠΙ ΙΠ / ΠΩΝΑ / ΚΤΟΣ *Strack* 166 .. .. VF/*nearly* VF £16

619 352-323 B.C. Æ *diobol.* ΗΡΑ above griffin l. ℞. ΑΒΔΗΡΙΤΕΩΝ. Laur. head of Apollo r. *Strack* 204 .. .. *good* F £9

620 Æ 15. ΑΒΔΗΡΙΤΩΝ. Head of Hermes r. ℞. ΕΠΙ / ΔΙΟΝΥΣ / Α. Griffin l. *Strack* 230 .. .. F 45/-

621 **Aenus** (Enez). 466-464 B.C. Æ *tetradrachm.* Head of young Hermes r., wearing close-fitting petasos. ℞. ΑΙΝΙ (retrograde) and goat r. within incuse square; boar's head in front. *May*, I, 19 .. .. RR, VF £500

622 464-460 B.C. Æ *diobol.* As last but much more severe style. ℞. Incuse square with head of caduceus and ΑΙ. *May*, VII, 37 .. .. F £20

623 412-409 B.C. Æ *tetradrachm.* Similar, but rather later style; Hermes's hair is a mass of curls; caduceus in front of goat. *May*, III, 255 .. .. *RR, good* F £350

624 Æ *diobol.* Similar type. *May*, IX, 293 .. .. VF £30

624A 398-395 B.C. Æ *tetradrachm.* Head of Hermes facing, turned slightly to l. ℞. ΑΙΝΙΟΝ. Goat r. poised over vine. *May* 348a .. .. .. RR, VF £600

625 **Maroneia.** 500-450 B.C. Æ *drachm.* ΜΑΡ. Forepart of prancing horse l. and two large pellets. ℞. Ram's head r. within incuse square. *B.M.C.* 7 .. .. F £45

626 450-400 B.C. Æ *tetradrachm.* ΜΑΡΩΝ. Horse prancing l.; above, kantharos. ℞. ΕΠΙ ΜΗΤΡΟΔΟΤΟ around linear square enclosing vine. *B.M.C.* 11 RR, VF/F £300

627 400-350 B.C. Æ *stater.* Horse prancing l. with loose rein; trident head to l. below. ℞. ΕΠΙ / ΙΗ / ΝΩ / ΝΟΣ. Linear square containing vine. *B.M.C.* 21 *good* F £70

628 Æ 15. Horse prancing r. ℞. ΜΑΡΩΝΙΤΩΝ. Type as preceding. *B.M.C.* 65
F 50/-

630

629 Maroneia. *After* 146 B.C. Æ *tetradrachm.* Young head of Dionysos, wearing ivy-wreath, r. ℞. ΔΙΟΝΥΣΟΥ ΣΩΤΗΡΟΣ ΜΑΡΩΝΙΤΩΝ. Dionysos standing l., holding bunch of grapes and two stalks of nartex; in field, two monograms. *B.M.C.* 48   F £12

630 Æ 24. Similar types and legends, only one monogram (*as illustration*). *B.M.C.* 75
                                                                                 good F 80/-

THRACIAN CHERSONESUS (Gallipoli).

631 Aegospotami. 4th Cent. B.C. Æ 18. Head of Demeter l. ℞. ΑΙΓΟΣΠΟ. Goat standing l. *B.M.C.* 2 ..   .. F £5

632 Alopeconnesus. 4th Cent. B.C. Æ 13. Head of Maenad r. ℞. ΑΛΩ. Kantharos. *B.M.C.* 2 ..   ..   *R, fair* 50/-

631   633

633 Cardia. 4th Cent. B.C. Æ 20. Head of Persephone l. ℞. ΚΑΡΔΙΑ. Lion l. *B.M.C.* 1–9 ..   ..   *fair* 21/-; F 45/-

634 Cherronesus (perhaps the later Cardia or Lysimachia), 480-350 B.C. Æ *hemidrachm.* Forepart of lion r., looking back. ℞. Quadripartite incuse square, the alternate depressions deeper, and containing a pellet, usually accompanied by letter or monogram in one quarter and a symbol in the opposite quarter (a very varied assortment). *B.M.C.* 8-52   ..   ..   VF/*good* F 75/-

635 Coela. *Caracalla.* Æ 18. ANTONINVS PIVS AVG. His bust r. ℞. AEL . MVNI . COELA. Prow r. *B.M.C.* 4 *var.*   ..   .. *fair* 35/-

636 Crithote. 350-281 B.C. Æ 12. Female head three-quarter r. ℞. ΚΡΙ below grain of corn. *Cf. B.M.C.* 1 ..   ..   *R, fair* 25/-

637 Elaeus. 350-281 B.C. Æ 18. Prow. ℞. ΕΛΑ in wreath. *Berlin M.C.* 4-10
                                                                                 F 50/-

638 Lysimachia. *After* 309 B.C. Æ 20. Veiled head of Demeter r. ℞. ΛΥΣΙΜΑ/ΧΕΩΝ across field, bunch of grapes below; all in barley-wreath. *B.M.C.* 7   .. F 50/-

639 Madytus. 4th Cent. B.C. Æ 19. Bull butting l., symbol above. ℞. ΜΑΔΥ. Dog seated r. stalk of barley to l. *B.M.C.* 1 ..   ..   *R, fair* 50/-

638   644A

640 **Sestus.** 350 B.C. Æ 17. Head of Persephone l. ℞. ΣΗ. Hermes standing l.; in field l., amphora. *B.M.C.* 3 .. .. F 50/–

641 2nd Cent. B.C. Æ 16. Head of Hermes l. ℞. ΣΗ. Lyre. *Grose* 4175
F/*fair* 30/–

642 *Hadrian.* Æ 16. ΑΔΡΙΑΝ ΚΑΙϹΑΡ. His bust l. ℞. ϹΗϹΤΙѠΝ. Lyre. *Grose* 4180
fair 40/–

ISLANDS OF THRACE.

643 **Imbros.** *After* 300 B.C. Æ 15. Head of Persephone r. ℞. ΙΜΒΡΟΥ. Hermes r. at altar, holding branch and patera. *B.M.C.* 1 .. .. F 60/–

644 Imperial Times. Æ 20. Head of Athena r. ℞. ΙΜΒΡΙΩΝ. Female standing l., holding cornucopiae. *B.M.C.* 8 .. .. *fair* 30/–

644A Æ 20. As before, but *rev.* type owl standing half-left, head facing. *B.M.C.* 6
F 50/–

645 **Lemnos : Hephaestia.** 350-280 B.C. Æ 12. As last. ℞. ΗΦΑΙ / ΣΤΙ. Ram r. *B.M.C.* 1 .. .. F 50/–

646 — **Myrina.** *ca.* 300 B.C. Æ 14. Similar. ℞. ΜΥΡΙ. Owl facing. *B.M.C.* 3
F 50/–

647 **Samothrace.** *ca.* 280 B.C. Æ 18. Similar. ℞. ΣΑΜΟ. Kybele enthroned l. *B.M.C.* 5 .. .. F 60/–

648 **Thasos.** 550-465 B.C. Æ *stater.* Satyr kneeling on r. knee, holding in his arms nymph clad in long chiton: archaic style. ℞. Quadripartite incuse square. *B.M.C.* 3
Plate IV .. .. *RR,* F/good F £50

649 Æ *drachm.* Similar type. *B.M.C.* 16. **Plate IV** .. .. .. R, F £20

650 Æ *obol* (8 grs.). Two dolphins in opposite directions. ℞. As preceding. *B.M.C.* 18
R, F £16

651 465-411 B.C. Æ *drachm.* *Obv.* Type as No. 648, but style not archaic. ℞. " Mill-sail " incuse. *B.M.C.* 32 .. .. VF £50

652 411-350 B.C. Æ Rhodian *tetradrachm.* Head of bearded Dionysos, wearing ivy-wreath l. ℞. ΘΑΣΙΟΝ. Herakles kneeling r., shooting with bow; in field r., round shield *B.M.C.* 36 .. .. *RRR,* VF/nearly VF £1200

652A Æ *didrachm.* Similar but symbol is a torch. .. .. .. *RRR, good* VF £150

652B Æ *drachm.* Similar but symbol is a lizard. *B.M.C.* 41 .. .. R, VF £50

653 Æ *quarter-drachm.* (*trihemiobol*). Satyr kneeling l., holding kantharos. ℞. ΘΑΣΙΩΝ. Amphora. *B.M.C.* 53 .. .. *fair* £5

654 Æ *eighth-drachm* (*tritemorion*). Head of bald and bearded satyr r. ℞. ΘΑΣΙ. Two dolphins in opposite directions. *B.M.C.* 60 .. .. R, VF £16

655 Æ *hemiobol.* Head of nymph l. ℞. ΑΘ. Dolphin r. *B.M.C.* 63 R, VF £20

656 *After* 146 B.C. Æ *tetradrachm.* Head of young Dionysos, wearing ivy-wreath, r. ℞. ΗΡΑΚΛΕΟΥΣ ΣΩΤΗΡΟΣ ΘΑΣΙΩΝ. Herakles standing l., holding club and lion's skin; in field l., monogram. *B.M.C.* 67-78 .. .. .. *nearly* F/F £6; VF £15

657 — Similar, with larger and thinner flan, of later and cruder style .. *good* F £8

658 — Similar, of very crude style; barbarous imitation .. .. F £5

THE EUROPEAN COAST OF THE PROPONTIS.

659 **Bisanthe.** *After* 280 B.C. Æ 14. Head of Apollo r. ℞. ΒΙΣΑΝ / ΘΗΝΩΝ. Tripod. *B.M.C.* 2 .. .. *R, fair* 32/6

660 **Byzantium** (Istanbul). 416-357 B.C. Æ *drachm.* Heifer standing on dolphin l. ℞. "Mill-sail" incuse. *B.M.C.* 1 .. .. F £8

661 357-340 B.C. Æ *tetradrachm.* Similar types. *B.M.C.* 11 .. .. R, F £15

662 664

662 Æ *hemidrachm.* Similar types. *B.M.C.* 15 .. .. *nearly* VF £5

663 3rd Cent. B.C. Æ 18. ΒΥΖΑΝ. Laur. head of Apollo r. ℞. ΔΡΑ / ΧΜΑ. Obelisk on base. *B.M.C.* 37 .. .. F 55/-

664 Roman Period. Æ 21. Head of young Dionysos r. ℞. ΒΥΖΑΝΤΙΩΝ. Vine branch with bunch of grapes. *B.M.C.* 44 .. .. F 40/-

665 *Severus Alexander.* Æ 30. ΑΥΤ . Μ . ΑΥΡ . ΑΛΕΞΑΝΔΡΟC ΑV. His laur. head r. ℞. ΑΝΤΩΝΕΙΝΙΑ ΒΥΖΑΝΤΙΩΝ CΕΒΑCΤΑ. Agonistic urn, containing two palms. *Cf. B.M.C.* 98 .. .. *fair* 60/-

666 **Byzantium and Calchedon in alliance.** *ca.* 221 B.C. Æ 24. Veiled bust of Demeter r. ℞. ΒΥΙΑΝ ΚΑΛΧΑ. Poseidon seated l. on rock. *B.M.C.* 2 .. F 90/-

667 **Byzantium and Nicaea.** *Trebonianus Gallus.* Æ 28. ΑΥΤΚΓΒΕΙΒ ΓΑΛΛΟCΑΥΓ. His laur. bust r. ℞. ΕΠΙ ΙCΑΥΡΙΚΟΥ Κ ΒΕΡΟ ΝΕΙΚΗC ΟΜΟΝΟΙΑ; ΝΙΚΑΕΩΝ in ex.; ΒΥΖΑΝΤΙΩΝ between two torches of fish-basket shape. *B.M.C.* 1 .. .. .. *fair*/F 70/-

668 **Perinthus.** 2nd-1st Cent. B.C. Æ 22. Busts of Sarapis and Isis, jugate, r. ℞. ΠΕΡΙΝΘΙΩΝ. Cow standing l.; beneath, foreparts of two Pegasoi conjoined; in field l., monogram, ΙΩ. *B.M.C.*—. *This type and monogram probably refer to the myth of Io who, metamorphosed into a white cow by Zeus, swam the Bosporus from Asia Minor to Europe* RR, VF £12

669 Imperial Times. *Caracalla.* Æ 43. ΑΥΤ . Κ . Μ . ΑΥΡ . CΕΟΥΗΡ ΑΝΤΩΝΙΝΟC . ΑΥΓ. His laur. bust dr. and cuir. r. ℞. ΠΕΡΙΝΘΙΩΝ above, ΝΕΩΚΟΡΩΝ in ex., ΑΚΤΙΑΠΥΘΙΑ across field. Two temples facing each other; above, two agonistic urns containing palm. *B.M.C.* 42 .. .. RR, F £35

669A *Gallienus.* Æ 36. Uncertain legend; laur. bust of emperor r. ℞. ΠΕΡΙΝΘΙΩΝ ΔΙC ΝΕΩΚΟΡΩΝ. Herakles, with lion-skin on shoulders, standing r., picking with mattock at heap of stones; at his feet, vase. *B.M.C.*— .. .. RRR, F/VF £25 *The reverse type represents one of the " Labours " of Heracles, viz. the cleaning of the stables of King Augeas by turning the course of the rivers Alpheus and Peneus through them.*

670 **Selymbria.** *Before* 450 B.C. Æ *drachm.* ΣΑ. Cock l. ℞. Incuse square of "mill-sail" pattern. *B.M.C.* 1 .. .. RR, *fair* £15

EASTERN COAST OF THRACE.

671 **Anchialus.** *Gordian III and Tranquillina.* Æ 26. AVTK M . ANT . ΓΟΡΔΙΑΝΟC AV . CAB. Their busts face to face; in ex., TPANKVΛΛINA. ℞. ΟVΛΠΙΑΝΩΝ ΑΓΧΙΑΛΕΩΝ. Hygieia standing r. *B.M.C.* 21 .. .. F £12

672 **Apollonia Pontica** (Sozopol). 5th Cent. B.C. *Æ drachm.* Gorgoneion. ℞. Anchor with crayfish to l., A to r. *Grose* 7314 .. .. *good* VF £25

673 400-375 B.C. *Æ diobol.* Head of Apollo facing. ℞. Similar with additional letters. *Grose* 7320-7322 .. .. F £5

674 **Mesembria.** 500-350 B.C. *Æ diobol.* Crested Corinthian helmet facing. ℞. ME ⋈ A between four spokes of wheel, surrounded by border of radiating lines. *B.M.C.* 2
R, VF £13

675 2nd-1st Cent. B.C. Æ 19. Female head, diademed, r. ℞. ME ⋈ AM / ΒΡΙΑΝΩΝ. Athena l., holding spear and shield. *B.M.C.* 8 .. .. *good* F/F 75/-

675   680

INLAND CITIES OF THRACE.

678 **Augusta Trajana** (Eski-Zaghra). *Septimius Severus.* Æ 31. AVK . Λ . CEΠΤΙ . CEVHPOC . Π. His laur. head r. ℞. AVΓΟVCTHC TPAIANHC. Eagle standing on altar facing, head r.; on either side, standard. *Grose* 4541 .. .. F £6

678A **Bizya.** Imperial Times. Æ 18. Head of young Dionysos r. ℞. ΒΙΖVHNΩΝ. Seilenos standing l. carrying kantharos and askos. *B.M.C.* 1 .. *fair, R* 37/6

678B *Philip I.* Æ 37. Greek legend. Laur. and dr. bust r. ℞. ΒΙΖVHNΩΝ. Nike and the emperor erecting trophy; below which, two captives. *B.M.C.* 13 F, R £15

679 **Deultum.** *Gordian III.* Æ 18. IMP . GORDIANVS AVG. Laur. bust l. ℞. COL . FL . PAC . DEVLT. (Colonia Flavia Pacensis Deultum). Concordia standing l., holding patera and cornucopiae. *B.M.C.* 17 *var.* .. .. F 65/-

680 **Hadrianopolis.** Imperial Times. Æ 20. Bare head of bearded Herakles r. ℞. ΑΔΡΙΑΝΟΠΟΛΙΤΩΝ. Club, quiver and bow *B.M.C.* 1 .. .. .. F 60/-

681 *Gordian III.* Æ 26. AVTK . M . ANTΩ . ΓΟΡΔΙΑΝΟC AV. His laur. bust r., draped. ℞. ΑΔΡΙΑΝΟΠ ΟΛΕΙΤΩΝ. Zeus seated l. on throne, eagle at his feet. *B.M.C.* 26
F 75/-

682 **Pautalia.** *Caracalla.* Æ 29. AVT . M . AVPH . ANTΩNEINOC. His laur. head r. ℞. ΟVΛΠΙΑC ΠΑVΤΑΛΙΑC. Fish-tailed serpent, four times coiled, rising erect, surrounded by radiate nimbus. *B.M.C.* 30 .. .. *fair* 65/-

683 **Philippopolis.** *Faustina Junior.* Æ 26. ΦΑVCTEINA CEBACTH. Her bust r., draped. ℞. ΦΙΛΙΠΠΟΠΟΛΕΙΤΩΝ. Demeter standing l., holding ears of corn and long torch. *B.M.C.* 13 .. .. *fair* 50/-

684 *Elagabalus.* Æ 18. AVTK . M . AVP . ANTΩNEINOC. Head r., laur. ℞. ΦΙΛΙΠΠΟΠ-ΟΛΕΙΤΩΝ NEΩKOP. Asklepios, standing facing, holding staff with serpent entwined. *B.M.C.* 48 .. .. F £5

685 **Serdica** (Sofia). *Geta.* Æ 18. A . C . KAI . ΓΕΤΑC. His laur. bust r., draped. ℞. CEPΔΩN. Hermes standing facing, head l. *Grose* 4538 .. .. .. *fair* 40/-

686 **Topirus.** *Caracalla.* Æ 24. AVTK . M . AVP . ANTΩNINOC. His laur. head r. ℞. ΟVΛΠΙΑC ΤΟΠΙΡΟV. Herakles seated l. on rock, holding club. *B.M.C.* 6 R, F £6

687 **Trajanopolis.** *Caracalla.* Æ 18. AVTK . M . AVPH . ANTΩNEINOC. His laur. head r. ℞. ΤΡΑΙΑΝΟΠΟΛΕΙΤΩΝ. Amphora with three palms. *Grose* 4545 .. *fair* 50/-

THRACIAN KINGS AND DYNASTS.

688 **Sparadocus,** *king of the Odrysae. ca.* 425 B.C. *Æ diobol.* ΣΠΑ. Fore-part of horse l. ℞. Incuse square within which eagle flying l. *B.M.C.* 1 .. .. F £16

689 **Seuthes III,** *king of the Odrysae. ca.* 324 B.C. Æ 22. Bearded male head r. ℞. ΣΕΟΥΘΟΥ. Rider on prancing horse r. *B.M.C.* 1 .. .. *fair* 90/-

690 **Lysimachus,** *king of Thrace.* 323-281 B.C. *N stater.* Head of deified Alexander the Great r., with horn of Ammon. ℞. ΒΑΣΙΛΕΩΣ ΛΥΣΙΜΑΧΟΥ. Athena helmeted, seated l., holding Nike and resting elbow on shield; in field l., star .. .. .. VF £80

690   691

691 *Æ tetradrachm.* Type as before. Various symbols, letters and monograms on *rev.* *good* F £22/10/-; *best style, good* VF £50

692 *Æ drachm.* Similar .. .. *good* F/F £7/10/-; VF £12/10/-

693 Æ 18. Young male head r., in close-fitting helmet. ℞. Legend as before. Lion springing r. *Grose* 4497 .. .. F 40/-

694 **Cavarus,** *the last Gaulish king in Thrace. ca.* 219-200 B.C. Æ 20. Laur. head of Apollo r. ℞. ΒΑΣΙΛΕΩΣ ΚΑΥΑΡΟΥ. Nike standing l. *B.M.C.* 1 .. .. F £6

695 **Rhoemetalces I,** *king of Thrace.* 11 B.C.-12 A.D. Æ 23. ΚΑΙΣΑΡΟΣ ΣΕΒΑΣΤΟΥ. Bare head of Augustus r. ℞. ΒΑΣΙΛΕΩΣ ΡΟΙΜΗΤΑΛΚΟΥ. Heads of Rhoemetalces and his wife, jugate, r. *B.M.C.* 4 .. .. *good* F/VF £6

DACIA.

696 *Imitation of tetradrachm of Philip II of Macedon.* Laur. head of Zeus r. ℞. Stylised horse and traces of rider. *Forrer* 281 .. .. VF £10

697 **Roman Province.** *Philip I.* Æ 30. IMP . M . IVL . PHILIPPVS AVG. His bust r., laureate, wearing cuirass and paludamentum. ℞. PROVINCIA DACIA AN . I . Dacia l., holding sword standing between eagle and lion. *B.M.C.—* .. .. .. F 60/-

PANNONIA.

698 *Imitation of tetradrachm of Philip II of Macedon.* Janus-head with features resembling those of Zeus as depicted on original. ℞. Stylised horse and rider r. *Forrer* 328 VF £20

699 — Similar to 696, on larger thin flan. Laureate head r., very barbarous. ℞. As last. *Forrer* 346 .. .. VF £10

MOESIA SUPERIOR.

700 **Viminacium.** *Gordian III.* Æ 23. IMP . GORDIANVS PIVS FEL . AVG. His radiate bust r. draped. ℞. P . M . S . COL . VIM. Moesia standing l. between bull and lion; AN IIII in ex. *B.M.C.* 12 .. .. F 65/-

701 *Philip I.* Æ 29. Similar type but laur. head and AN VI. *B.M.C.* 21 .. F 80/-

702 *Etruscilla.* Æ 29. Type as last but AN XII. *B.M.C.* 32 .. .. *fair*/F 60/-

MOESIA INFERIOR.

703 **Callatis.** Imperial Times. Æ 21. Bust of Demeter r., veiled. ℞. ΚΑΛΛΑΤΙΑΝΩΝ. The Dioskuri galloping r. *B.M.C.* 9 .. .. R, F 65/-

704 **Dionysopolis.** *Gordian III.* Æ 28. ΑΥΤΚ . Μ . ΑΝΤΩΝΙΟC ΓΟΡΔΙΑΝΟC ΑΥΓ. Laur. and draped bust of the emperor r., facing head of Sarapis l. ℞. ΔΙΟΝΥCΟΠΟΛΕΙΤΩΝ. Hygieia standing r. *B.M.C.* 4 .. .. R, *fair* 60/-

705 **Istrus.** 400-300 B.C ⃝R *drachm* Two young male heads facing, side by side, one of them inverted. ℞. ΙΣΤΡΙΗ. Sea-eagle l. on dolphin; below, A. *B.M.C.* 2
nearly VF/F £12

706 *Septimius Severus.* Æ 30. ΑΚ . Λ . ϹΕΠΤ . ϹΕΥΗΡΟϹ Π. His laur. head r. ℞. ΙϹΤΡΙΗΝΩΝ. Kybele seated on throne r.; lion before. *Pick* 495 .. .. .. *fair* 55/-

707 **Marcianopolis.** *Septimius Severus.* Æ 26. ΑΥ . Κ . Λ . ϹΕΠ . ϹΕΥΗΡΟϹ. His laur. and draped bust r. ℞. VI ΦΑVϹΤΙΝΙΑΝΟΥ ΜΑΡΚΙΑΝΟΠΟΛΙΤΩΝ. Kybele seated l. between two lions. *B.M.C.* 4 .. .. F 90/-

708 *Caracalla and J. Domna.* Æ 26. ΑΝΤΩΝΙΝΟϹ ΑΥΓΟΥϹΤΟϹ ΙΟΥΛΙΑ ΔΟΜΝΑ ϹΕ. Their busts face to face. ℞. VII . ΚVΝΤΙΛΙΑΝΟΥ ΜΑΡΚΙΑΝΟΠΟΛΙΤΩΝ. As last, but only one lion. *Pick* 673 .. .. *fair* 75/-

709 *Diadumenian.* Æ 24. Μ. ΟΠΕΛΛΙΟΝ ΑΝΤΩΝΕΙΝΟΝ Κ. Bare-headed bust, dr., r. ℞. ΜΑΡΚΙΑΝΟΠΟΛΕΙΤΩΝ. Artemis running r., holding bow; beside her, hound. *B.M.C.* 39
F £9

710 **Nicopolis ad Istrum.** *Septimius Severus.* Æ 18. ΑV . Κ . Λ . Ϲ . ϹΕΥΗΡΟϹ. His laur. bust r., draped. ℞. ΝΙΚΟΠΟΛΙΤΩΝ ΠΡΟϹΙϹ. Apollo Sauroktonos r., hand on tree. *Pick* 1355 .. .. *fair* 45/-

711 **Odessus.** *After* 200 B.C. Æ 18. Head of Apollo, laur., r. ℞. ΟΔΗϹΙΤΩΝ. Great God reclining l., holding patera and cornucopiae. *B.M.C.* 3 .. .. *fair* 45/-

711A *Caracalla.* Æ 25. ΑVΤΚΜΑVΡϹΕVΗΡΟ ϹΑΝΤΩΝΕΙΝΟ Ϲ. His laur. head r. . ℞. ΟΔΗϹϹΕΙΤΩΝ. Sarapis standing facing, looking l., holding caduceus and patera over altar. *B.M.C.* 13 .. .. F 85/-

711B *Time of Gordian III.* Æ 27. ΑVΤ . Μ . ΑΝΤ . ΓΟΡΔΙΑΝΟϹ ΑVΓ. Busts face to face of Gordian r. and Great God l. ℞. ΟΔΗϹϹΕΙΤΩΝ. Demeter standing l., holding ears of corn and long torch; in field l., Ε. *B.M.C.* 19 .. .. *nearly* F £7

712 **Tomis.** 2nd and 1st cent. B.C. Æ 26. Bearded head of Θεὸς Μέγας (the " Great God " of Odessus) wearing taenia. ℞. ΤΟΜΙ, eagle and ΤΙΜΟ (magistrate's name) in oak-wreath. *B.M.C.* 1 .. .. R, F £6

713 *Lucilla.* Æ 21. ΛΟΥΚΙΛΛΑ ϹΕΒΑϹΤ. Bust r. ℞. ΜΗΤΡΟΠ . ΠΟΝΤΟV ΤΟΜΕΩϹ. Athena l., holding Nike. *B.M.C.* 14 .. .. F £5

713A *Caracalla.* Æ 28. ΑΚ . Μ . ΑV . ΑΝΤΩΝΙΝΟϹ. Laur. bust r. ℞. Legend as last. Emperor at altar standing l., holding patera and sceptre. *Pick* 2901 .. F 90/-

DANUBIAN DISTRICT : SARMATIA.
For map see page 114.

714 **Olbia.** 6th-5th cent. B.C. Æ 65 *cast.* Gorgon-head facing. ℞. ΑΡΙΧ. Eagle, wings open, standing r. on dolphin. *Berlin M.C.* 1 .. .. .. RRR, F £100

715 Æ 37 *cast.* As before, but ΟΛΒΙ and eagle l. *Berlin M.C.* 13 .. F/*fair* £25

716 Æ 24×7 in shape of dolphin, *cast*: one side is flat and inscribed ΘΥ. *B.M.C.* 21
RR, *fair* £10; F £20

717 *Ca.* 350 B.C. ⃝R *stater.* Head of Demeter l. ℞. ΟΛΒΙΟ. Sea-eagle standing l. on dolphin, wings open, head r. *B.M.C.* 1. **Plate IV** .. .. .. RRR, F £100

718 3rd Cent. B.C. Æ 23. Bearded head of river-god Borysthenes l. ℞. ΟΛΒΙΟ. Battle-axe and bow; in field, different letters and monograms. *B.M.C.* 4-12 .. *fair* 30/-

719 *Ca.* 150 B.C. ⃝R *drachm.* Laur. head of Apollo r.; countermarked with helmet. ℞. ΟΛΒΙΟ. Lyre. *Zograf* 33, 15 .. .. F £17

720 Æ 18. Similar, but countermark, male head .. .. F 75/-

721 **Olbia.** 120-63 B.C. Æ 14. Head of Tyche l. ℞. ΟΛΒΙΟ. Naked archer kneeling l., discharging bow. *B.M.C.* 17 .. .. F 40/–

722 138-161 A.D. Æ 25. ΟΛΒΙΟΠΟΛΕΙΤωΝ. Laur. head of Apollo r. ℞. ΑΛΟΘΥ ΑΔΕΛΦΟΥ Eagle l., between three monograms. *Zograf* 34, 13 .. .. VF £7

723 **Tyra.** *ca.* 300 B.C. Æ *drachm* (86 grs.). Bust of Demeter facing. ℞. ΤΥΡΑΝΟΝ. Bull rushing l. *Grose* 4313 .. .. *RRR*, F £120

TAURIC CHERSONESUS (The Crimea).

For map see page 114.

724 **Cherronesus** (near Sebastopol). 350-330 B.C. Æ 20. ΧΕΡ. Warrior, wearing conical helmet, kneeling l. on r. knee behind his shield, and holding spear. ℞. Artemis in galloping quadriga r. *B.M.C.* 5 .. .. *R, good* F £8

725 330-300 B.C. Æ 19. Artemis kneeling r. on r. knee, holding arrow and bow. ℞. ΧΕΡ. Griffin running l. *B.M.C.* 6 .. .. *good* F £5

726 300-250 B.C. Æ 19. ΧΕΡ. Artemis l., kneeling on prostrate stag which she pierces with a spear. ℞. Bull l. butting; club below; in ex. ΔΙΑΓΟΡΑ. *B.M.C.* 7 F 80/–

727 **Panticapaeum** (formerly Apollonia, now Kerch). 5th Cent. B.C. Æ *diobol.* Lion's mask facing. ℞. ΑΠΟΛ in angles of cross. *B.M.C.* Apollonia 1 .. *good* F £20

728 375-340 B.C. Æ 19. Head of bearded Pan r. ℞. ΠΑΝ. Forepart of running griffin l.; beneath, sturgeon l. *B.M.C.* 20 .. .. VF/F £5

729 325-300 B.C. Æ *stater.* Head of bearded Pan l., crowned with ivy. ℞. ΠΑΝ. Horned griffin l., with spear between teeth, standing on ear of corn. *B.M.C.* 4 VF £500

730 Æ 18. Head of young Pan l., crowned with ivy. ℞. ΠΑΝ. Lion's head l.; below sturgeon l. *B.M.C.* 21 .. .. *fair* 30/–; F 65/–

731 300-250 B.C. Æ 16. As last. ℞. ΠΑΝ. Bow and arrow. *B.M.C.* 28 .. F 55/–

732 Æ 16. Head of bearded Pan l. ℞. ΠΑΝ. Head of ox. l. *B.M.C.* 17 .. F 75/–

733 200-175 B.C. Æ 19. As last. ℞. ΠΑΝΤΙ. Cornucopiae between the pilei of the Dioskuri. *B.M.C.* 39 .. .. *fair*/F 60/–

734 100-75 B.C. Billon *didrachm.* Head of Dionysos r., crowned with ivy. ℞. ΠΑΝΤΙ / ΚΑΠΑΙ / ΤΩΝ within ivy-wreath. *B.M.C.* 11 .. .. .. F £10; VF £20

735 Æ 21. Laur. head of Apollo r. ℞. Similar legend. Tripod lebes. *B.M.C.* 35 *good* F/F 90/–

736 Æ 14. ΠΑΝΤΙΚΑΠ between rays of eight-pointed star. ℞. Tripod-lebes. *B.M.C.* 48 F 45/–

KINGS OF THE SCYTHIANS.

737 **Acrosandrus.** *ca.* 100 B.C. Æ 18. Head of Zeus r. ℞. ΒΑΣΙΛΕ . ΑΚΡΟΣΑΝΔΡ. Cornucopiae .. .. *RR, fair* £6

738 **Coson.** *ca.* 50 B.C. Æ *stater.* ΚΟΣΩΝ. Three men in Roman togas walking l. (copied from a denarius of Brutus). ℞. Eagle l., standing on sceptre, holding wreath in claw. *B.M.C.* 2 .. .. F £40

NORTHERN GREECE.

Thessaly		19 Peumata ?	35 Pelagia ?
1 Atrax		20 Phacium	*Epirus*
2 Cierium		21 Phalanna	36 Ambracia
3 Crannon		22 Pharcadon	37 Buthrotum
4 Demetrias		23 Pharsalus	38 Cassope
5 Gomphi		24 Pherae	39 Elea
6 Gyrton		25 Scotussa	40 Nicopolis
7 Halus		26 Thebae	41 Pandosia
8 Heraclea Trachinia		27 Tricca	42 Phoenice
9 Homolium		*Is. of Thessaly*	43 Dodona
10 Lamia		28 Peparethus	*Acarnania*
11 Larissa		29 Sciathus	44 Alyzia
12 Larissa Cremaste		*Illyricum*	45 Anactorium
13 Meliboea		30 Amantia	46 Argos Amphilochicum
14 Melitaea		31 Apollonia	47 Leucas
15 Metropolis		32 Epidamnus-	48 Metropolis
16 Oeta		Dyrrachium	49 Oeniadae
17 Orthe		33 Oricus	50 Stratus
18 Pelinna		34 Damastium ?	51 Thyrrheium

THESSALY.

739 The Aenianes. 400-344 B.C. Æ *hemidrachm.* Laur. head of Zeus l. ℞. ΑΙΝΙΑΝΩΝ. Warrior hurrying l., hurling javelin r. *B.M.C.* 2 .. .. .. *good* F £15

740 168-143 B.C. Æ *tetrobol.* Head of Athena r. ℞. Same legend. Slinger (Phemius) discharging sling, r. *B.M.C.* 13 .. .. VF/F £10

741 Æ 15. Head of Zeus, laur., r. ℞. ΑΙΝΙΑΝΩΝ. Slinger r. *B.M.C.* 20 .. F 35/-

742 Atrax. 400-344 B.C. Æ 18. Head of nymph r. ℞. ΑΤΡΑΓΙΟΝ. Free horse standing r. *B.M.C.* 1 .. .. *fair*/F 35/-

743 Æ 17. Head of Apollo l. ℞. ΑΤΡΑΓΙΟΝ. Bull r. *Not in B.M.C.* R, F 75/-

744 Cierium. 350-190 B.C. Æ 12. Head of Poseidon l. ℞. ΚΙΕΡΙΕΙΩΝ. Arne kneeling, playing with astragali. *B.M.C.* 5 .. .. F 45/-

745 Crannon. *After* 400 B.C. Æ 17. Horseman galloping r. ℞. ΚΡΑΝΝΟ. Hydria mounted on wheels. *B.M.C.* 4 .. .. F 60/-

745A Æ 16. Laur. head of Zeus r. ℞. ΚΡΑΝΝΩΝΙΩΝ. Horseman prancing r. *B.M.C.* 7/8 F 45/-

746 Demetrias (Magnesia). *c.* 290 B.C. Æ *hemidrachm.* Head of Artemis r. ℞. ΔΗΜΗΤΡΙΕΩΝ. Prow r.; on l., mon. *B.M.C.* 1 .. .. R, F £10

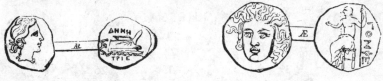

746   747

747 Gomphi. 300-200 B.C. Æ 18. Head of nymph of the city, three-quarter l. ℞. ΓΟΜΦΕ. Zeus Palamnaeus seated r., holding sceptre. *B.M.C.* 3 F/*fair* 27/6

748 Gyrton. 300-200 B.C. Æ 20. Head of Zeus, laur., l. ℞. ΓΥΡΤΩΝΙΩΝ. Horse r.: below, ΔΗ and bunch of grapes. *B.M.C.* 7 .. .. .. F/VF 65/-

749 Halus. 300-200 B.C. Æ 14. Head of Zeus r. ℞. ΑΛΕ. Phryxus on ram flying r. *B.M.C.* 4 .. .. F 40/-

750 Heraclea Trachinia (Oetaea). 300-190 B.C. Æ 15. Head of lion l. ℞. ΗΡΑ. Club within olive-wreath. *B.M.C.* 7 .. .. F 40/-

751 Homolium. 300-200 B.C. Æ 20. Head of Philoktetes, in conical hat, r. ℞. ΟΜΟΛΙΚΟΝ. Coiled serpent r. *Grose* 4579 .. .. R, *fair* 37/6

752 Lamia. Chief town of the Malians. 400-344 B.C. Æ *hemidrachm.* Head of young Dionysos l. ℞. ΛΑΜΙΕΩΝ. Amphora. *B.M.C.* 2 .. .. .. VF £7

753 Æ *obol.* Similar type. *B.M.C.* 4 .. .. F/VF 80/-

754 Æ *hemidrachm.* As before but legend ΜΑΛΙΕΩΝ. *B.M.C.* Malienses 1 *nearly* F 50/-

755 Æ 16. Head of nymph r. ℞. ΛΑΜΙΕΩΝ. Herakles kneeling r., shooting with bow. *B.M.C.* 10 .. .. F 40/-

756 Æ 15. *Obv.* Similar. ℞. ΛΑΜΙ. The sick Philoktetes reclining on rock l. *B.M.C.* 6 *fair* 30/-

759

757 **Larissa.** *Before* 450 B.C. Æ *drachm.* Youth standing r., restraining unruly bull r. ℞. ΛΑΡΙΣ (last three letters retrograde). Bridled horse galloping r. *B.M.C.* 16
nearly VF £30

758 450-400 B.C. Similar, but *obv.* type to l. and ΛΑΡΙΣΑΙΑ on *rev.* *B.M.C.* 33 VF £40

758A Æ *obol.* Horse galloping l. ℞. Nymph Larissa l. playing with ball. *Cf. B.M.C.* 41
almost VF £12/10/–

759 400-344. Æ *didrachm.* Head of nymph Larissa facing slightly to l., hair flowing. ℞. ΛΑΡΙΣΩΝ. Bridled horse trotting r. *B.M.C.* 55 *RR, nearly* VF £200

760 Æ *drachm.* Similar but free horse feeding r., l. forefoot raised. *B.M.C.* 57. **Plate IV**
nice style, VF £40

760A — Head of nymph r., wearing sphendone. ℞. ΛΑΡΙΣΑΙΑ. Horse cantering l. *B.M.C.* 51 *var.* **Plate IV** .. .. VF £40

761 — Another, as No. 759, but mare r. with foal r. behind. *B.M.C.* 63
nearly VF/F £25

762 Æ 17. Head of nymph r., hair rolled. ℞. As preceding, but type l. *B.M.C.* 92 *var.* .. .. F 30/–

763 **Larissa Cremaste.** 302-286 B.C. Æ 17. Head of Achilles l. ℞. ΛΑΡΙ. Thetis l. on hippocamp, holding shield. *B.M.C.* 1 .. .. *good* F 65/–

764 **The Magnetes.** 196-146 B.C. Æ *drachm.* Head of Zeus, laur., r. ℞. ΜΑΓΝΗΤΩΝ. Artemis holding bow, seated l. on prow of galley: to l., dolphin; to r., monograms. *B.M.C.* 1 .. .. *R,* VF £30

765 Æ 19. Head of Zeus, laur., l. ℞. ΜΑΓΝΗΤΩΝ. Centaur r., holding branch. *B.M.C.* 7
F 45/–

The Malienses, *see* Lamia, especially 754

765A **Meliboea.** Æ 11. Head of nymph r. ℞. ΜΕΛΙ. Bunch of grapes *fair* 25/–

766 **Melitaea.** 350 B.C. Æ 14. Head of Zeus r. ℞. ΜΕΛΙ. Bee. *Grose* 4646
fair 27/6

767 **Metropolis.** 400-344 B.C. Æ 19. Head of Apollo, laur., r. ℞. ΜΗΤΡΟΠΟΛΙΤΩΝ. Artemis r., holding dove. *B.M.C.* 4 .. .. F/*fair* 40/–

768 **Oeta.** 400-344 B.C. Æ *obol.* Head of lion l. ℞. ΟΙΤΑ. Quiver with strap, and strung bow. *B.M.C.* 3 .. .. *R,* F £5

769 196-146 B.C. Æ 17. Young male head. ℞. ΟΙΤΑΙΩΝ. Spear-head and jaw-bone of boar. *B.M.C.* 11 .. .. *fair*/F 30/–

770 **Orthe.** 350-200 B.C. Æ 22. Head of Athena r. ℞. ΟΡΘΙΕΙΩΝ. Forepart of horse r. springing from rock upon which grow trees; all within wreath. *Grose* 4655
R, F £5

771 **Pelinna.** 450-400 B.C. Æ *diobol.* Horseman galloping l., holding two lances. ℞. ΠΕΛΛΙ. Warrior advancing l., with spear and round shield. *B.M.C.* 1 *RR,* F £10

772 **The Perrhaebi.** 480-400 B.C. Æ *obol.* Horse galloping r. ℞. ΠΕΡΑ. Athena adv. r., with spear and shield: all in incuse square. *B.M.C.* 4 .. *R,* F £7

773 196-146 B.C. Æ 19. Head of Zeus r. ℞. ΠΕΡΡΑΙΒΩΝ. Hera seated r. *Grose* 4665 .. .. F 75/–

774 **Peumata.** 302-286 B.C. Æ 12. Head of Nymph r. ℞. ΠΕΥΜΑΤΙΩΝ around large monogram of the Achaeans, ΑΧ .. .. *RR, fair* 40/–

775 **Phacium.** 300-200 B.C Æ 20. Similar. ℞. ΦΑΚΙΑΣΤΩΝ. Horseman r. *B.M.C.* 1 .. .. *R, fair* 40/–

776 **Phalanna.** 400-344 B.C. Æ *drachm.* Young male head (? Ares) r. ℞. ΦΑΛ-ΑΝΝΑΙΩΝ. Bridled horse r. *B.M.C.* 1 .. .. *RR,* VF/F £45

777 Æ 18. *Obv.* as preceding. ℞. Legend as preceding: head of nymph r. *B.M.C.* 5
R, F 75/–

778 **Pharcadon.** 480-400 B.C. Æ *hemidrachm.* Youth r., restraining forepart of unruly bull. ℞. ΦΑΡΚΑΔ. Forepart of galloping horse, r. *B.M.C.* 1 .. .. F £10

779 **Pharsalus.** 480-440 B.C. Æ *hemidrachm.* Head of Athena r. of archaic style; serpents on helmet. ℞. ΦΑΡ. Horse's head r. *B.M.C.* 1. **Plate IV** *RR,* F £25

780 440-400 B.C. Similar, but more advanced style, ΦΑΡ. *B.M.C.* 2 .. F £17/10/–

781 Æ *obol.* As before. *B.M.C.* 5 .. .. VF £20

782 **Pharsalus.** 400-344 B.C. Æ *drachm.* As before. ℞. ΦΑΡΣ. Thessalian rider r.; magistrate's name in ex. *B.M.C.* 6 .. .. VF £45

783 300-190 B.C. Æ 20. Head of Athena, helmeted, three-quarter l. ℞. ΦΑΡΣΑ. Horseman galloping r.; beyond him, second rider r. *B.M.C.* 21 .. .. .. F 40/-

784 **Pherae.** 4th Cent. B.C. Æ *hemidrachm.* Head of Hekate l.; behind, torch. ℞. ΦΕΡΑΙΟΥΝ. Nymph Hypereia l., placing r. hand on lion's-head fountain: in wreath, l., ΑΣΤΟ. *B.M.C.* 20 .. .. RR, F £25

785 *Alexander.* 369-357 B.C. Æ 14. Forepart of bull r., head facing. ℞. ΑΛΕΞΑΝΔΡΟΥ· Forepart of horse prancing r. *B.M.C.* 18 .. .. *fair* 30/-

786 *c.* 300 B.C. Æ 25. Head of Hekate facing, holding torch. ℞. ΦΕΡΑΙΩΝ. Hekate seated on horse galloping r. *B.M.C.* 22 .. .. F 70/-

782   792

787 **Scotussa.** 480-400 B.C. Æ *drachm.* Forepart of horse r. ℞. ΣΚΟ. Corn-grain. *B.M.C.* 1 .. .. RR, F £30

788 300-190 B.C. Æ 18. Head of Ares, helmeted, r. ℞. ΣΚΟΤΟΥΣΣΑΙΩΝ. Horse prancing r.; below, Φ. *B.M.C.* 5 .. .. *green patina,* VF £7

789 **Thebae.** 302-286. Æ *hemidrachm.* Head of Demeter r. ℞. ΘΗΒΑΙΩΝ. Protesilaos leaping ashore r. from prow. *B.M.C.* 1 .. .. RR, *good* F £30

790 **Tricca.** 480-400 B.C. Æ *hemidrachm.* Thessalian youth r. restraining forepart of unruly bull. ℞. ΤΡΙΚΚΑΙΩΝ. Forepart of free horse r. *B.M.C.* 6 F/*good* F £12

791 300-190 B.C. Æ 22. Head of nymph Tricca r. ℞. ΤΡΙΚΚΑΙΩΝ. Asklepios seated r. feeding serpent with a bird. *B.M.C.* 17 .. .. R, F 75/-

792 **Thessalian Confederacy.** 191-146 B.C. Æ *double victoriatus.* Head of Zeus r., wearing oak-wreath. ℞. ΘΕΣΣΑΛΩΝ. Athena Itonia r., striking with spear and holding shield: in field, ΠΟΛΙ. *B.M.C.* 4 .. .. .. *nearly* VF/*good* F £8

793 — Similar, but above on *rev.* ΦΙΛΟΞΕΝΙΔΗΣ; in ex. ΔΑΜΟΘΟΙΝΟΣ. *B.M.C.* 33
                                                                     good VF £14

794 Æ *drachm.* ΓΑΥΑΝΑ. Laur. head of Apollo r. ℞. As No. 792, but ΠΟΛΥ. *B.M.C* 38 .. .. VF £11

795 Æ *hemidrachm* Similar, but laur. head of Zeus on *obv.* *B.M.C.* 44 .. R, VF £17

796 Æ 22. Head of Apollo, laur., r. ℞. ΘΕΣΣΑΛΩΝ. Type as preceding. *Cf. B.M.C.* 29
                                                                            F 35/-

797 Æ 18. ΙΠΠΑΤΑΣ. Head of Athena r. ℞. ΘΕΣΣΑΛΩΝ. Horse trotting r. *B.M.C.* 62
                                                                            F 35/-

798 **Thessaly: Imperial Times.** *Hadrian.* Æ 22. Laur. bust of emperor r. ℞. ΟΧ ΝΙΚΟΜΑΧΟΥ preceded by monogram: type as No. 792. *B.M.C.* 77 F/VF £5

799 *Caracalla.* Æ 22, *three assaria.* Laur. bust of emperor r. ℞. ΘΕΣΣΑΛΩΝ. Nike in three-horsed chariot r.: in ex., ΚΟΙΝΟΝ. *B.M.C.* 83 .. .. .. M/*fair* 22/6

800 **Islands of Thessaly: Peparethus** (Scopelos), 500-480 B.C. Æ *tetradrachm (plated).* Bunch of grapes. ℞. Crested helmet r., in incuse square. *Not in B.M.C. Babelon* 1864
                              RR, *large chisel-cuts on rev., otherwise* VF £40

801 Imperial Times. Æ 18. Head of Dionysos r. ℞. ΠΕΠΑΡΗΘΙΩΝ. Kantharos with palm beside it. *B.M.C.* 9 .. .. *fair* 27/6

802 **Sciathus.** 400-200 B.C. Æ 16. Head of Hermes r. ℞. ΣΚΙΑΘΙ. Caduceus. *B.M.C.* 1 .. .. R, F £5

ILLYRICUM.

802A **Amantia.** 230-168 B.C. Æ 20. ΘΟΙ. Head of Dodonean Zeus r. ℞. ΑΜΑΝΤΩΝ. Thunderbolt: beneath, ΞΕ; all in oak-wreath. *B.M.C.* 1 .. .. *R, fair* 40/-

803 **Apollonia.** 350-300 B.C. Æ Corinthian *stater.* Pegasos with pointed wing flying r. ℞. ΑΠΟΛ. Head of Athena r. *B.M.C.* 1 .. .. *RR,* F £25

804 229-100 B.C. Æ *drachm* or *victoriatus.* Name of mint-master. Cow suckling calf. ℞. ΑΠΟΛ and name of magistrate. Stellate or floral pattern in double linear square VF 75/-

805 Æ *hemidrachm.* ΔΑΜΟΦΩΝ. Fire of the Nymphaeum. ℞. ΑΠΟΛΛΩΝΙΑΤΑΝ. Pedum. *B.M.C.* 44 *var.* .. .. *RR,* F £8

806 Æ 27. Head of Apollo l.; behind, two monograms; below, ΞΕ. ℞. ΑΠΟΛΛΩΝΙΑΤΑΝ. Obelisk; all in laurel-wreath. *B.M.C.* 60 .. .. *fair* 30/-

807 *After* 100 B.C. Æ *drachm* or *denarius.* ΔΩΡΙΩΝΟΣ. Head of Apollo l. ℞. ΑΠΟΛ. Three nymphs dancing round fire: in ex., ΔΕΙΝΩΝ. *B.M.C.* 67 .. VF £12

808 **Epidamnus Dyrrhachium** 450-350 B.C. Æ *stater.* Cow r., looking back, suckling calf. ℞ ΔΥΡ around double floral pattern in linear square; below, club l. *B.M.C.* 1 .. .. VF £30

809 350-300 B.C. Æ Corinthian *stater.* Pegasos flying r. with pointed wing, Δ below. ℞. Head of Athena r.; to r. above, dolphin; behind neck, club. *B.M.C.* 4 VF/F £13

810 250-229 B.C. Æ *drachm.* Hd. of Herakles in lion's skin r. ℞. Pegasos flying r. *B.M.C.* 27 .. .. VF £6

811 229-100 B.C. Æ *drachm.* Type as No. 808, but to r., magistrate's name and symbol on *obv.*; ΔΥΡ and another magistrate's name on *rev.* .. .. .. *nearly* VF 50/-

812 Æ 16. Head of Zeus r. ℞. ΔΥΡ and magistrate's name. Tripod-lebes. *B.M.C.* 169 .. .. F 30/-

813 **Oricus.** 230-168 B.C. Æ 17. Laur. head of Apollo. ℞. ΩΡΙΚΙΩΝ. Obelisk of Apollo Agyieus; all in wreath. *B.M.C.* 1 .. .. *R, fair* 40/-

808   816

814 **KINGS OF ILLYRICUM: Monunius.** *c.* 290 B.C. Æ *stater.* Cow suckling calf; above, jaw-bone of Calydonian boar. ℞. ΔΥΡ ΒΑΣΙΛΕΩΣ ΜΟΝΟΥΝΙΟΥ. Double floral pattern within double linear square. *B.M.C.* 2 .. .. .. *RR,* F/VF £35

815 **Ballaeus.** *c.* 150 B.C. Æ 16. His head r. ℞. ΒΑΛΛΑΙΟΥ. Artemis running l. *B.M.C.* 3 .. .. *R, fair* 70/-

816 **ISLANDS OF ILLYRICUM: Issa.** 4th cent. B.C. Æ 23. Head of Athena r. ℞. ΙΣ. Goat standing r. *B.M.C.* 1 .. .. *R, fair* 45/-

817 **Pharos.** 4th Cent. B.C. Æ 24. Laur. head of Zeus l. ℞. ΦΑΡΙΩΝ. Goat standing l. *B.M.C.* 1 .. .. *fair* 35/-

818 2nd Cent. B.C. Æ 19. Young male head, laur., r. ℞. ΦΑ. Kantharos. *B.M.C.* 12 *fair* 30/-

819 **ILLYRIO-EPIROTE SILVER COINAGE: Damastium.** *ca.* 400 B.C. *Stater* or *tetradrachm.* Laur. head of Apollo r. ℞. ΔΑΜΑΣΤΙΝΩΝ. Tripod-lebes. *May* 64. **Plate IV** .. .. VF £100

820 — Another, of much ruder style. *May* 98b .. .. *fair* £15

820A **Pelagia.** 4th cent. B.C. *Stater.* Similar type to last but ΠΕΛΑΙ and knife on l. of tripod. *B.M.C.* 2 .. .. *RRR,* F £50

EPIRUS.

821 **Ambracia.** 450-320 B.C. Æ Corinthian *stater*. Pegasos with pointed wing flying l., A below. ℞. Head of Athena r., with A and symbol .. .. *good* F £12

822 238-168 B.C. Æ *drachm* or *victoriatus*. Laur. and veiled head of Dione l. ℞. AM. Obelisk, etc.: all in laurel-wreath. *B.M.C.* 1 .. .. *R*, F £8

823 Æ 16. Similar, but *obv.* type r.; *rev.* legend AMBP. *B.M.C.* 5 .. VF/F 60/–

824 Æ 19. Head of Zeus r. ℞. AMBP. Griffin running r.: magistrate's name in ex. *B.M.C.* 29 .. .. F 42/6

825 **Athamanes.** 220-190 B.C. Æ 17. Type as No. 823. ℞. AΘAMANΩN. Athena l., holding owl and spear. *B.M.C.* 3 .. .. *R*, F 65/–

825A **Buthrotum.** Augustus. Æ 24. CAESAR AVGVSTVS in oak-wreath ℞. GRAECINVS QVIN . TERT BVTHR. Lituus. .. .. *RR, fair* 52/6

826 **Cassope.** Late 4th Cent. B.C. Æ 18. Head of Aphrodite r. ℞. KAΣΣΩΠAIΩN. Coiled serpent, head erect. *B.M.C.* 1 .. .. *fair* 27/6

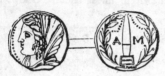

822 827

827 238-168 B.C. Æ *drachm*. Head of Zeus r., monogram behind. ℞. Same legend. Eagle r.; all within oak-wreath. *B.M.C.* 8 .. .. F £7

828 Æ 17. Head of Dionysos r. ℞ Same legend. Amphora; all in wreath. *B.M.C.* 14
fair 25/–

829 **Elea.** *Before* 340 B.C. Æ 20. Head of Demeter facing. ℞. EΛEAI. Kerberus l. *B.M.C.* 3 .. .. *RR*, F £5

830 **Molossi.** *Before* 340 B.C. Æ 17. MOΛOΣΣΩN around rim of shield decorated with thunderbolt. ℞. Thunderbolt in laurel wreath. *B.M.C.* 3 .. *RR*, VF £8

831 **Nicopolis.** *Caracalla.* Æ 24. Laur. bust of emperor r. ℞. NEIKOΠOΛEΩΣ. Nike in biga r. *Not in B.M.C.* .. .. F £6

831A **Pandosia.** 238-168 B.C. Æ 19. AΠAΣ. Head of Zeus l. ℞. ΠAN. Thunderbolt: all within oak-wreath. *B.M.C.* 1 .. .. *RR, fair* 45/–

832 **Phoenice.** Imperial Times. Æ 15. ΦOINIKAIEΩN. Head of Zeus r. ℞. IEPEVC . . . Palm-branch. *B.M.C.* 4 .. .. *RR*, F £5

833 **Kings of Epirus : Pyrrhus.** 295-272 B.C. Æ *octobol*. Head of Persephone r. ℞. BAΣIΛEΩΣ ΠYPPOY. Athena in fighting attitude l. *B.M.C.* 9 *nearly* VF/F £90

834 Æ 22. Similar, but *rev.* type Demeter seated r. on throne. *B.M.C.* 26 F/VF 85/–

835 **Regal Period.** *Before* 238 B.C. Æ 20. Head of Zeus l. ℞. AΠ. Thunderbolt; all within wreath. *B.M.C.* 5 .. .. F 37/6

836 — As preceding, *obv.* type r. *B.M.C.* 7 .. .. F/*fair* 25/–

837 **Epirote Republic.** 238-168 B.C. Æ *didrachm*. Jugate heads, r., of Zeus Dodonaeus, crowned with oak, and Dione, wearing laureate stephane and veil. ℞. AΠEIPΩ-TAN Bull charging r.; all within oak-wreath. *Cf. B.M.C.* 8 *R*, VF/F £60

838 Æ *drachm*. Head of Zeus r., crowned with oak. ℞. ΑΠΕΙΡΩΤΑΝ. Eagle standing r., with wings closed; all in oak-wreath. *B.M.C.* 23 .. .. .. F £5; EF £20

839 Æ *drachm* (reduced to weight of victoriatus). *Obv.* type as 837. ℞. ΑΠΕΙΡΩΤΑΝ. Thunderbolt; all within oak-wreath. *B.M.C.* 42 .. .. .. VF/F £10

840 Æ *hemidrachm* (weight of half-victoriatus). *Obv.* type as 838. ℞. as preceding. *B.M.C.* 44 .. .. VF/F £10

841 Æ 22. Head of Zeus l., crowned with oak. ℞. ΑΠΕΙΡΩΤΑΝ and thunderbolt within oak-wreath. *B.M.C.* 46 .. .. F 35/–

842 *Struck at* **Dodona**. *After* 168 B.C. Æ 26. ΙΕΡΕΥΣ. Head of Zeus r. ℞. ΜΕΝΕ-ΔΗΜΟΣ ΑΡΓΕΑΔΗΣ. Bust of Artemis r. *B.M.C.* 68 .. .. F 60/–

CORCYRA.

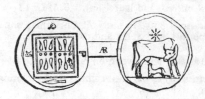

845

843 500-450 B.C. Æ *stater*. Cow l., head r., suckling calf. ℞. Double stellate or floral pattern within linear square; all in incuse square. *B.M.C.* 34 .. VF/EF £20

844 450-400 B.C. Æ *stater*. Similar, but whole *rev.* type in a circle and letter κ. *B.M.C.* 60 good F/F £8

845 400-300 B.C. Æ *stater*. Similar, but neater workmanship: *obv.* type r. ; on *rev.* legend ΚΟΡ. *B.M.C.* 126 .. .. *nearly* VF £10

846 Æ *hemidrachm*. Amphora. ℞. ΚΟΡ. Star of eight rays. *B.M.C.* 135 good F £5

847 338-300 B.C. Corinthian *stater*. Pegasos with pointed wing r. ℞. ΚΟΡ. Head of Athena r.; amphora behind. *B.M.C.* 6 .. .. .. *nearly* VF/VF £20

848 300-229 B.C. Æ *drachm*. Κ I. Amphora between kantharos and oenochoe. ℞. ΚΟΡΚΥΡΑΙ. Floral star of eight rays. *B.M.C.* 198 .. .. .. F/VF £12

849 Æ 16. Bull's head and shoulders r. ℞. Monogram in wreath. *B.M.C.* 215 fair 25/–

850 Æ 17. Prow r.: above, magistrate's name. ℞. ΚΟ. Kantharos. *B.M.C.* 259 F/fair 30/–

851 229-48 B.C. Æ *didrachm*. Head of young Dionysos, crowned with ivy, r. ℞. Pegasos r.: below, monogram. *B.M.C.* 362 .. .. good F £10

852 — Another, palm in mouth of Pegasos and hindlegs resting on prow of galley. *B.M.C.* 369. **Plate IV** .. .. VF £20

853 Æ *half-victoriatus*. Head of Aphrodite r., Β behind. ℞. Pegasos with pointed wing, monogram below. *B.M.C.* 392 .. .. *nearly* VF/F £7

854 Æ 23. Head of young Herakles, in lion-skin, r. ℞. ΚΟΡΚΥΡΑΙΩΝ. Prow of galley inscribed ΝΙΚΑ: in field, l., ΛΥ. *B.M.C.* 482 .. .. F 50/–

855 Æ 16. Head of Dionysos r. ℞. ΚΟ. Kantharos. *B.M.C.* 396 .. F 32/6

856 Æ 20. Head of Dionysos r. ℞. Amphora and monogram. *B.M.C.* 422 F 35/–

857 Æ 26. Jugate heads of young Herakles and nymph Corcyra r. ℞. As 854, but with names of magistrates ΑΡΙCΤΕΑC and ΑΡΙCΤΩΝΟC in addition. *B.M.C.* 497 F 75/–

858 *After* 48 B.C. Æ 27. ΚΟΡΚΥΡΑΙWΝ. Bust of Apollo r.: in front, lyre. ℞. ΖΕΥC ΚΑCΙΟC. Zeus Kasios seated l. on throne, holding sceptre. *B.M.C.* 578 good F 90/–

859 Æ 19. ΑΓΡΕΥC. Agreus (Aristaeus) standing l., holding cornucopiae. ℞. As preceding. *B.M.C.* 587 .. .., ... *fair* 20/–

860 *Severus*. Æ 26. Greek legend. Laur. bust of emperor r. ℞. ΚΟΡΚVΡΑΙΩΝ. Galley under sail r. *B.M.C.* 662 .. .. fair/F 75/–

861 *Caracalla*. Æ 26. ΜΑ ΑV ΑΝΤΩΝΕΙΝΟC ΑV ΒΡΙΤ. Laur. bust r. ℞. Similar to preceding. *B.M.C.* 678 .. .. F £5

ACARNANIA.

862 **Alyzia.** 350-250 B.C. Æ Corinthian *stater*. Pegasos with pointed wing flying r.; below, A. ℞. ΑΛΥΙΑΙΩΝ. Head of Athena r.; to l., pudenda virilia. *B.M.C.* 6   F   £14

862   863

863 **Anactorium.** 350-300 B.C. Æ Corinthian *stater*. Similar, but A͡N monogram in field on *obv.*, ANACTOPIEΩN on *rev.* and laurel-leaf. *B.M.C.* 14 ..   ..   *good* F   £10

864 **Argos Amphilochicum.** 350-270 B.C. Æ Corinthian *stater*. Similar, but A on *obv.* ℞. Similar, but type to l. and ΑΡΓΕΙ and crested helmet as symbol. *B.M.C.* 8
F/*good* F   £8

865 — Another, with ΑΜΦΙ, ΑΒΡ and javelin on *rev. B.M.C.* 14   ..   *good* F   £12

866 Æ 16. Head of Hermes (?) r. ℞. ΑΡΓΕΙΩΝ. Dog reclining r., looking back. *B.M.C.* 8 ..   ..   F   40/-

867 Æ 15. Head of Pallas, helmeted, r. ℞. ΑΡΓΕΙΩΝ. Owl l. *B.M.C.* 10   F/VF   50/-

868 **Leucas.** *c.* 500 B.C. Æ Corinthian *stater*. Bridled Pegasos with curled wing flying l., Λ below. ℞. Head of Athena r. of archaic style within incuse square. *B.M.C.* 1
fair/F £7; *good* F   £18

869 460-420 B.C. Æ *diobol*. Pegasos with pointed wing flying l., Λ below. ℞. Pegasos with curled wing walking r., Λ below. *B.M.C.* 134   ..   ..   *good* F   £12

870 400-330 B.C. Æ Corinthian *stater*. Pegasos with pointed wing flying r., Λ below. ℞. Head of Athena r., with Λ and symbol in field   ..   ..   *good* F/VF   £10

871 Æ *drachm.* Similar. ℞. Head of Aphrodite l. *B.M.C.* 114   ..   *nearly* VF   £6

872 330-250 B.C. Æ *stater*. Another, similar to No. 870, but type to l.: style of Athena rather harder, different symbols ..   ..   VF   £10

873 4th Cent. B.C. Æ 16. Monogram and head of man-headed bull r. ℞. Monogram and trident. *B.M.C.* 21 ..   ..   F   45/-

874 Æ 18. Bellerophon thrusting with lance on prancing Pegasos r. ℞. Chimaera at bay r., ΛΕΥΚΑ in ex. *B.M.C.* 34 ..   ..   F   45/-

875 Æ 15. Laur. head of Apollo l. ℞. ΛΕΥ above prow of galley. *B.M.C.* 68
nearly F   30/-

876 *After* 168 B.C. Æ *didrachm.* Statue of Artemis r. on base, holding aplustre; beside her, stag r.; in front, ear of corn; behind, sceptre surmounted by bird; all within wreath. ℞. ΛΕΥΚΑΔΙΩΝ. Prow of galley r., bound with laurel; above, ΑΥΣΙΜΑΧΟΣ and female head. *B.M.C.* 94   ..   ..   R, F   £12/10/-

877 Æ 18. Somewhat as last. *B.M.C.* 116   ..   ..   F   37/6

878 Æ 18. Head of young Herakles in lion's skin r. ℞. ΛΕΥΚΑΔΙΩΝ above club, magistrate's name below. *B.M.C.* 132-170 ..   ..   *fair*   25/-

879 Æ 16. Head of Apollo r. ℞. As before, but lyre. *B.M.C.* 171-191   *fair*/F   25/-

880 **Metropolis.** *c.* 300 B.C. Æ Corinthian *stater*. Pegasos with pointed wings, flying l., MH monogram below. ℞. Head of Athena l., WA in monogram and round shield to r. *B.M.C.* 1 .. .. *RRR*, F £50

881 **Oeniadae.** 230-168 B.C. Æ 21. Head of Zeus, laur., r. ℞. OINIAΔAN. Bearded head of man-headed bull, Achelous, r. *Б.М.C.* 6-14 .. .. F 37/6; VF 85/-

881A **Stratus.** 350-250 B.C. Æ Corinthian *stater*. Pegasus flying r., Σ below r. ℞. Head o Athena r.; head of Achelous behind; ΣΤΡΑΤΙΩΝ in front .. .. *RRR*, F £50

882   888

882 **Thyrrheium.** 350-250 B.C. Æ Corinthian *stater*. Pegasos with pointed wing l., ΘY below. ℞. Head of Athena l., Θ to l., Y and Boeotian shield to r. *B.M.C.* 15
F/good F £8

883 Æ 14. Head of Athena l. ℞. ΘYP. Owl r. *B.M.C.* 7 .. .. .. F 30/-

884 *After* 168 B.C. Æ *didrachm* (?). Ξ ΕΝΟΜΕΝΗΣ to l. and above beardless man-headed bull, Achelous, r. ℞. ΘYPPEIΩN. Apollo Aktios seated l., holding bow. *B.M.C.* 13
Plate IV .. .. *RR, good* F £50

885 **Acarnanian League.** 229-168 B.C. Æ *didrachm*. ΛYKOYPΓOΣ. Head of man-headed bull, beardless, r. ℞. AKAPNANΩN. Apollo Aktios seated l. on throne, holding bow; to l., monogram EΘ. *B.M.C.* 6 .. .. *R*, VF £75

886 Æ 21. Head of Zeus r. ℞. AKR monogram. Head of Achelous r.: above, trident. *B.M.C.* 15 .. .. F 32/6

887 Æ 20. Head of Athena l. ℞. Head of Achelous l. *B.M.C.* 21 F/VF 40/-

AETOLIA.

888 **Aetolian League.** 279-168 B.C. N *stater*. Head of Athena r.; behind, owl. ℞. Aetolia wearing kausia, seated r. on pile of shields, holding spear and Nike; before, monogram. *B.M.C.* 1 .. .. *RR*, VF £350

889 Æ *hemidrachm* (often called a *drachm*). Head of Atalanta r., wearing kausia, hair loose. ℞. AITΩΛΩN. Boar r.: in ex., monogram and spear-head. *Cf. B.M.C.* 16-26 .. .. *good* F 75/-; EF/VF £8

889A Æ 16. As last, without mon. and spear-head. *B.M.C.* 27 .. .. .. *fair* 25/-

890 Æ 17. Young male head, wearing laurel-wreath, r. ℞. AITΩΛΩN. Spear-head and jaw-bone of boar r.: between them, KΛEI *B.M.C.* 58 .. .. .. F 35/-

891 Æ 16. Head of Athena r. ℞. AITΩΛΩN. Herakles standing facing. *B.M.C.* 69
F 30/-

CENTRAL GREECE.

Locris	7 Chaeroneia	17 Thebes	25 Salamis
1 Opus	8 Copae	18 Thespiae	
2 Scarpheia	9 Chaeroneia		*Megaris*
3 Thronium	10 Haliartus	*Euboea*	26 Aegosthena
4 Amphissa	11 Lebadeia	19 Carystus	27 Megara
	12 Mycalessus	20 Chalcis	28 Pagae
Phocis	13 Orchomenus	21 Eretria	
5 Delphi	14 Pharae	22 Histiaea	*Aegina*
	15 Plataea		29 Aegina
Boeotia	16 Tanagra	*Attica*	*Corinthia*
6 Acraephia		24 Eleusis	30 Corinth

LOCRIS

892 **The Locri Opuntii** (chief town, Opus). 387-369 B.C. Æ *obol.* ΟΠΟΝ. Amphora. Ŗ. Rosette of pellets within star of sixteen rays. *B.M.C.* 4 .. F/VF £9

893 369-338 B.C. Æ *stater.* Head of Persephone, wearing wreath of corn, l. Ŗ. ΟΠΟΝΤΙΩΝ. Ajax, helmeted and armed with sword and shield, in fighting attitude r.: serpent on inner side of shield, kantharos between legs. *B.M.C.* 8-12.. EF, *nice style* £200

894 — Another, griffin on shield, olive-branch and broken spear between legs of Ajax. *B.M.C.* 30 .. .. *nearly* VF £65

895 Æ *hemidrachm.* Similar types .. .. *good* F £7

896 Æ *obol.* ΟΠΟΝ. Amphora. ℞. Star of sixteen rays. *B.M.C.* 36 .. F 60/–
897 338-300 B.C. Æ *obol.* Similar but, ΛΟΚΡ on *obv.* *B.M.C.* 45 .. F/VF 90/–
898 Æ 13. Head of Apollo, laur., l. ℞. ΛΟ. Bunch of grapes. *B.M.C.* 54 F 32/6
899 Æ 14. Head of Athena r. ℞. ΛΟΚΡΩΝ. Bunch of grapes. *B.M.C.* 57 F 30/–
900 Imperial Times. Æ 17. Head of Persephone r. ℞. ΟΠΟΥΝΤΙΩΝ. Ajax r. fighting. *B.M.C.* 86 .. .. F 50/–
901 **Scarpheia.** *ca.* 338 B.C. Æ 17. Female head r. ℞. ΣΚΑΡΦΕΩΝ. As last. *B.M.C.* 1 R, *fair* 40/–
902 **Thronium.** 2nd Cent. B.C. Æ 18. Laur. head of Apollo r. ℞. ΘΡΟΝΙΕΩΝ. Spear head and jawbone of Calydonian boar. *B.M.C.* 2 .. .. .. R, *fair* 50/–
903 **Locri Ozolae. Amphissa.** 2nd Cent. B.C. Æ 17. As last. ℞. ΑΜΦΙΣΣΕΩΝ. As last but between the two objects bunch of grapes, star and monogram. *B.M.C.* 1 R, *fair* 40/–

PHOCIS.

904 550-371 B.C. Æ *triobol.* Bull's head facing. ℞. ΦΟΚΙ. Female head of archaic style r., hair turned up under fillet: all within incuse square. *B.M.C.* 12
good F/F £12
905 — Similar, hair differently arranged. *B.M.C.* 25 .. ..F £7/10/–
906 Æ *obol.* ΦΟ. Bull's head facing. ℞. Forepart of boar r., within incuse square. *B.M.C.* 35 .. .. VF £7/10/–
907 371-357 B.C. Æ 16. Head of Athena almost facing. ℞. Φ in wreath. *B.M.C.* 66 F 32/6
908 Æ 22 *trichalkon.* ΦΩΚΕΩΝ. Three bull's heads with pellets facing, arranged in triangular pattern. ℞. T in laurel wreath. *B.M.C.* 91 .. .. RR, VF/EF £15
909 357-346 B.C. Æ *triobol.* Bull's head facing. ℞. ΦΩ. Head of Apollo, laur., r.: behind, lyre. *B.M.C.* 78 .. .. F £7
910 339-146 B.C. Æ 19. ΕΛ above bucranium facing bound with sacrificial fillet. ℞. ΦΩΚΕΩΝ. Laur. head of Apollo r. *B.M.C.* 105 .. .. *fair* 27/6

911 **Delphi.** 500-480 B.C. Æ *trihemiobol.* Ram's head r., dolphin r. below. ℞. Goat's head facing between two dolphins. *B.M.C.* 4 .. .. .. R, VF/F £15
912 Æ *tritartemorion.* Head of negro (Delphos) r. ℞. As last. *B.M.C.* 7 F £12
913 371-357 B.C. Æ *trihemiobol.* Type as No. 911, but with ΔΕΛ on *rev.* .. F £8
914 *Faustina I.* Æ 24. ΘΕΑ ΦΑVCTEINA. Bust r. ℞. ΔΕΛΦΩΝ. Temple of Apollo viewed from an angle: within, statue of Apollo, leaning on column. *B.M.C.* 33 RR, F/VF £12/10/–

BOEOTIA

915 **Acraephia.** 456-446 B.C. Æ *obol.* Boeotian shield. ℞. AK. Kantharos
RR, F £20
916 **Chaeroneia.** 387-374 B.C. Æ *hemidrachm.* Boeotian shield. ℞. ΧΑΙ. Club. *Bab.* ccii, 15 .. .. R, F £40
917 **Copae.** 387-374 B.C. Æ *obol.* Boeotian shield. ℞. ΚΩΠΑΙΩΝ. Forepart of rushing bull. *B.M.C.* 1 .. .. RR, F £18
918 **Coroneia.** *c.* 387-374 B.C. Æ *obol.* Boeotian shield. ℞. ΚΟ below head of Gorgon with protruded tongue. *B.M.C.* 7 .. .. .. RR, F £12/10/–
919 **Haliartus.** 550-480 B.C. Æ *stater.* Boeotian shield, the rim of which is divided into eight compartments. ℞. Incuse of "mill-sail" pattern; in centre, H with top and bottom closed by two strokes. *B.M.C.* 6 .. .. .. R, F £30
919A **Lebadeia.** 146-27 B.C. Æ 13. Head of Athena r. ℞. ΛΕ in wreath. *B.M.C.* 2 R, *fair* 32/6
920 **Mycalessus.** *c.* 387-374 B.C. Æ *obol.* Boeotian shield. ℞. ΜΥ. Thunderbolt. *B.M.C.* 1 .. .. R, F £16

921 **Orchomenus.** 600-480 B.C. Æ *obol*. Corn-grain. ℞. Incuse square divided into five unequal compartments, within two of which, ᴴᴿ. *B.M.C.* 13   R, F £12

922 480-456 B.C. Æ *hemiobol*. Types as preceding, without legend. *Cf. B.M.C.* 19   R, VF/F £20

923 387-374 B.C. Æ *obol*. EP. Three corn-grains. ℞. Horse prancing r. *B.M.C.* 25 ..   ..   R, F £10

924 **Pharae.** 550-480 B.C. Æ *stater*. Boeotian shield. ℞. Incuse of "mill-sail" pattern, with Φ in centre. *B.M.C.* 1 ..   ..   RR, F/VF £45

924A **Plataea.** 387-374. Æ *hemidrachm*. Boeotian shield. ℞. ΠΛΑ. Head of Hera r., wearing stephanos. *B.M.C.* 1 ..   ..   RR, F £35

925 **Tanagra.** 600-550 B.C. Æ *drachm* (95 grs.). Boeotian shield, in side openings of which, ᴴ ᴴ. ℞. "Mill-sail" incuse. *B.M.C.* 2 ..   ..   R, VF £25

926 550-480 B.C. Æ *drachm*. Boeotian shield. ℞. "Mill-sail" incuse, in alternate depressions of which, T T. *B.M.C.* 7 ..   ..   R, F/VF £20

927 456-446 B.C. Æ *obol*. Boeotian shield. ℞. TA. Forepart of horse r. *B.M.C.* 27   good F/F £7

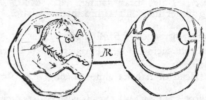

928 387-384 B.C. Æ *stater*. Boeotian shield. ℞. Forepart of horse r., his shoulders bound with wreath; head divides TA. *B.M.C.* 29 ..   ..   ..   R, F £45

928A 338-315 B.C. Æ 21. Boeotian shield. ℞. TAN in plain concave field   fair 32/6

929 **Thebes.** 550-480 B.C. Æ *stater*. Boeotian shield, the rim divided into twelve compartments. ℞. "Mill-sail" incuse, with + in circle in centre. *B.M.C.* 4   F/VF £25

930 Æ *obol*. Similar. *B.M.C.* 12 ..   ..   F 75/-

931 Æ *hemiobol*. Half Boeotian shield. ℞. Similar. *B.M.C.* 17 ..   ..   F £5

932 456-446 B.C. Æ *hemidrachm*. Boeotian shield. ℞. + in circle and amphora in incuse square. *B.M.C.* 27 ..   ..   F £7

933 446-426 B.C. Æ *stater*. Boeotian shield. ℞. ΘΕΒΑ. Female figure (? Harmonia) seated r. on chair, legs crossed, holding in l. hand Corinthian helmet: all in incuse square. *B.M.C.* 42 ..   ..   RRR, F/VF £300

934 426-395 B.C. Æ *stater*. Boeotian shield. ℞. ΘΕ. Head of bearded Dionysos r., wearing wreath of ivy. *B.M.C.* 54 ..   ..   F/fair £20

935 Æ *hemiobol*. Boeotian shield. ℞. Club between Θ and ivy-leaf. *B.M.C.* 53   F £6

936 Æ *stater*. Boeotian shield, across one end of which, club. ℞. ΘΕ. Amphora; all in rectangular incuse. *B.M.C.* 72 ..   ..   R, VF £50

937 Æ *hemidrachm*. Boeotian shield. ℞. ΘΕΒΗ. Kantharos: above, club. *B.M.C.* 78   good F £8

938 395-387 B.C. Æ *stater*. Boeotian shield. ℞. ΘΕ. Amphora with ivy leaf at l. handle. *B.M.C.* 74 ..   ..   VF £30

939 — Another; similar. ℞. ΘΕ. Amphora; to l., bow. *B.M.C.* 94 ..   VF £30

940 Æ *tritemorion*. Three Boeotian half-shields; in centre, Θ. ℞. As *obv*. *B.M.C.* 105   F £5

934   943

941 378-338 B.C. Æ *stater.* Boeotian shield. ℞. ΑΡΚΑ. Amphora with two ivy-leaves on each handle. *B.M.C.* 117 .. .. VF £25

942 — Similar, with ΔΙΩ on *rev.*, and no ivy-leaves. *B.M.C.* 134 .. *nearly* VF £15

943 — Similar, with ΕΠ ΑΜ on *rev. B.M.C.* 136. *See illus. on p.* 88 .. .. F £10

944 Æ *obol.* Boeotian shield, club across one end. ℞. ΘΕ. Head of young Herakles, wearing lion-skin, r. *B.M.C.* 169 .. .. F £8

945 315-288 B.C. Æ 11. *Obv.* type as *rev.* of preceding. ℞. ΘΗΒΑΙΩΝ between club and thyrsos. *B.M.C.* 201 .. .. VF 45/-

946 146-27 B.C. Æ 19. ΘΗΒΑΙΩΝ. Bust of Tyche, turreted, r. ℞. Female figure standing r., holding kantharos. *Not in B.M.C., and perhaps overstruck on earlier coin, as there are traces of uncertain legend in rev. field* .. .. .. F 50/-
See also Nos. 950-954, which were probably struck at Thebes.

947 **Thespiae.** 387-374 B.C. Æ *stater.* Boeotian shield. ℞. ΘΕΣΠΙΚΟΝ. Head of Aphrodite Melainis r., large crescent before, smaller crescent below. *B.M.C.* 9
RRR, F £400

947A Æ *obol.* Boeotian shield. ℞. ΘΕS above crescent. *B.M.C.* 4 .. F £5

948 338-315 B.C. Æ *hemidrachm.* Boeotian shield. ℞. ΒΟΙ. Kantharos: club above, crescent on r. *B.M.C.* 53. **Plate IV** .. .. F 70/-

949 146-27 B.C. Æ 15. Female head r., veiled. ℞. ΘΕΣΠΙΕΩΝ. Lyre; all within wreath *B.M.C.* 14 .. .. F 40/-

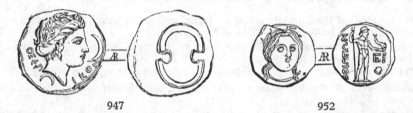

947   952

950 **Boeotia in genere.** 288-244 B.C. Æ 21. Helmeted head of Athena r. ℞. ΒΟΙ-ΩΤΩΝ. Trophy of arms. *B.M.C.* 64 .. .. ∴. F 40/-

951 Æ 18. Head of young Herakles, wearing lion-skin, r. ℞. ΒΟΙΩΤΩΝ. Winged Athena or Nike r., with thunderbolt and aegis. *B.M.C.* 66 .. .. .. F/VF 60/-

952 220-197 B.C. Æ *drachm.* Head of Demeter, three-quarter right. ℞. ΒΟΙΩΤΩΝ. Poseidon standing half-right with trident and dolphin. *B.M.C.* 76 .. .. VF £17/10/-

953 196-146 B.C. Æ *drachm.* Laur. head of Poseidon r. ℞. ΒΟΙΩΤΩΝ. Nike standing l., monogram in field. *B.M.C.* 92-100 .. .. .. *nearly* VF/F £9

954 Æ 12. Boeotian shield. ℞. ΒΟΙΩΤΩΝ. Trident; to r., dolphin. *B.M.C.* 108
fair 25/-

EUBOEA.

955 **Carystus.** 480-445 B.C. Æ *didrachm.* Cow r., with head turned back, suckling calf. ℞. Cock r. and Κ in incuse square. *B.M.C.* 1 .. .. .. RRR, F £150

955A 369-336 B.C. Æ *didrachm.* As before, but ΚΑΡΥΕΣ and without the incuse square. *B.M.C.* 7 .. .. RR, VF £120

956 **Carystus.** 196-146 B.C. Æ 18. Head of young Herakles, wearing lion-skin, r. ℞. ΚΑ. Head and neck of bull three-quarter r.: to r., monogram. *B.M.C.* 19   F 45/-

957 Æ 18. Veiled head of Hera r. ℞. ΚΑΡΥ. Bull butting r. *B.M.C.* 23 .. F 35/-

958 Æ 17. Head of Poseidon r. ℞. ΚΑΡΥΣΤΙΩΝ. Dolphin entwined around trident. *B.M.C.* 24 .. .. F 35/-

959 **Chalcis.** *c.* 520 B.C. *Æ tetrobol.* Eagle r. carrying off serpent. ℞. Wheel of four spokes within incuse triangle. *Grose* 5668 .. .. RR, F £50

960 369-336 B.C. *Æ drachm.* Female head r., hair rolled. ℞. ΧΑΛ. Eagle flying r., holding serpent in beak and claws: below, trophy. *B.M.C.* 50 .. *good* F 75/-

961 — Similar, with caduceus below eagle. *B.M.C.* 53 .. .. F 50/-

962 *Æ hemidrachm.* *Obv.* as preceding. ℞. ΧΑΛ. Eagle r., devouring hare. *B.M.C.* 57 F 85/-

963 Æ 13. Head of Hera facing. ℞. ΧΑΛ. Eagle flying r., holding serpent. *B.M.C.* 70 F 32/6

964 196-146 B.C. *Æ octobol.* Female head r., hair rolled. ℞. ΧΑΛΚΙ. Eagle standing r. about to attack serpent ready to strike, three monograms before. *B.M.C.* 87 R, VF £30

965 Æ 16. Head of Hera, facing, placed on capital of Ionic column. ℞. Eagle flying r., holding serpent: below, ΑΑΘ. *B.M.C.* 98 .. .. *fair* 25/-

966 *Nero.* Æ 20. ΝΕΡΩΝ ΚΑΙCΑΡ. His laur. head r. ℞. CΤΡΑ . ΤΙ . ΚΛΑΥ . ΕΥΘΥΚΛΙΕ . ΧΑΛ. Head of Hera r., on capital of Ionic column. *B.M.C.* 108 .. .. F/*fair* 50/-

967 **Eretria.** *c.* 500 B.C. *Æ obol.* Bull's head facing. ℞. Octopus. *B.M.C.* 33 F £8

968 480-445 B.C. *Æ drachm.* Cow r., head l., scratching herself. ℞. Sepia in incuse square. *B.M.C.* 26 .. .. RR, VF/EF £75

969 369-336 B.C. *Æ drachm.* Head of nymph l. ℞. ΕΥ. Head and neck of bull three-quarter r. *B.M.C.* 8 .. .. *nearly* VF £20

970 Æ 13. Bull standing r. ℞. ΕΥΒΟΙ retrograde. Bunch of grapes. *B.M.C.* 30 *nearly* F 25/-

969   971

971 196-146 B.C. *Æ octobol.* Head of Artemis r., bow and quiver over shoulder. ℞. ΕΡΕΤΡΙΕΩΝ. Ox recumbent r.; ΦΑΝΙΑΣ in ex. *B.M.C.* 41 .. RR, F/VF £80

971A Æ 18. Veiled female head r. ℞. ΕΥΒΟΙΕΩΝ. Bull butting r. *B.M.C.* 39-44 F 35/-
Some of the coins struck at Eretria were probably for a federal coinage for all Euboea.

972 **Histiaea.** 369-336 B.C. *Æ drachm.* Head of Maenad r., wearing vine-wreath. ℞. Bull walking r.: in background, vine with two bunches of grapes: in ex., ΙΣΤΙ. *B.M.C.* 4 VF £20

973 196-146 B.C. *Æ tetrobol.* *Obv.* as preceding. ℞. ΙΣΤΙΑΙΕΩΝ. Nymph Histiaea seated r. on stern of galley, holding trophy-stand: below, trident-head l. *B.M.C.* 36 VF 75/-

974 — Similar, without trident-head. *B.M.C.* 99 .. .. *good* F 50/-
There are a very large number of varieties of this coin.

975 Æ 17. Female head r. ℞. ΙΣΤΙΑ ΙΕΩΝ. Bunch of grapes. *B.M.C.* 134 *fair* 25/-

ATTICA.

976 **Athens.** *c.* 600 B.C. Æ *three-eighth obol* (*trihemitetartemorion*) (4 grs.). Pomegranate.
℞. Incuse square. *Svoronos* 44 .. .. *R*, F £15

977 Æ *obol.* Wheel of four spokes. ℞. Incuse square. *Sv.* 56 .. R, VF £30

978 *c.* 594-562 B.C. Æ *drachm.* Type as preceding. *Sv.* 58 .. .. *R*, F £30

979 Æ *obol.* Gorgon-head facing. ℞. Incuse square. *Sv.* 67 .. RR, F £16

980 560-490 B.C. Æ *tetradrachm.* Head of Athena, of very archaic style, r., wearing close-fitting crested helmet and round ear-ring. ℞. AΘE. Owl standing r., head facing and wings closed; behind, spray of olive; all in shallow incuse. *B.M.C.* 3
RR, lumpy fabric, fair £60

981 — Similar, with the decoration on the helmet-crest well shown, and fabric almost globular. *B.M.C.* 3 .. .. VF £250

982 — Similar, slightly larger and flatter fabric: head of Athena in very crude style, and olive-spray and A off *rev. B.M.C.* 4 .. .. VF £175

983 Æ *obol.* Similar types. *Sv.* 49. *B.M.C.* 30 .. .. *fair* £15

981   984

984 490-430 B.C. Æ *tetradrachm.* Head of Athena r., of archaic style, wearing round ear-ring and close-fitting crested helmet adorned with three upright olive leaves and floral ornament. ℞. AΘE. Owl r., head facing and wings closed; behind, spray of olive and crescent: all in incuse square. *Cf. B.M.C.* 43 .. .. .. EF £75

985 — Similar, of later archaic style and rougher fabric, hair in normal single lock across forehead. *B.M.C.* 46 .. .. F £18; VF £35

986 — Similar, of still later and rougher work. *B.M.C.* 62 .. .. F £15; VF £30

987 Æ *drachm.* Similar types. *B.M.C.* 74 .. .. *good* F £10

988 Æ *triobol.* Obv. as preceding. ℞. AΘE. Owl standing facing between two olive-branches. *B.M.C.* 82 .. .. *fair* 65/-

989 Æ *obol* (10.5 grs.). *Obv.* as preceding. ℞. AΘE. Owl r., head facing and wings closed; behind, olive leaf with berry; all in incuse square. *B.M.C.* 96 .. VF £10

990 Æ *hemiobol* (5.5 grs.). Similar types. *B.M.C.* 112 .. .. . F 60/-; EF £9

991 Emergency base-metal issue of 406 B.C. (referred to by Aristophanes in " The Frogs " produced in 405 B.C.). *Tetradrachm* of types as 985, originally plated, but with plating almost entirely gone .. .. *RRR*, F £25

992 — *drachm* of the same issue .. .. *RRR, fair* £8

993 430-322 B.C. Æ *tetradrachm.* Types as 985, but the eye of Athena is shown in *profile* instead of in the archaic style: the execution of the coins is not as good as that of the earlier tetradrachms. *B.M.C.* 132 .. .. .. F/VF £10; VF £16; EF £35

994 Æ *drachm* (68 grs.). Types as preceding. *B.M.C.* 150 .. .. .. F £7

995 Æ *tetrobol.* Obv. as preceding. ℞. AΘE. Two owls standing r. and l., heads facing. *B.M.C.* 160 .. .. F £6

996 Æ *triobol.* Obv. as preceding. ℞. AΘE. Owl facing between olive branches. *B.M.C.* 162 .. .. *fair* 32/6; VF £8

997 Æ *diobol.* Obv. as preceding. ℞. AΘE. Double-bodied owl, head facing. *B.M.C.* 176 .. .. F 90/-

998 Æ *obol.* Obv. as preceding. ℞. AΘE. Four crescents back to back, in incuse square. *B.M.C.* 180 .. .. *fair* 35/-; VF £10

999 Æ *tritartemorion* (¾ *obol*). Obv. as preceding. ℞. AΘE within three crescents. *B.M.C.* 183 .. .. F £9

1000 Æ *tetartemorion* (¼ *obol*). Obv. as preceding. ℞. AΘE and crescent. *B.M.C.* 197
F £7

1001 406-393 B.C. Æ 14. *Obv.* as preceding. ℞. AΘ. Two owls r. and l., heads facing: all within olive-wreath. *B.M.C.* 209 .. .. F 40/-

1002 393-322 B.C. Æ 16. Head of Athena, wearing crested Corinthian helmet, r. ℞. AΘH. Owl l., head facing: all in olive-wreath. *B.M.C.* 240 .. F/VF 60/-

1002A 297-255 B.C. Æ *triobol.* Type as 996. *Svor.* 21, 49 .. .. nearly VF £7

1003 229-197 B.C. Æ *tetradrachm (new style).* Head of Athena Parthenos r., wearing earring, necklace and close-fitting helmet with triple crest, adorned in front with the foreparts of several horses abreast, on the side with Pegasos, and on the back with an aplustre-like scroll. ℞. AΘE. Owl r., wings closed and head facing, standing on amphora which lies on its side; in field, l., monogram: in field r., monogram and symbol, pilei of the Dioskuri; all within olive wreath. *B.M.C.* 296 .. R, F/VF £25

1004 Æ *drachm.* Types as last; Σ to l., ear of corn to r. *B.M.C.* 292 .. .. F £10

1005 196-87 B.C. Æ *tetradrachm.* As preceding, but style not so good: magistrate's names AMΦIAΣ and OINOΦIΛOΣ in *rev.* field, and symbol, Demeter or Persephone standing l. holding two torches. *B.M.C.* 317 .. .. F/VF £20

1006 Æ *drachm.* Types as preceding: in *rev.* field abbreviated magistrate's names HPA APIΣTO and ΦIΛA: in field, l., club and bow in case. *Cf. B.M.C.* 335 RRR, VF £35

1007 Æ *tetradrachm.* Types as preceding, but magistrate's names on *rev.* ΔIONYΣI, ΔIONYΣI and APIΣ: symbol, Helios in quadriga facing: on amphora, B, and below, ΣΦ. *B.M.C.* 380 *var.* VF £27/10/-

1008 — Similar types as preceding, with magistrate's names EYMAPEIΔHΣ, KΛEOMEN and ΔH: on amphora, E, and below, ΣT: symbol Triptolemus in biga of serpents l. *B.M.C.* 405 *var.* .. .. VF £30

1009 — Similar, with EYMHΛOΣ, ΦEOΞENIΔHΣ; symbol, figure of Theseus or Ares facing, with spear; A on amphora, EΠ below. *B.M.C.* 406 .. .. VF £25

1010 — Similar, with ΞENOKΛHΣ and APMOΞENOΣ: E on amphora: symbol, figure of Q. Caecilius Metellus seated facing, laureate and holding spear. *Not in B.M.C.* RRR, VF £45

1011 86-83 B.C. Æ *tetradrachm.* Types as preceding, but with griffin on helmet, no AΘE and no magistrate's names on *rev.*: in field l. and r., monograms MAP and TAM (Marcus Tamias, quaestor), and A on amphora. *B.M.C.* 519 RR, VF/EF £45

1012 220-83 B.C. Æ 18. Head of Athena, wearing crested Corinthian helmet, r. ℞. AΘE. Zeus standing r., hurling thunderbolt; before him, eagle r.: in field, r., cornucopiae. *B.M.C.* 543 .. .. F 37/6

1013 Æ 20. *Obv.* as preceding. ℞. AΘE. Statue of Apollo Delios facing, holding figures of the three Charites and strung bow. *B.M.C.* 564 .. .. *fair* 27/6

1014 Æ 20. *Obv.* as preceding. ℞. AΘE. Sphinx seated r. *B.M.C.* 570 .. F 45/-

1015 Æ 21. Gorgon-head facing. ℞. AΘE. Athena adv. r., with spear and aegis. *B.M.C.* 578 .. .. R, F 50/-

1016 Æ 21. Head of Artemis r. ℞. AΘE. Athena standing r., holding owl and patera. *B.M.C.* 585 .. .. *fair* 22/6

1017 220-83 B.C. Æ 17. Head of Zeus r. Æ. AΘE. Head of bearded Dionysos r., wearing ivy-wreath. *B.M.C.* 604 .. .. F/VF 60/-

1018 Æ 15. Head of Artemis r. ℞. AΘE. Cicada. *B.M.C.* 616 .. R, F 50/-

1019 Æ 12. Cicada. ℞. AΘE. Amphora and palm. *B.M.C.* 618 .. .. F 40/-

1020 Æ 10. Head of Artemis r. ℞. AΘE. Plemochoë: all in olive-wreath. *B.M.C.* 647 F 40/-

1021 Æ 10. Head of Apollo r. ℞. AΘE. Two ears of corn on one stalk. *B.M.C.* 664 F 40/-

1022 Imperial Times. Æ 21. Head of Athena, wearing crested Corinthian helmet, r. ℞. ΑΘΗΝΑΙΩΝ. Athena Promachos standing facing, head l., holding spear and shield. *B.M.C.* 676. **Plate IV** .. .. *good* F/F 50/–

1023 Æ 22. *Obv.* as preceding. ℞. ΑΘΗΝΑΙΩΝ. Athena Parthenos facing, head l., holding Nike, and resting l. hand on shield adorned with Gorgon-head. *B.M.C.* 682
F 40/–

1025 Æ 22. *Obv.* as preceding. ℞. ΑΘΗΝΑΙΩΝ. Athena standing as preceding, but to l., olive-tree. *B.M.C.* 694 .. .. F 45/–

1026 Æ 21. *Obv.* as preceding. ℞. ΑΘΗΝΑΙΩΝ. Athena in biga r., holding spear. *B.M.C.* 705 .. .. F/fair 32/6

1027 Æ 17. *Obv.* as preceding. ℞. ΑΘΗΝΑΙΩΝ. Owl in olive-tree. *B.M.C.* 716
F 37/6

1028 Æ 21. *Obv.* as preceding. ℞. ΑΘΗΝΑΙΩΝ. Table, on which bust of Athena r., and wreath: below table, amphora. *B.M.C.* 721 .. .. .. F/VF 65/–

1029 Æ 21. *Obv.* as preceding. ℞. ΑΘΗΝΑΙΩΝ. Apollo Lykeios standing r., resting l. hand on lyre. *B.M.C.* 750 .. .. F/fair 30/–

1030 Æ 22. *Obv.* as preceding. ℞. ΑΘΗΝΑΙΩΝ. Bearded Dionysos seated r. on throne, holding kantharos and thyrsos. *B.M.C.* 758 .. .. .. R, F 70/–

1031 Æ 23. *Obv.* as preceding. ℞. ΑΘΗ. Theseus r., raising rock beneath which are the sword and sandals of Aegeus. *B.M.C.* 760 .. .. RRR, *fair* 85/–

1032 Æ 21. *Obv.* as preceding. ℞. ΑΘΗΝΑΙΩΝ (retrograde). Theseus l., attacking with club the Minotaur, who is beaten to his knees l. *B.M.C.* 763 *var.* RRR, F £7

1033 Æ 21. Head of Athena, wearing crested Corinthian helmet, r. ℞. ΑΘΗΝΑΙΩΝ. Themistokles on galley r. *B.M.C.* 787 .. .. *fair* 35/–

1034 Æ 20. *Obv.* as preceding. ℞. ΑΘΗ. Miltiades in military dress placing a captive Persian before a trophy. *B.M.C.* 791 .. .. RRR, F £8

1035   1035A

1035 Æ 22. *Obv.* as preceding. ℞. ΑΘΗΝ[ΑΙΩΝ]. Northern view of the rock of the Akropolis, with the Parthenon and the Propylaea on summit, with the statue of Athena Parthenos between them: in the side of the rock, the grotto of Pan. *B.M.C.* 802
R, F £8

1035A Æ 21. *Obv.* as preceding. ℞. ΑΘΗΝΑΙΩΝ. Theatre of Dionysos with the Propylaea and Parthenon on the Akropolis in background. *B.M.C.* 807 .. R, F £8

1036 **Eleusis.** 350-300 B.C. Æ 15. Triptolemos seated l. in winged car drawn by serpents, holding corn-ears. ℞. ΕΛΕΥΣΙ below boar standing r. on Eleusinian βάκχος: the whole in wreath of corn. *B.M.C.* 1 .. .. F 50/–

1037 Æ 17. As preceding, but above the boar, ΕΛΕΥΣΙ: no wreath *B.M.C.* 12 *good* F 75/–

1038 Æ 16. Triptolemos mounting winged car drawn by serpents. ℞. ΕΛΕΥ (in ex.). Boar r.: all in corn-wreath. *B.M.C.* 10.. .. .. F 50/–

1039 Æ 23. Head of Demeter r. ℞. ΕΛΕΥΣ. Plemochoë on basis. *B.M.C.* 29 *fair* 25/–

1040 **Salamis.** 350-318 B.C. Æ 16. Female head r., wearing stephane. ℞. ΣΑΛΑ. Shield of Ajax, on which, sword in scabbard with strap. *B.M.C.* 1 F/fair 30/–

MEGARIS.

1040A Aegosthena. *Severus.* Æ. 17. His laur. head r. ℞. ΑΙΓΟϹΘΕΝΙ. Infant Zeus suckled by goat r. *B.M.C.* 1 .. .. *RR, fair* 37/6

1041 Megara. 400-338 B.C. Æ *pentobol.* Head of Apollo, laur., 1. ℞. ΜΕΓΑ and Η between five crescents, which radiate from a centre. *B.M.C.* 2 .. *R, F* £12

1042 Æ *triobol.* Similar, but ΜΕΓ and three crescents. *B.M.C.* 3 .. *R, fair* 75/-

1043 *After* 307 B.C. Æ *drachm.* Laur. head of Apollo r. ℞. ΜΕΓΑΡΕΩΝ. Lyre. *B.M.C.* 8 .. .. *R, F* £15

1043A Æ *hemidrachm.* As before. *B.M.C.* 10 .. .. *R, F* £8

1044 Æ 19. Similar, but legend on *obv.* *B.M.C.* 15 .. .. .. F 50/-

1045 Æ 16. As No. 1043, but *rev.* type: tripod-lebes. *B.M.C.* 16 .. .. F 35/-

1046 Æ 14. Prow of galley l. ℞. ΜΕΓΑ between two dolphins. *B.M.C.* 28 F 35/-

1047 Æ 14. ΜΕΓΑ. Prow. l. ℞. Obelisk of Apollo Karinos between two dolphins upwards. *B.M.C.* 35 .. .. *fair* 25/-

1048 *Septimius Severus.* Æ 23. Greek legend. His laur. head r. ℞. ΜΕΓΑΡΕ ΩΝ. Demeter standing r., lighting a large torch. *B.M.C.* 48 .. .. .. *fair* 30/-

1049 Pagae. *Commodus.* Æ 19. As last. ℞. ΠΑΓΑΙ ΩΝ. Artemis running r. *Grose* 6001 .. .. F £5

AEGINA.

1050 700-550 B.C. Æ *stater.* Sea-turtle with smooth shell, with row of dots down the centre. ℞. Incuse square divided into eight triangular compartments. *B.M.C.* 10
fair £12; *good* F £40

1051 Æ *drachm.* Similar types. *B.M.C.* 39 .. .. *R, F* £22

1052 Æ *triobol.* Similar types. *B.M.C.* 46 .. .. F £10

1053 Æ *obol.* Similar types. *B.M.C.* 57 .. .. *fair* £6

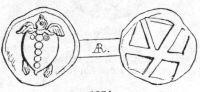

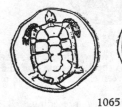

1054   1065

1054 550-480 B.C. Æ *stater.* Sea-turtle with smooth shell with a row of dots down the back and three across the top. ℞. Incuse square divided by broad bars into five compartments. *B.M.C.* 85 .. .. F £25

1055 Æ *drachm.* Somewhat similar. *B.M.C.* 105 .. .. .. *R, F* £17

1056 Æ *obol.* Similar types. *B.M.C.* 115 .. .. F £8

1057 Æ *hemiobol.* Similar. *B.M.C.* 132 .. .. *fair*/F £8

1058 480-431 B.C. Æ *stater.* Tortoise, with structure of shell shown and divided into thirteen plates. ℞. as preceding. *B.M.C.* 146. **Plate IV** .. .. .. VF £40

1059 — Similar, with the incuse pattern on *rev.* much more formal .. *good* F £30

1060 Æ *drachm.* Similar type, but in l. lower compartment of *rev.*, two dots. *B.M.C.* 170
nearly VF £20

1061 Æ *triobol.* Similar types, but *rev.* incuse of usual pattern: in one compartment, a crescent. *B.M.C.* 176 .. .. F £15

1062 — Similar, without crescent .. .. *fair* £6

1063 Æ *obol.* As last .. .. *good* F £10

1064 Æ *drachm.* A I. Tortoise, with structure of shell shown and divided into plates. ℞. Incuse pattern of usual type, in two compartments of which, A I. *B.M.C.* 184
R, VF £30

1065 *After* 404 B.C. Æ *stater.* As illustration on previous page. *B.M.C.* 187　F £27

1066 Æ 12. A between two dolphins upwards. ℞. Incuse square of usual pattern. *B.M.C.* 206 .. .. *fair* 25/–

CORINTHIA.

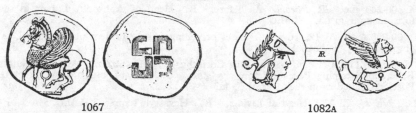

1067   1082A

1067 **Corinth.** 620-540 B.C. Æ *stater.* Pegasos, with curled wing, walking l.; ϙ below. ℞. Incuse of swastika pattern. *B.M.C.* 2 .. .. R, *good* F £60

1068 — Another, similar, but Pegasos flying. *B.M.C.* 6 .. .. .. R, *fair*/F £20

1069 Æ *hemidrachm.* Forepart of Pegasos, with curled wing, l. ℞. Incuse of swastika pattern. *B.M.C.* 38 .. .. F £15

1070 Æ *obol.* As last. *B.M.C.* 45 .. .. *fair*/F £7

1071 540-430 B.C. Æ *stater.* Pegasos, with curled wing, flying r.; below, ϙ. ℞. Head of Athena r., hair in queue, wearing Corinthian helmet and necklace; all in incuse square. *B.M.C.* 65 .. .. F £15; *good* F £24

1072 — Similar, but *rev.* in finer style and with ϙ behind head. *B.M.C.* 75. **Plate IV**
off centre, good F/VF £30

1073 Æ *hemidrachm.* Forepart of Pegasos, with curled wing, r. ℞. Head of Aphrodite, of archaic style, hair in queue, r.; all in incuse square. *B.M.C.* 91.. .. *fair* £6

1074 — Similar, but with hair rolled. *B.M.C.* 92 .. .. *fair* £7

1075 Æ *diobol.* Head and neck of Pegasos, r. ℞. Δ in incuse square. *B.M.C.* 103
F £12

This piece and the next are perhaps the earliest where the value (i.e. denomination) is placed on a coin.

1076 Æ *trihemiobol.* Pegasos, with curled wing, flying l. ℞. Τ Ρ Ι Η. Gorgon-head facing. *B.M.C.* 105 .. .. *fair* £6

1077 430-400 B.C. Æ *stater.* Pegasos, with curled wing, flying r., ϙ below. ℞. Head of Athena r., hair in queue, trident behind. *B.M.C.* 113 .. *good* F/VF £18

1078 Æ *trihemidrachm.* Bellerophon riding on Pegasos r.; below, ϙ. ℞. Chimaera r. *B.M.C.* 116 .. .. RR, *fair* £22

1079 Æ *drachm.* Pegasos, with pointed wing, flying l.; below, ϙ. ℞. Head of Aphrodite, hair rolled, r. *B.M.C.* 118 .. .. R, F £10

1080 400-338 B.C. Æ *stater.* Pegasos, with curled wing, walking l.: below, ϙ. ℞. Head of Athena r., wearing Corinthian helmet over leather cap: to l., statue of Poseidon wielding trident: to r., dolphin. *B.M.C.* 167 .. .. R, F/VF £22/10/–

1081 — Another. Pegasos, with pointed wing, flying l. ℞. Similar head of Athena r., rose behind, the whole within incuse. *B.M.C.* 130. **Plate IV**
EF, *of fine bold style in high relief* £30

1082 — Another, types to r., thymiaterion behind. *B.M.C.* 141 .. F/VF £10

1082A — Another, Pegasos as last. ℞. Head of Athena r., helmet bound with olive; to l., beaded serpent r. *B.M.C.* 138 .. .. F £7/10/–

1083 Æ *drachm.* Pegasos, with pointed wing, flying l. ℞. Head of Aphrodite l., hair in saccos. *B.M.C.* 184 .. .. *nearly* VF £6

1084 — Similar, but types to r. *B.M.C.* 186 .. .. F 60/–

1085 Æ *hemidrachm.* Forepart of Pegasos, with curled wing, l. ℞. Head of Aphrodite l. *B.M.C.* 191 .. .. F/*good* F £5

1086. Æ *diobol.* *Obv.* Type as No. 1083. ℞. Pegasos, with curled wing, trotting r. *B.M.C.* 203 .. .. F 75/–

1087 — Similar, but both types to l. *B.M.C.* 207 .. .. *fair* 35/–

1088 338-300 B.C. Æ *stater*. Pegasos, with pointed wing, flying l.: below, ?. ℞. Head of Athena l., wearing Corinthian helmet over leather cap: in field, ΔI and figure of Artemis running l. holding two torches. *B.M.C.* 314 .. .. VF £14

1089 Æ *hemidrachm*. Pegasos, with pointed wing, flying r. ℞. Head of Aphrodite l., with flowing hair. *Cf. B.M.C.* 266 .. .. F 60/-

1090 Æ *diobol*. Pegasos, with pointed wing, flying l. ℞. Pegasos, with curled wing, trotting l. *B.M.C.* 270 .. .. *fair* 30/-; F 75/-

1090A 300-243 B.C. Æ *drachm*. As before. ℞. Head of Aphrodite l., hair in saccos; to r., monogram ΠΑ. *B.M.C.* 408 .. .. *good* F £5

1091 400-300 B.C. Æ 12. *Obv.* Type as preceding. ℞. Trident upwards: to l., Δ and amphora. *Cf. B.M.C.* 448 .. .. F 27/6

1092 Imperial Times (Colonia Laus Julia Corinthus). *Julius Caesar.* Æ 23. CORINTHVM. Bellerophon taming Pegasos before city gate. ℞. P. TADI. CHILO/C.IVLI. NICEP/II.VIR. Poseidon seated r. on rock. *B.M.C.* 483 .. .. *fair* £7

1092A *Tiberius.* Æ 21. Head of Livia r. ℞. Hexastyle temple. *B.M.C.* 514-5 F £6

1093 Æ 15. Pegasos flying l. ℞. INST (in monogram). CAS II VIR. Trident. *B.M.C.* 529 .. .. F 50/-

1092   1096   1096A   1097

1094 *Caligula.* Æ 20. C CAESAR AVGVS. Bare head r. ℞. Pegasos flying r. *B.M.C.* 531 *fair*/F 40/-

1095 *Nero.* Æ 19. NERO CLAVD CAES AVG. Bare head of Nero r. ℞. ISTHMIA within wreath of parsley, etc. *B.M.C.* 565 .. .. F 60/-

1096 *Hadrian.* Æ 20. Bust of Hadrian r. ℞. Bellerophon on Pegasos r., attacking Chimaera. *B.M.C.* 593 .. .. *fair* 40/-

1096A *Lucius Verus.* Æ 26. Bare head of L. Verus r. ℞. C.L.I.COR below circular temple of Melikertes surrounded by three trees; within temple, Melikertes lying on dolphin r. *B.M.C.* 624 .. .. *fair* 60/-

1097 *Severus.* Æ 25. Laur. bust of Severus r. ℞. C L I COR. Fountain-nymph Peirene seated l., pouring water from vase; before, Pegasos r., drinking: in background, Acrocorinthus surmounted by temple of Aphrodite. *B.M.C.* 654 .. .. .. *fair* 70/-

1098 *Caracalla.* Æ 19. Radiate bust of Caracalla r. ℞. COL IVL L COR. Two wrestlers. *Not in B.M.C.* .. .. *fair* 45/-

1099 Without name of emperor. Æ 15. COR. Pegasos flying r. ℞. COR. Melikertes on dolphin r. *B.M.C.* 681 .. .. *fair* 45/-

1100 Æ 15. *Obv.* as preceding. ℞. S E. Isthmos standing facing, holding a rudder in each hand. *B.M.C.* 682 .. .. *fair* 40/-

COLONIES OF CORINTH.

See:—

In Bruttium:—Locri Epizephyrii (299); Mesma (305)

In Sicily:—Syracuse (433, 440)

In Illyricum:—Apollonia (803); Epidamnus-Dyrrachacium (809)

In Epirus:—Ambracia (821)

In Corcyra (847)

In Acarnania:—Alyzia (862); Anactorium (863); Argos Amphilochicum (864-5); Leucas 868-72); Metropolis (880); Stratus (881A); Thyrrheium (882)

THE PELOPONNESUS.

Phliasia	Is. off Elis	23 Pylus	Arcadia
1 Phlius	Cephallenia:	24 Thuria	35 Alea
	12 Cranii		36 Asea
Sicyonia	13 Pale	Laconia	37 Caphyae
2 Sicyon	14 Pronni	25 Gythium	38 Cleitor
	15 Same	26 Lacedaemon	39 Heraea
Achaia	Ithaca:		40 Lycoa
3 Aegae	16 Ithaca	Is. of Cythera:	41 Mantineia
4 Aegeira	Zacynthus:	27 Cythera	42 Megalopolis
5 Aegium	17 Zacynthus		43 Orchomenos
6 Ceryneia		Argolis	44 Pallantium
7 Dyme	Messenia	28 Argos	45 Pheneus
8 Patrae	18 Messene	29 Cleonae	46 Phigaleia
9 Pellene	19 Asine	30 Epidaurus	47 Psophis
	20 Corone	31 Hermione	48 Stymphalus
Elis	21 Cyparissia	32 Methana	49 Tegea
10 Elis	22 Mothone	33 Tiryns	50 Thelpusa
11 Olympia		34 Troezen	

PHLIASIA.

1101 **Phlius.** 430-370 B.C. Æ *obol.* Forepart of bull l., butting, head turned full-face. Ŗ. Φ in shallow incuse, circle with pellet at each corner. *B.M.C.* 9 .. F £7

1102 400-360 B.C. Æ 12. Bull butting l.: above, I. Ŗ. Φ between four pellets. *B.M.C.* 16
F 35/-

1103 370-322 B.C. Æ *hemidrachm.* Bull l., head facing, l. fore-knee on ground. Ŗ. Φ in ivy-wreath. *B.M.C.* 18 .. .. *fair* £5

1104 Æ *trihemiobol.* Similar, but I above. Ŗ. Wheel with four spokes, Φ in one quarter and bunch of grapes in each of the others. *B.M.C.* 24 .. .. .. F £15

SICYONIA.

1105 **Sicyon.** *Before* 431 B.C. Æ *hemiobol.* Dove with closed wings standing l. Ŗ. ΣΗ. Dove flying r.; all in incuse square. *B.M.C.* 12.. .. .. .. *fair* 70/-

1106 431-400 B.C. Æ *stater.* ΣΕ. Chimaera prowling l. Ŗ. Dove flying l. within olive-wreath. *B.M.C.* 22 .. .. VF/*nearly* VF £24

1107 Æ *drachm.* Dove l. alighting. Ŗ. Similar. *B.M.C.* 26 .. *nearly* VF/F £10

1108 400-300 B.C. Æ *stater.* ΣΕ. Chimaera r. Ŗ. Dove flying l.; in field, A: all in olive wreath. *B.M.C.* 48 .. .. VF £25

1109 Æ *hemidrachm.* ΣΙ. Chimaera l. Ŗ. Dove flying l.: to r., NO. *B.M.C.* 118
good F 65/-

1110 — Similar; but with pellet to r. *B.M.C.* 124 .. .. .. *fair*/F 27/6

1111 Æ *hemiobol.* Apollo kneeling on one knee r. Ŗ. ΣΕ in olive-wreath. *B.M.C.* 77
fair/F 50/-

1112 Æ *obol.* Σ. Dove alighting r. Ŗ. Ꝫ. Dove flying r. *B.M.C.* 125 .. F 50/-

1113 Æ 15. Dove flying l. Ŗ. ΜΕ. Wreath: all within olive-wreath. *B.M.C.* 151
F 25/-

1114 250-146 B.C. Æ *hemidrachm.* *Obv.* As preceding. Ŗ. ΘΡΑΣΥΚΛΗΣ around large Σ; all in incuse square. *B.M.C.* 194 .. .. *fair* 40/-

1115 — Similar, with magistrate's name ΠΟΛΥΚΡΑ. *B.M.C.* 199 .. .. VF £5

1116 Æ 18. Head of Apollo r. Ŗ. ΣΙ. Dove flying l.: 'above, ΑΙΝΕΑΣ. *B.M.C.* 234
F 35/-

1117 Æ 16. Magistrate's name, dove flying l. Ŗ. ΣΙ within olive-wreath. *B.M.C.* 215-224 .. .. *fair*/F 22/6

1118 Imperial Times: *Nero.* Æ 21. ΝΕ . ΚΑΙ . ΖΕΥC ΕΛΕΥΘΕΡΙΟC. Head of Nero, r. Ŗ. ΕΠΙ Γ ΙΟΥ ΠΟΛΥΑΙΝΟΥ ΔΑ CΙ. Nero on horseback l. *Not in B.M.C.: Cook "Zeus,"* *Vol. II, p.* 97, *fig.* 55 .. .. RR, F £9

ACHAIA.

1119 **Aegae.** 480-370 B.C. Æ *triobol.* ΑΙC. Forepart of goat l. Ŗ. ΑΙCΑΙΟΝ. Head of Dionysos r. *B.M.C.* 4 .. .. F £15

1120 **Aegeira.** 370-280 B.C. Æ 12. Head of Athena r. Ŗ. ΑΙΓΙ. Forepart of goat in wreath. *B.M.C.* 2 .. .. R, *fair*/F 42/-

1121 **Aegium.** 146-31 B.C. Æ 22. ΑΙΓΙΕΩΝ. Laur. head of Zeus r. Ŗ. ΘΕΟΞΙΟΣ ΚΛΗΤΑΙΟΣ. Zeus standing r., hurling thunderbolt. *B.M.C.* 4 *nearly* VF/F 60/-

1122 **Dyme.** *After* 146 F.C. Æ 16. Head of Athena. Ŗ. ΔΥ in wreath.
R, F 50/-

1123 **Patrae.** 250-146 B.C. Æ *hemidrachm.* Head of Aphrodite r. ℞. ΔΑ / MACIAC and monogram in olive-wreath. *B.M.C.* 2 .. .. F £7

1124 146-32 B.C. Æ 19. Bust of Athena, helmeted, l. ℞. Poseidon r., wielding trident: around, magistrate's names. *B.M.C.* 5 .. .. F 37/6

1125 Æ 21. Head of bearded Herakles r. ℞. Athena r., with spear and shield: around, magistrate's names. *B.M.C.* 7-13 .. .. F 40/-

1126 *Augustus* (posthumous). Æ 27. DIVVS AVGVSTVS PATER. His rad. head l. ℞. COL . A . A . PATRENS. Founder ploughing l. *B.M.C.* 19 .. .. F £5

1127 *Claudius.* Æ 26. TI . CLAVDIVS, etc. His bare head l. ℞. COL . A . A . PATR XXII. Legionary eagle between two standards. *B.M.C.* 21 .. .. .. *nearly* F 60/-

1128 *Domitian.* Æ 25. Laur. head of Domitian r. ℞. COL A A PATRENS. Colonist ploughing with yoke of oxen. *B.M.C.* 26 .. .. F 60/-

1129 *Commodus.* Æ 24. Laur. bust of Commodus r. ℞. Artemis Laphria standing r., holding bow. *Not in B.M.C.* .. .. *fair*/F 50/-

1123   1130

1130 **Pellene.** 370-280 B.C. Æ *hemidrachm.* Laur. head of Apollo r. ℞. ΠΕΛ within olive-wreath. *B.M.C.* 1 .. .. VF £15

1131 Æ 14. Similar. ℞. ΠΕ monogram above ram's head, all within olive-wreath. *B.M.C.* 10 .. .. *nearly* F 25/-

1132 **Achaean League.** 370-360 B.C. Æ *hemidrachm.* Head of Zeus r. ℞. AX monogram within wreath. *B.M.C.* 1 .. .. R, *fair* £10

1133 Æ 14. Similar. *B.M.C.* 2 .. .. *fair* 30/-

ACHAEAN LEAGUE, 280-146 B.C.

The League was reformed in B.C. 280 and gradually town after town in the Peloponnesus joined it, so in the end most of the peninsular had a uniform coinage. The date after the town is the date of its joining the League.

1135   1137

1134 **ACHAIA : Aegeira** (274 B.C. ?). Æ *hemidrachm.* Laur. head of Zeus. ℞. AX monogram, AP at sides, forepart of goat above; all within laurel wreath. *B.M.C.* 16 *good* F/VF 75/-

1135 **Aegium** (275 B.C.). Æ *hemidr.* Same type, but ΑΙΓΙΕ ΩΝ on *obv.*; ΑΡΙ / CTO / ΔΑ / ΜΟC on *rev.* *B.M.C.* 24 .. .. *good* F/VF 65/-

1136 **Ceryneia** (273 B.C.). Æ 18. Zeus Amarios standing l. ℞. ΑΧΑΙΩΝ ΚΑΡΥΝΕΩΝ. Achaia seated l. *Clerk* 15 .. .. F 40/-

1137 **Dyme** (280 B.C.). Æ *hemidr.* As No. 1134; but ΔΥ, mon. and fish on *rev.* *B.M.C.* 29 VF 90/-

1138 **Patrae** (280 B.C.). Æ *hemidr.* Similar, but dolphin, three mon. and ΠΑ on *rev.* *B.M.C.* 42 .. .. VF 70/-

1139 **Pellene** (274 B.C. ?). Æ 18. As No. 1136, but ΑΡΧΕΜΑΧΙ on *obv.* and ΑΧΑΙΩΝ ΠΕΛΛΑΝΕΩΝ on *rev.* *Clerk* 19 .. .. *fair* 21/-

1140 **SICYON** (251 B.C.). Æ *hemidr.* As No. 1134, but dove flying r., two mon. and ΝΙ. *B.M.C.* 44 .. .. VF 85/-

1141 **CORINTH** (243 B.C.). Æ *hemidr.* Similar, but Pegasos flying r., ΑΣ and Κ. *Clerk* 111 .. .. F 50/-

1142 **MEGARIS:** (243 B.C.). Æ *hemidr.* As 1134, but lyre, ΔΩΡΟ. *B.M.C.* 7 F 40/-

1143 **ARGOLIS : Argos** (228 B.C.). Æ *hemidr.* Similar, but monogram above and wolf's head below. *B.M.C.* 87 .. .. VF 85/-

1144 **Epidaurus** (243 B.C.). Æ *hemidr.* Similar, but coiled serpent, head erect, and ΣΩΣΙ. *B.M.C.* 91 .. .. *good* F 65/-

1145 **Hermione** (229 B.C.). Æ *hemidr.* Similar, but tripod ΙΣ and three monograms. *Clerk* 173 .. .. R, VF £8

1146 **ARCADIA : Alea** (*before* 234 B.C.). Æ 19. As No. 1136. ΑΧΑΙΩΝ ΑΛΕΑΤΑΝ on *rev.* *Clerk* 50 .. .. *nearly* F 37/6

1147 **Asea** (194 B.C.). Æ 21. As No. 1136. ΞΕΝΙΑΣ on *obv.* ΑΣΕΑΤΑΝ ΑΧΑΙΩΝ on *rev.* *B.M.C.* 161 .. .. *fair* 27/6

1148 **Callista** (194 B.C. ?). Æ 19. As No. 1136. ΑΝΤΑΝΔΡΟΣ on *obv.*, ΚΑΛΛΙΣΤΑΤΑΝ ΑΧΑΙΩΝ on *rev.* *Clerk* 57 .. .. *fair* 32/6

1149 **Caphyae** (227 B.C.). Æ *hemidr.* As No. 1134, but head of Athena, ΚΑ and monogram. *B.M.C.* 109 .. .. VF £5

1150 **Cleitor.** Æ *hemidr.* Similar, but ΚΛΗ and head of Helios. *Clerk* 179 R, VF £8

1151 **Lycoa** (?). Æ *hemidr.* Similar, but dolphin, ΛΥ ΑΡ. *B.M.C.* 110 R, F 75/-

1152 **Mantineia** (*before* 222 B.C.). Æ *hemidr.* Similar, but trident and head, ΔΙ and mon. *B.M.C.* 98 .. .. VF 90/-

1153 — now called **Antigoneia.** Another, similar, but no symbols, ΑΝ ΣΩ. *B.M.C.* 107 *nearly* VF 75/-

1154 **Megalopolis** (234 B.C.). Æ *hemidr.* Similar, but syrinx, ΚΙ and Ξ. *Clerk* 212 *nearly* VF 60/-

1155 **Pallantium** (194 B.C.). Æ *hemidr.* Similar, but trident-head, ΠΑΛ. *B.M.C.* 124 VF 90/-

1156 **Pheneus** (234 B.C.). Æ 18. As No. 1136. ΜΝΑΣΙΛΑΟΣ on *obv.*, ΦΕΝΕΩΝ ΑΧΑΙΩΝ on *rev.* *Clerk* 83 .. .. F 42/-

1157 **Phigaleia** (208 B.C.). Æ 21. Similar, but ΚΛΕΟΔΙΧΟΣ on *obv.*, ΦΙΓΑΛΕΩΝ ΑΧΑΙΩΝ on *rev.* *Clerk* 80 .. .. *fair* 27/6

1158 **Tegea** (222 B.C.). Æ *hemidr.* As No. 1134, but ΤΕ. *Clerk* 223 .. .. VF 70/-

1159 **ELIS** (191 B.C.). Æ *hemidr.* Similar, but thunderbolt, ΓΑ and two mon. *B.M.C.* 61 *nearly* VF 60/-

1160 — Another, with ΚΑΛΛΙΠΟΣ on *obv.*, thunderbolt, Φ and two mon. on *rev.* *B.M.C.* 71 VF 90/-

1161 **MESSENE** (191 B.C.). Æ *hemidr.* As No. 1134, but ΜΕΣ. *B.M.C.* 77 VF/*good* F 70/-

1162 **LACONIA : Lacedaemon.** Æ *hemidr.* Similar, but the caps of the Dioskuri, ΕΥ and mon. *B.M.C.* 79 .. .. *good* VF £8

ELIS.

1163 **Olympia,** 510-471 B.C. Æ *stater.* Eagle flying l., holding serpent in beak. ℞. Nike winged, wearing long chiton, running r., holding wreath; all in circular incuse. *Cf. B.M.C.* 5, *and Seltman,* " *Temple Coins of Olympia* " *No.* 30 *RR, fair, several bankers' stamps on obv.* £40

1164 — Eagle flying l. with hare; five countermarks. ℞. ΓΑ. Thunderbolt. *Seltman* 32b. **Plate V** .. .. *good* F £85

1165 471-370 B.C. Æ *stater.* Eagle flying r., tearing hare. ℞. Thunderbolt with large widespread wings, in dotted square within incuse square. *B.M.C.* 25 *var.*, *and Seltman* 90 .. .. *RR, fair, banker's stamp on each face* £40

1166 — Zeus seated l., holding sceptre: before him, eagle flying l. ℞. Α Ϝ. Nike seated l., holding sceptre: all in incuse square. *Not in B.M.C.*: *Pozzi colln.* 1826, *and Seltman* 99 .. .. *RRR, fair, two bankers' stamps on obv.* £120

1167 — Eagle standing r., wings spread, holding serpent in beak and claws. ℞. Ϝ Α. Thunderbolt: all in circular incuse. *B.M.C.* 27 *var.*, *and Seltman* 137 *RR,* F £60

1168 — Eagle standing r. on hare, wings closed. ℞. Ϝ Α. Thunderbolt, the lower part of which is composed of an insect's body and wings: all in olive wreath. *Not in B.M.C.*: *Seltman* 143 .. .. *RRR, only three specimens recorded,* VF/F £250

1168A — Eagle's head l. ℞. Winged thunderbolt within olive wreath. *Seltman* 150. **Plate V** .. .. *RR, good* F £300

1169 Æ *hemidrachm.* Eagle, wings spread, r., head l. ℞. Ϝ Α. Winged thunderbolt: all in circular incuse. *B.M.C.* 23 .. .. R, VF £40

1170 — Head of eagle l.: below, leaf. ℞. As preceding. *B.M.C.* 41 *RR,* F/VF £25

1171 Æ *stater*. Head of Hera r., wearing stephanos adorned with flowers. ℞. ꜰ ᴀ. Wingless thunderbolt; all in olive-wreath. *B.M.C. 55, and Seltman* 272
R, finest style, VF £200

1172 — Similar, with ʜ ᴘ ᴀ above *obv.* type. *B.M.C. 61, and Seltman* 243 RR, F £100

1173 370-362 ʙ.ᴄ. Æ *stater*. ꜰ ᴀ. Head of Olympia r., hair in sphendone. ℞. Eagle, with wings closed, l.: all in olive-wreath. *B.M.C. 75 var. and Seltman* 324
RR, F/VF £100

1173ᴀ — ꜰᴀᴧᴇɪΩɴ. Laur. head of Zeus l. ℞. Eagle r., with closed wings, standing on the capital of an Ionic column. *B.M.C.* 73 .. .. .. RR, F £200

1174 — Head of Hera r., wearing stephanos inscr. ꜰᴀᴧᴇɪΩɴ. ℞. ꜰ retrograde. Eagle, wings spread, l., head r.: all in olive-wreath. *B.M.C. 101 var. and Seltman* 355
R, F/VF £100

1175 Æ *obol*. Head of Hera r. ℞. ꜰ ᴀ. Thunderbolt. *Not in B.M.C.* .. F £10

1176 362-312 ʙ.ᴄ. Æ *stater*. ꜰ ᴀ. Head of Zeus, laureate, r. ℞. ꜰ ᴀ. Eagle standing r. on Ionic capital, wings closed: in field, r., thunderbolt. *Not in B.M.C.: Seltman* 196 *var.* .. .. *RRR, in finest style of the period, almost* VF £300

1177 271-191 ʙ.ᴄ. Æ *hemidrachm*. Head of Hera r. ℞. ꜰ ᴀ. Eagle r., head l.: in field, r., thunderbolt. *Not in B.M.C.* .. .. F £14

1178 Æ 20. Laur. head of Zeus r. ℞. Free horse trotting l.; ᴧʏ below; ꜰᴀ and thunderbolt above .. .. *nearly* VF 75/-

1179 146-43 ʙ.ᴄ. Æ 20. Head of Zeus, laur., r.: below ᴅ. ℞. ꜰᴀᴧᴇɪΩɴ in olive-wreath. *Cf. B.M.C.* 149 .. .. VF 90/-

ISLANDS OFF ELIS.

1180 **CEPHALLENIA : Cranii.** *Before* 431 ʙ.ᴄ. Æ *triobol*. ᴋᴘᴀɴɪ. Ram l. ℞. Bow in incuse square. *B.M.C.* 2 .. .. *good* F/VF £9

1181 431-330 ʙ.ᴄ. Æ *obol*. Ram's head r. ℞. ᴋᴘᴀ. Ram's foot r. *B.M.C.* 32 F £5

1182 Æ 15. Forepart of ram l. ℞. Bow in oblong incuse. *B.M.C.* 18 .˙. F 35/-

1183 Æ 14. Ram's head l. ℞. as No. 1181. *B.M.C.* 37 .. .. *fair*/F 25/-

1184 Æ 17. Kephalos standing r., resting on spear. ℞. Monogram. *B.M.C.* 42
fair 21/-

1185 Æ 17. Bull's head facing. ℞. ᴋ. *B.M.C.* 48 .. .. .. F/*fair* 25/-

1186 **Pale.** 431-370 ʙ.ᴄ. Æ *drachm*. ᴨᴀ. Young male head r. ℞. ᴋᴇꜰᴀ[ᴧᴏΣ]. Kephalos seated r. on rock, holding spear. *B.M.C.* 2 .. .. F £8

1187 370-189 ʙ.ᴄ. Æ 15. Large ᴨ, within which, barley-corn upright. ℞. Dolphin over waves. *B.M.C.* 36 .. .. *fair* 22/6

1188 **Pronni.** *c.* 370 ʙ.ᴄ. Æ *triobol*. Head of Kephalos l. ℞. ᴨᴘΩɴɴΩɴ. Club. *B.M.C.* 1 .. .. R, *nearly* VF £17

1189 **Same.** 370-189 ʙ.ᴄ. Æ 15 Young male head r. ℞. ΣᴀᴍᴀɪΩɴ. Hound seated r., fore-paw raised. *B.M.C.* 25 .. .. F 35/-

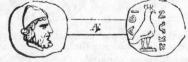

1186   1191

1190 **ITHACA.** 300-191 ʙ.ᴄ. Æ 17. Head of Odysseus, wearing pointed cap, r. ℞. ɪΘᴀᴋΩɴ. Head of Athena, helmeted, r. *B.M.C.* 14 .. .. F 40/-

1191 Æ 15. *Obv.* as preceding. ℞. ɪΘᴀᴋΩɴ. Cock r. *B.M.C.* 18 .. .. F 37/6

1192 **ZACYNTHUS.** *c.* 370 B.C. Æ *stater.* Laur. head of Apollo r. ℞. ΔΙΩΝΟΣ divided by tripod: Ι Α between legs. *B.M.C.* 33 .. .. .. *RR*, VF £200

1192A Æ *third.* Similar. ℞. Ι Α and tripod within wreath. *B.M.C.* 24   *fair* £6

1193 *After* 350 B.C. Æ 15. Similar, but rather barbarous. ℞. ΙΑ below forepart of Pegasos r. *B.M.C.* 52 .. .. F 35/-

1194 *M. Aurelius.* Æ 19. Laur. head of Aurelius r. ℞. ΖΑΚΥΝΘΙΩΝ. Pan standing r., holding bunch of grapes in r. hand and the young Dionysos on l. arm. *B.M.C.* 93   F 65/-

1192   1195

MESSENIA.

1195 **Messene.** 370-280 B.C. Æ *tetradrachm.* Head of Demeter, crowned with corn, l. ℞. ΜΕΣΣΑΝΙΩΝ. Zeus Ithomates standing r., holding thunderbolt and eagle. *B.M.C.* 1   *RRR, good* F £120

1196 Æ 20. Head of Demeter r. ℞. ΜΕ in monogram. Type as preceding; to r., tripod .. .. *fair* 25/-

1197 280-146 B.C. Æ *hemidrachm.* Diad. head of Zeus r. ℞. ΜΕΣ and tripod within wreath. *B.M.C.* 13 .. .. VF £5

1198 Æ 20. Head of Demeter l. ℞. As No. 1195; in field, tripod, wreath and ΔΙΩΝ. *B.M.C.* 34 .. .. *fair* 25/-

1199 Æ 20. Head of Demeter r. ℞. ΜΕ in monogram: Zeus standing r., holding sceptre and eagle; before him, tripod; behind, ΝΙΚΑΡΧΟΣ. *B.M.C.* 37   *RR, dark-green patina,* EF/F £7

1200 **Asine.** *Septimius Severus.* Æ 21. ΛΟV . C . CEOVHPOC. His laur. head r. ℞. ΑCΙΝΑΙΩΝ. Draped female figure standing facing. *B.M.C.* 1   *R, fair* 55/-

1201 **Corone.** *c.* 200 B.C. Æ *hemidrachm.* Head of Athena r. ℞. ΚΟΡ and bunch of grapes within ivy-wreath. *B.M.C.* 1 .. .. *nearly* F £8

1201A **Cyparissia.** *Caracalla.* Æ 22. Greek legend. Bust r. ℞. ΚΥΠΑΡΙCCΙΕWΝ. Athena standing. l. *B.M.C.* 3 .. .. *fair* 50/-

1201B **Mothone.** *Plautilla.* Æ 22. ΦΟVΛΒ ΠΛΑVΤΙΛΑΝ. Bust r. ℞ ΜΟΘΩΝΑΙΩΝ. Isis standing l. *B.M.C.* 5 .. .. *RR, fair* £7

1202 **Pylus.** *Geta.* Æ 22. His bust r. ℞. ΠVΛΙWΝ. Statue of goat reclining r. on plinth. *B.M.C.* 3 .. .. *R, fair* 60/-

1203 **Thuria.** *c.* 200 B.C. Æ 22. Diad. head of Zeus r. ℞. ΘΟΥ ΝΙΚΩΝΥΜΟΣ. Athena standing l. *B.M.C.* 2 .. .. *R, fair* 30/-

LACONIA.

1203A **Gythium** (the port of Sparta). *Severus.* Æ 22. His laur. head r. ℞. ΓVΘΕΑΤWΝ. Zeus seated l., holding thunderbolt and sceptre. *B.M.C.* 1 .. .. .. *R,* F £6

1204 **Lacedaemon** (Sparta). *Areus.* 309-265 B.C. Æ *tetradrachm.* Head of king, diademed, l. ℞. ΛΑ. The Apollo of Amyclae r., helmeted and holding spear and bow; beside him, goat r.; in field, l., wreath. *B.M.C.* 1 .. .. *RR,* F/VF £150

1205 266-210 B.C. Æ 23. Eagle standing l. on thunderbolt. ℞. ΛΑ. Thunderbolt. *B.M.C.* 4 .. .. F 50/-

1206 196-146 B.C. Æ *tetrobol.* Diad. head of Herakles r. ℞. ΛΛ. Amphora between caps of the Dioscuri, monogram. *B.M.C.* 11 .. .. *good* F/F £8

1207 146-32 B.C. Æ 23. ΛΥΚΟΥΡΓΟC. Head of Lycurgus r. ℞. ΛΛ. Club and caduceus combined, between monogram and I: all in wreath. *B.M.C.* 20 *var.* F/VF 80/-

1208 Æ 18. Head of bearded Herakles r. ℞. ΛΛ and ΛΥ. Club: all in wreath. *B.M.C.* 41 *var.* .. .. F 40/-

1209 Æ 20. Head of Zeus r. ℞. ΛΛ. Type as previous: in field, ΕΠΙ ΕΥΡΥΚΛΕΟΣ. *B.M.C.* 63 .. .. *fair* 25/-

1210 Æ 18. Heads of the Dioskuri, jugate, r. ℞. ΛΛ. Two amphorae: all in wreath. *B.M.C.* 35-40 .. .. F/*fair* 35/-

1211 **Cythera** (island off Laconia). 3rd-3nd Cent. B.C. Æ 18. Diad. head of Aphrodite r. ℞. ΚΥ. Dove flying r. *B.M.C.* 2 .. .. F 50/-

ARGOLIS.

1212 **Argos.** 468-421 B.C. Æ *hemidrachm.* Forepart of wolf, at bay, l. ℞. Α in shallow square incuse, in upper part of which two deeper incuses; across field, three pellets. *B.M.C.* 5 .. .. *good* F 90/-

1213 — Similar, with ΣΟ before wolf: no pellets. *B.M.C.* 16 .. .. F/*fair* 45/-

1214 Æ *obol.* Wolf's head l. ℞. As preceding, pellet below Α. *B.M.C.* 23 .. F 65/-

1215 Æ *hemiobol.* Η with top and bottom closed by strokes. ℞. As preceding, but no pellet. *B.M.C.* 27.. .. .. *RR,* F £5

1216 421-350 B.C. Æ *stater.* Head of Hera r., wearing stephanos decorated with floral ornaments. ℞. ΑΡΓΕΙΩΝ. Wolf l. between two dolphins in opposite directions. *B.M.C.* 33 .. .. *RR,* F/VF £275

1216A Æ *tritartemorian.* As before. ℞. Τ Τ Τ. Temple-key bound with fillets. *B.M.C.* 42. *Another example of the value being on a Greek coin* .. .. *R,* VF £10

1217 Æ *drachm.* Similar type l. ℞. ΑΡΓΕΙΩΝ. Diomedes advancing r., holding sword and the Palladium : to l., swan r. *B.M.C.* 46 .. .. .. *R, good* F £60

1218 Æ *trihemiobol.* Similar type r. ℞. ΑΡ. The Palladium r. *B.M.C.* 48 *R,* F/*fair* £10

1219 350-228 B.C. Æ *hemidrachm.* Forepart of wolf r. ℞. Α: in field, Z ΕΥ and small eagle on base r.: all in incuse square. *B.M.C.* 64 .. .. F 45/-

1220 — Similar, with ΦΑ and club in *rev.* field. *B.M.C.* 82 .. .. .. VF 90/-

1221 Æ *trihemiobol.* Forepart of wolf l. ℞. ΑΡ. Crested Corinthian helmet l. *B.M.C.* 88 .. .. *fair* 50/-

1222 Æ 12. Wolf's head l. ℞. Α: below, helmet l. *B.M.C.* 101 .. .. F 30/-

1223 Æ 18. Head of Hera r., wearing stephanos inscr. ΑΡΓΕ. ℞. Athena l., with shield and spear. *B.M.C.* 106. **Plate V** .. .. F 40/-

1224 228-146 B.C. Æ *hemidrachm.* Forepart of wolf r. ℞. Α: below, radiate head of Helios; in field, ΞΕΝΟΦΙΛΟΥ: all in incuse square. *B.M.C.* 117 .. F/VF 65/-

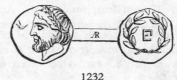

1225   1232

1225 — Forepart of wolf l. ℞. Α: below, eagle: in field, ΙΕ ΡΩ[ΝΟΣ]: all in incuse square. *B.M.C.* 114 .. .. VF/EF £6

1226 Æ 17. Hd. of Hera r. ℞. Quiver between helmet and Η with closed top and bottom. *B.M.C.* 142 .. .. *fair* 22/6

1227 **Argos.** *L. Verus.* Æ 23. Laur. bust of emperor r. ℞. ΑΡΓΕΙΩΝ. Hera seated l., holding patera and sceptre. *B.M.C.* 159 .. .. R, F £6

1228 Æ 25. *Obv.* as 1227. ℞. ΑΡΓ. Hero r., fighting serpent: to r., nurse Hypsipyle fleeing r.: below serpent, infant Opheltes on ground. *Not in B.M.C.* M/*fair* 45/–

1229 *Severus.* Æ 24. Laur. bust of emperor r. ℞. ΑΡΓΕΙUΝ. Acropolis-rock surmounted by tetrastyle temple. *B.M.C.* 165 .. .. *fair* 50/–

1230 **Cleonae.** 471-421 B.C. Æ *obol.* Head of Herakles l. ℞. κ within incuse square. *B.M.C.* 4 .. .. R, F £10

1231 Late 4th Cent. B.C. Æ 14. Head of Herakles r. ℞. ΚΛΕΩ in parsley wreath F 50/–

1232 **Epidaurus.** 350-323 B.C. Æ *hemidrachm.* Laur. head of Asklepios l. ℞. Ε Π mon. within laurel-wreath. *B.M.C.* 1. *Illustrated on page* 103 .. .. F £15

1233 323-240 B.C. Æ 17. Head of Asklepios, laur., r. ℞. ΕΠ in monogram: Epione standing l., pouring from phial into patera: to r., cupping-vessel. *B.M.C.* 12 F 50/–

1234 **Hermione.** 370-300 B.C. Æ 15. Head of Demeter l. ℞. ΕΡ and flaming torch within corn-wreath. *B.M.C.* 8 .. .. F 40/–

1235 **Methana.** 370-300 B.C. Æ 15. Head of Hephaistos r. ℞. ΜΕ mon. in wreath of corn. *B.M.C.* 1 .. .. R, *fair* 30/–

1236 **Tiryns.** 370-300 B.C. Æ 12. Head of Apollo r. ℞. ΤΙRVΝ. Palm-tree. *B.M.C* 4 .. .. F 37/

1237 **Troezen.** 431-400 B.C. Æ *drachm.* Head of Athena l. ℞. ΤΡΟ and trident-head within incuse square. *B.M.C.* 3 .. .. R, *nearly* VF £30

1238 *After* 322 B.C. Æ 13. Head of Athena l. ℞. ΤΡΟ. Trident-head and dolphin. *B.M.C.* 12 .. .. F 40/–

ARCADIA.

1239 **The Arcadians.** 480-417 B.C. Æ *triobol.* Zeus Aphesius seated on throne r., head l., holding sceptre: to r., eagle flying r. ℞. Head of Artemis r.: all in incuse square. *B.M.C.* 2 .. .. F £12

1240 Æ *obol.* Zeus Aphesius seated l. ℞. ΑΡ. Head of Artemis l.; all in incuse square. *B.M.C.* 12 .. .. F 75/–

1241 Æ *triobol.* *Obv.* as preceding. ℞. ΑΡΚΑ. Head of Artemis r., hair in queue: all in incuse square. *B.M.C.* 25 .. .. F £5

1242   1251

1242 363-280 B.C. Æ *stater.* Head of Zeus l. ℞. ΑΡΚ mon. Pan seated l. on rock, holding a lagobolon; below, syrinx and ΟΛΥ. *B.M.C.* 48. **Plate V** *RRR, good* F/F £350

1243 Æ *triobol.* Similar, but Δ *B.M.C.* 51 .. .. *nearly* VF £8

1244 Æ *obol.* Head of young Pan l. ℞. Monogram Α Ρ; below, syrinx. *B.M.C.* 55 *nearly* VF £6

1245 Æ 20. Head of Zeus, laur., l. ℞. As last, all within wreath. *B.M.C.* 75 F 37/6

1246 280-234 B.C. Æ *triobol.* *Obv.* as preceding. ℞. Pan seated l. on rock, r. hand raised: before him, eagle flying l.: in field, ΑΔ. *B.M.C.* 78 .. .. VF/F 90/–

1247 — Similar, with monogram ΑΡ and ΔΔ in *rev.* field. *B.M.C.* 82 .. .. F 55/–

1248 *Antinous.* Æ 18. ΒΕΤΟΥΡΙΟC. Bust of Antinous r. ℞. ΤΟΙC ΑΡΚΑCΙ. Horse r. *B.M.C.* 90 .. .. R, *fair* £10

1249 **Alea.** 430-370 B.C. Æ 13. Head of Artemis r. ℞. ΑΛ below strung bow. *B.M.C.* 1 .. .. F 50/–

1250 **Caphyae.** 3rd Cent. B.C. Æ 13. Head of Athena. ℞. ΚΑΦ in corn-wreath. *B.M.C.* 1 .. .. R, *fair* 30/–

1251 **Cleitor.** 370-240 B.C. Æ *hemidrachm.* Head of Helios, radiate, facing. ℞. ΚΛΗ. Bull butting r.; above, centaur r. *B.M.C.* 4 .. .. *RR,* VF £21

1252 Æ *obol.* Head of Athena l. ℞. ΚΛΗ. Free horse prancing r. *B.M.C.* 8 VF £14

1253 Æ 15. Similar. *B.M.C.* 10 .. .. F 50/-

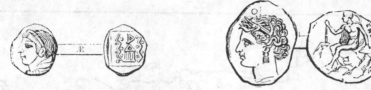

1254   1261

1254 **Heraea.** 550-490 B.C. Æ *triobol.* Head of goddess l. ℞. ΕΡΑ between zigzag lines and dots. *B.M.C.* 7 .. .. *R, fair* £6

1254A 420-322 B.C. Æ *trihemiobol.* Head of Athena l. ℞. Three Ε's back to back, all in incuse square. *B.M.C.* 11 .. .. F £10

1255 Æ 14. Similar. ℞. Η with four dots around. *B.M.C.* 23 .. .. F 35/-

1256 **Mantineia.** 5th Cent. B.C. Æ *obol.* Acorn. ℞. Large Μ, ΜΑΝ below. *B.M.C.* 8 F £8

1257 *After* 370 B.C. Æ 16. Head of Athena r. ℞. ΜΑΝ. Poseidon seated on rock l. *B.M.C.* 19 .. .. *fair/F* 27/6

1258 **Megalopolis.** 234-146 B.C. Æ *triobol.* Head of Zeus, laur., l. ℞. ΜΕΓ. Type as No. 1246. *B.M.C.* 1-11 .. .. F 55/-; VF £6

1259 **Orchomenus.** 370-300 B.C. Æ 18. Artemis kneeling r., holding bow in l. hand. ℞. ΕΡΧΟΜΕΝΙΩΝ. Callisto seated l., pierced by arrow and falling back: behind her, young Arkas stretching out his arms. *B.M.C.* 1 .. .. .. *R, fair* 35/-

1260 **Pheneus.** 431-370 B.C. Æ 16. Head of Hermes r. ℞. ΦΕΝΕΩΝ. Ram standing r. *B.M.C.* 8 .. .. *fair* 25/-

1261 *After* 362 B.C. Æ *drachm.* Head of Demeter l. ℞. ΦΕΝΕΩΝ. Hermes, holding caduceus, seated l. on rocks. *B.M.C.* 14 .. .. *RR,* F £150

1261A Æ *hemidrachm.* Head of Demeter l. ℞. ΦΕΝΙΚΟΝ. Bull standing r., Π below *B.M.C.* 15 .. .. F £10

1265   1268A

1262 **Psophis.** *c.* 460 B.C. Æ *obol.* Forepart of stag r. ℞. ΧΟ and fish within incuse square. *B.M.C.* 3 .. .. *R, nearly* VF £25

1263 **Stymphalus.** 400-362 B.C. Æ *obol.* Head of young Herakles r. ℞. ΣΤΥΜΦΑΛΙΟΝ retrograde. Head and neck of Stymphalian bird r. *B.M.C.* 2 .. *RR,* VF £50

1264 **Tegea.** 420-370 B.C. Æ *trihemiobol.* Gorgoneion facing; above, Τ. ℞. Three Ε's back to back (*i.e.,* mark of value). *B.M.C.* 1 .. .. *R,* F £20

1265 370-340 B.C. Æ 17. Head of Athena r. ℞. ΤΕΓΕΑ. Telephus r., suckled by doe: on l., Μ. *B.M.C.* 15 .. .. *fair* 30/-

1266 *After* 146 B.C. Æ 22. ΑΛΕΟΣ. Head of Aleus, bearded, r. ℞. ΤΕΓΕΑΤΑΝ. Cepheus standing r. facing Athena standing l., who hands him the head of Medusa; between them, Sterope r. holding vase. *B.M.C.* 20 .. .. *R, fair* 60/-

1267 Æ 19. Female head (? Eileithuia) l. ℞. ΤΕΓΕΑΤΑΝ. Athena standing r., placing head of Medusa in vase held by Sterope standing l. *B.M.C.* 22 .. .. F 45/-

1268 **Thelpusa.** 400-370 B.C. Æ *obol.* Head of Demeter Erinys r. ℞. ΕΡΙΩΝ. Horse prancing r. *Grose* 7026 .. .. *RR,* F £27/10/-

1268A *After* 146 B.C. Æ 17. Head of Demeter Erinys rad. r. ℞. ΘΕΛ in wreath. *B.M.C.* 1 .. .. *fair/F* 40/-

CRETE.

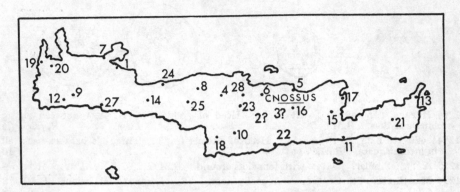

1 Aptera	10 Gortyna	19 Phalasarna
2 Arcadia ?	11 Hierapytna	20 Polyrhenium
3 Arsinoe ?	12 Hyrtacina	21 Praesus
4 Axus	13 Itanus	22 Priansus
5 Chersonesus	14 Lappa	23 Rhaucus
6 Cnossus	15 Latus	24 Rhithymna
7 Cydonia	16 Lyttus	25 Sybrita
8 Eleutherna	17 Olus	27 Tarra
9 Elyrus	18 Phaestus	28 Tylisus

1269 **Aptera.** 400-300 B.C. Æ *stater.* ΑΠΤΕΡΑΙΩΝ. Head of Artemis of Aptera r., hair rolled. Ɍ. ΠΤΟΛΙΟΙΚΟΣ. Warrior standing l., holding spear and shield, raises r. hand in adoration of sacred tree: in field, ΑΠ mon. *B.M.C.* 3 .. *R, good* F £75

1270 250-67 B.C. Æ *hemidrachm.* Head of Artemis of later style, hair rolled and with stephane. Ɍ. ΑΠΤΑΡΑΙΟΝ. Warrior advancing l., ΝΙ and ΚΑ in field. *B.M.C.* 8 *good* F £20

1271 Æ 16. Similar type but no letters in field. *B.M.C.* 20 .. .. .. *fair* 30/-

1271A **Arcadia.** 330-280 B.C. Æ *drachm.* Head of Zeus Ammon r. Ɍ. ΑΡΚΑΔΩΝ. Athena standing l. *B.M.C.* 1 .. .. *RRR,* F £35

1271B **Arsinoe.** 3rd cent. B.C. Æ 12. Head of Athena r. Ɍ. ΑΡΣΙ. Two dolphins. *B.M.C.* 5 .. .. *R, fair* 35/-

1272 **Axus.** 300-67 B.C. Æ 13. Head of Zeus r. Ɍ. ϹΑΞΙΩΝ. Τɾipod: above, thunderbolt. *B.M.C.* 9 .. .. *fair* 35/-

1273 Æ 20. Head of Zeus r. Ɍ. ΑΞ. Winged thunderbolt. *B.M.C.* 12 *fair*/F 40/-

1274 **Chersonesus.** 370-300 B.C. Æ *stater*. Laur. head of Artemis Britomartis r. ℞. ΧΕΡΣΟΝΑΣΙΟΝ. Apollo seated r. on omphalos holding lyre; to r., thymiaterion. *B.M.C.* 1 *variety*. **Plate V** .. ..*RR, good* F £100

1275 — Another. Head of Artemis Britomartis l. ℞. ΧΕΡΣΟ retrograde. Herakles l., rushing to attack with club raised. *B.M.C.* 3 .. .. *RR, good* F/F £70

1276 300-200 B.C. Æ 13. Head of Athena, helmeted, r. ℞. ΧΕΡ. Prow of galley r. *B.M.C.* 11 .. .. *fair* 25/-

1277 Æ 17. As preceding, but head l. *B.M.C.* 10 .. .. .. *fair*/F 35/-

1278 **Cnossus.** *c.* 450 B.C. Æ *obol*. Minotaur running l. ℞. Star of four rays. *Svor.* 9 .. .. *fair* £5

1279 400-350 B.C. Æ *stater*. Head of Demeter or Persephone in wreath of corn r. ℞. Labyrinth of meander pattern with Κ inside; to l., arrow; to r., sword in sheath. *Svor.* 48 .. .. F/*good* F £55

1280 — Another, similar, but hair rolled. ℞. ΒΡΙΩΝ. Square labyrinth. *Svor.* 65 F £65

1281   1293

1281 350-300 B.C. Æ *stater*. Head of Hera l., wearing stephanos; circular countermark before neck. ℞. ΚΝΩΣΙΩΝ below square labyrinth; to l., arrow-head and Α; to r., thunderbolt and Ρ. *B.M.C.* 24 .. .. *good* F £100

1281A Æ *drachm*. Similar but ΚΝΟΣΙ. *B.M.C.* 26 .. .. *good* VF/VF £55

1282 Æ 13. Star of sixteen rays. ℞. Square labyrinth. *B.M.C.* 34 F/*fair* 35/-

1283 300-200 B.C. Æ *hemidrachm*. Laur. head of Apollo l. ℞. ΚΝΩ below square labyrinth; to l., ΑΓΕΙ; to r., thunderbolt. *Svor.* 90 .. .. F £16

1284 *About* 200 B.C., *in alliance with Gortyna*. Æ 18. Bull galloping l., carrying Europa with her veil flying above her head. ℞. ΚΝΩΣΙΩΝ. Square labyrinth: above, star. *B.M.C.* 36 .. .. VF £6

1285 200-67 B.C. Æ *tetradrachm*. Diad. head of Zeus (or Minos) r. ℞. ΚΝΟΣΙΟΝ around square labyrinth. *B.M.C.* 43 .. .. VF £100

1286 — Another, similar, but head of Zeus l. *B.M.C.* 44. **Plate V** VF/*good* F £85

1287 Æ 26. Head of Zeus r.: in front, half-thunderbolt. ℞. ΚΥΔΑΣ. Eagle standing r., wings spread. *B.M.C.* 53 .. .. .. *fair* 35/-; EF/VF, *green patina* £10

1288 Æ 21. Head of Artemis r. ℞. ΘΑΡΣΥΔΙΚΑΣ. Quiver with strap. *B.M.C.* 66 *fair* 30/-

1289 *Caligula and Germanicus*. Æ 22. Bare head either side. *Svor.* 202 .. *fair* 50/-

1290 **Cydonia** (Canea). 400-300 B.C. Æ *stater*. Female head r. wreathed with grapes and vine-leaves; two countermarks. ℞. ΚΥΔΩΝ. Kydon l., stringing bow; in front, hound r. *Svor.* 3 .. .. *RR, nearly* VF/*fair* £85

1291 Æ *obol*. Head of Pan l. ℞. ΚΥ. Hound seated r. *Svor.* 18 .. .. F £10

1292 Æ 12. Young male head r. ℞. ΚΥΔΩ. Hound seated r. *B.M.C.* 15 F 60/-

1293 200-67 B.C. Æ *tetradrachm*.. Head of Artemis (Diktynna) r, bow and quiver at neck: magistrates name, ΠΑΣΙΩΝ in three lines across field. ℞. ΚΥΔΩΝΙΑΤΑΝ in three lines across field. Artemis (Diktynna) standing facing, looking l., holding long torch; on l., seated hound looks up at her. *B.M.C.* 22 .. .. *RR, nearly* VF £200

1293A Æ 23. Head of Apollo, laur., r. ℞. ΚΥΔΩΝΙΑΤΑΝ. Nike standing l., with wreath and palm. *Svor.* 58 .. .. *fair* 40/-

1294 *Augustus*. Æ 20. Head of Augustus l. ℞. ΚΥΔΩΝΙΑΤΑΝ. Hound r., suckling infant. *B.M.C.* 34 .. .. *fair* 50/-

1295A

1295 Eleutherna. 431-300 B.C. Æ *stater.* Head of Apollo r. of crude style. ℞. ΕΛΕΥΑΡ. Apollo standing facing holding stone and strung bow. *B.M.C.* 2 .. *good* F/F £60

1295A — Laur. head of Zeus r. ℞. ΕΛΕΥΘΕ. Nude Apollo standing half l., holding stone and bow. *B.M.C.* 3 .. .. *RR, good* F £160

1296 300-200 B.C. Æ 18. Head of Apollo, laur., r. ℞. ΕΛΕΥΘΕΡΝΑΙΩΝ. Apollo seated l. on omphalos, holding stone. *B.M.C.* 16 .. .. F 65/-

1297 Elyrus (Rhrodhooani). 4th Cent. B.C. Æ *drachm.* ΕΛΥΡΙΟΝ. Head of Cretan goat. ℞. Bee. *B.M.C.* 2 .. .. *RR,* F £50

1298 Gortyna. *Before* 431 B.C. Æ *drachm.* Bull recumbent l., looking back. ℞. Lion's scalp in linear square: around, in archaic lettering, retrograde, ΓΟΡΤΥΝΟΣ ΤΟ ΦΑΙΜΑ. *Svor.* 17 .. .. *RRR,* F £100

1299 431-300 B.C. Æ *didrachm.* Europa r., wearing chiton and peplos over lower limbs, seated in tree, resting r. hand on tree and head on l. hand. ℞. Bull r., looking back. *Svor.* 58 .. .. *RR,* F/VF £75

1300 — *Obv.* Similar to preceding. ℞. Bull r., looking back, raising rear r. hoof. *Svor.* *plate* xiv, 13 (*obv.*) *and* 6 (*rev.*) .. .. *RR, fair*/F £25

1301 — Similar *obv.* type, but to l. ℞. Bull adv. r., looking back. *Svor.* 29. *Overstruck on coin with double linear border divided into small squares* .. .. *RR,* F £75

1302 — *Obv.* Similar to No. 1299, but Europa raises veil with both hands. ℞. Bull l., looking back and licking lifted l. rear hoof: below, indication of ground. *Svor.* 65 *RR, fair*/F £40

1303 — Europa seated l. in tree, r. hand raised to head, and eagle with outspread wings on her lap. ℞. ΓΟΡΤΥΝ. Bull r., looking back and licking raised r. hind hoof; below, gad-fly. *Svor.* 76 .. .. *RR,* F/VF £65

1304 300-200 B.C. Æ 17. Europa seated in tree r., head facing; behind her, on tree, eagle. ℞. ΓΟΡΤΥ ΝΙΩΝ. Europa on bull l. *B.M.C.* 41 .. .. *fair* 32/6

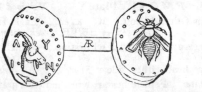

1297   1304A

1304A 200-67 B.C. Æ Attic *drachm* (60 gr.) Diad. head of Zeus r. ℞. ΓΟΡΤΥΝΙΩΝ. Apollo seated l. on rock holding bow and arrow; in field r., B. *B.M.C.* 49 *RR,* F £50

1304B Æ *drachm* (46 gr.) Similar but H below head and no arrow. *B.M.C.* 51 *R,* F £37/10/-

1305 Hierapytna (Gierapetra). 200-67 B.C. Æ *didrachm.* Female head r., wearing turreted head-dress. ℞. ΙΕΡΑΠΥΤΝ. Palm-tree; to l., eagle r.; in field r., upwards ΜΕΝΕΣΘΕΝΗΣ: all in laurel-wreath. *B.M.C.* 5 .. .. *R,* VF £75

1306 Æ 16. Star of six rays. ℞. ΙΕΡΑ ΦΑΛΑ. Palm-tree. *Svor.* 34 .. *fair* 32/6

1306A Hyrtacina. 4th cent. B.C. Æ *drachm.* ΥΡΤΑΚΙΝΙΩΝ. Goat's head r.; behind, arrow-head. ℞. Bee: in field r., rose. *B.M.C.* 1 .. .. .. *RRR,* F £75

1307 **Itanus.** 5th Cent. B.C. Æ *didrachm.* Glaukos, represented as a human being above the waist with a fishes tail below, r., raising both hands. ℞. Star of eight rays, between two of which, pellet; all in shallow incuse square. *B.M.C.* 1 *RR, fair/F* £100

1308 4th Cent. B.C. Æ *drachm.* Head of Athena l. ℞. ITANIΩN. Eagle standing l., looking back, within shallow incuse; in field to r., Glaukos r. holding trident. *B.M.C.* 13 VF/F £32

1310 Æ *obol.* Similar. ℞. ITANIΩN. Star of eight rays. *B.M.C.* 19 .. VF £15

1311 **Lappa.** 4th Cent. B.C. Æ *hemiobol.* Head of bull facing. ℞. Λ. *Svor.* 6 *R, good* F £15

1312 2nd Cent. B.C. Æ 14. Head of Apollo r. ℞. ΛΑ. Lyre. *Svor.* 24 .. *fair* 35/–

1313 Æ 15. Head of Artemis r. ℞. Bull's head facing. *Svor.* 18 .. .. F 60/–

1314 Æ 12. Bull's head facing. ℞. Λ. *Svor.* 8.. .. .. .. *good* F 50/–

1315 **Latus.** 2nd Cent. B.C. Æ 14. Head of Artemis l. wearing stephane. ℞. ΛΑΤΙΩΝ. Hermes walking r. carrying lit torch. *Svor.* 1 .. .. *R,* F £5

1316 **Lyttus** (Xyda). 430-400 B.C. Æ *stater.* Eagle flying l., border of dots. ℞. ΛΥΤΤSΘΝ above boar's head r., all in square. *B.M.C.* 2. **Plate V** .. .. .. VF £80

1317 400 B.C. and later. Æ *stater.* Somewhat similar but ΛΥΤΤΙΟΝ and boar's head l. *B.M.C.* 10 .. .. F £48

1318 300-200 B.C. Æ 16. Head of Zeus r. ℞. ΛΥΤΤΙΩΝ. Eagle r., wings spread; in field, r., boar's head r. *B.M.C.* 23 .. .. F 45/–

1319 Æ 16. ΛΥΤΤΙΩΝ. Eagle r., wings spread. ℞. ΛΥΤΤΙ. Boar's head r. *Cf. B.M.C.* 27 .. .. *good* F 60/–

1320 Æ 12. Eagle flying r. ℞. ΛΥΤΤΙΩΝ. Boar's head l. *B.M.C.* 29 .. F 37/6

1321 **Olus.** 3rd Cent. B.C. Æ *hemidrachm.* Head of Artemis Britomartis l. ℞. Λ with O inside it, within laurel wreath. *Svor.* 2 .. .. *R,* F £40

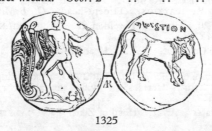

1325

1322 **Phaestus.** *Before* 431 B.C. Æ *stater.* Europa seated on bull advancing l. ℞. Lion's scalp within linear square, around which, in archaic characters and retrograde, ΦΑΙΣΤΙΩΝ ΤΟ ΠΑΙΜΑ: all in incuse square. *B.M.C.* 1 .. .. .. *RRR,* F £150

1323 431-400 B.C. Æ *stater.* Herakles, naked, standing facing, resting r. hand on club and holding bow and lion-skin in l.; to l., serpent; to r., tree. ℞. Bull l., hobbled; all within wreath. *B.M.C.* 8: *Svoronos, pl.* xxiii, 9. **Plate V** .. *RR,* F £36

1324 Æ *hemidrachm.* Youthful male head r. ℞. Bull's head facing. *B.M.C.* 25 *R,* F £12

1325 360-300 B.C. Æ *stater.* Herakles l., seen from behind, with club raised above to attack the Hydra. ℞. ΦΑΙΣΤΙΩΝ above bull advancing r. *Svor.* 58. **Plate V** F/VF £75

1326 3rd Cent. B.C. Æ 18. Talos, winged, running r., hurling stone with r. hand and holding another stone in l. ℞. ΦΑΙΣΤΙΩΝ. Hound r., on the scent. *B.M.C.* 27 *fair* 32/6; F 65/–

1327 **Phalasarna.** 431-300 B.C. Æ *stater.* Large head of Artemis Diktynna r., hair doubly bound with narrow fillet. ℞. ΦΑ between prongs of trident-head. *B.M.C.* 1 *RR, nearly* VF £75

1328 **Polyrhenium.** 400-330 B.C. Æ *hemidrachm.* ΠΥΘΟΔΩΡΟΥ. Head of Artemis Diktynna l. R. ΠΟΛ. Bull's head, facing, decorated with fillets. *Svor.* 16 F £20

1329 330-280 B.C. Æ *drachm.* ΠΟΛ / ΥΡΗΝ / ΙΩΝ. Bull's head facing. R. ΠΟΛΥ / ΡΗΝ above and below spear-head r. *Svor.* 13 .. .. F £15

1330 Æ 11. Round shield with bull's head in centre. R. ΠΟΛΥ. Spear-head. *B.M.C.* 15 .. .. *fair* 21/-; F/VF 60/-

1331 220-67 B.C. Æ *hemidrachm.* Bust of Artemis Diktynna facing. R. ΠΟΛΥΡΗΝΙΩΝ. Apollo l., holding bow. *B.M.C.* 20 .. .. F £12

1332 *Caligula and Germanicus.* Æ 21. Greek legend and head either side. *B.M.C.* 23 F £7

1333 **Praesus.** 400-300 B.C. Æ *stater.* Zeus seated l. on throne, head facing, holding eagle and sceptre. R. ΠΡΑΙΣ. Zeus standing r., hurling thunderbolt. *Not in B.M.C.:* *Svoronos*, pl. xxvii, 21 .. .. *RRR, fair* £70

1334 — Similar to preceding, inscr. ΑΚΡΑΙΟΣ. R. ΠΡΑΙΣΙΟΝ retrograde: bull walking r. *B.M.C.* 5 *var.*: *Svoronos*, xxvii, 2 .. .. *RR,* F £90

1335 **Priansus.** 430-200 B.C. Æ *stater.* Goddess seated l. beneath palm-tree, caressing serpent who rises to her hand. R. ΠΡΙΑΝΣΙΕΩΝ. Poseidon standing l., holding dolphin and trident. *B.M.C.* 1 .. .. *RRR,* F £125

1335A Æ *drachm.* Female head (Artemis ?) r. R. ΠΡΙΑΝΣΙΕΩΝ. Palm-tree between dolphin and rudder. *B.M.C.* 5 .. .. *R, nearly* F £25

1336 *c.* 200 B.C. Æ 17. Similar. *B.M.C.* 12 .. .. *fair* 30/-

1337 **Rhaucus.** 430-300 B.C. Æ *stater.* Poseidon, naked, walking r., holding trident and leading horse. R. ΡΑΥΚΙΟΝ. Trident-head. *Cf. B.M.C.* 1-5 *RR,* F £75

1338 300-166 B.C. Æ 20. Head of Poseidon r. R. ΡΑΥΚΙΩΝ. Trident-head between two dolphins. *B.M.C.* 8 .. .. *fair*/F 37/6

1339 **Rhithymna.** 4th Cent. B.C. Æ 12. Head of Athena r. R. ΙΡ. Trident. *B.M.C.* 4 .. .. *R, fair* 35/-

1340 **Sybrita.** 4th Cent. B.C. Æ *stater.* Youthful Dionysos riding l. on panther, and holding thyrsos. R. ΣΥΒΡΙΤΙΩΝ. Hermes l., tying sandal on r. leg; before, caduceus. *B.M.C.* 1 .. .. *RRR, good* F £350

1340A 4th Cent. B.C. or later. Æ 21. Head of Zeus. R. ΣΥΒΡΙΤΙΩΝ. Jawbone of animal. *B.M.C.*— .. .. *R,* F 65/-

1341 **Tanus.** 4th Cent. B.C. Æ *obol.* Young male head r. R. ΤΑΝΙΤ. Head of Hermes. *Svor.* 3 .. .. *R,* F £12

1342 **Tarra.** 4th Cent. B.C. Æ 10. Head of goat. R. ΤΑ mon. Bee. *Svor.* 2 *R, fair* 35/-

1343 **Tylisus.** 4th Cent. B.C. Æ *stater.* Head of Hera r. wearing stephanos. R. ΤΥΛΙΣΙΟΝ. (retrograde). Apollo, naked, standing holding goat's head and bow; in field, shrub. *Svor.* 1 .. .. *RR, nearly* F £90

1344 **Crete as Roman Province.** *Caligula.* Æ *drachm.* Greek legend. His bare head l. R. Rad. head of Augustus r. *B.M.C.* 3 .. .. .. *R,* VF/*good* F £40

1345 *Claudius.* Æ 24. Greek legend. His bare head r. R. Emperor galloping r.; statue r. on podium behind. *Svor.* 18 .. .. *good* F £6

1346 *Trajan.* Æ *drachm.* IMP CAES NER TRAIA OPTIM AVG GER DAC PART. Laur. bust of Trajan r. R. ΔΙΚΤΥΝΝΑ ΚΡΗΤ. Diktynna seated l., holding javelin and the infant Zeus; on either side, one of the Curetes. *B.M.C.* 16 .. .. *RR,* VF £27

1347 *Hadrian.* Æ 15. Laur. bust of Hadrian r. R. Κ Κ. Altar. *B.M.C.* 33 F 40/-

THE AEGEAN ISLANDS

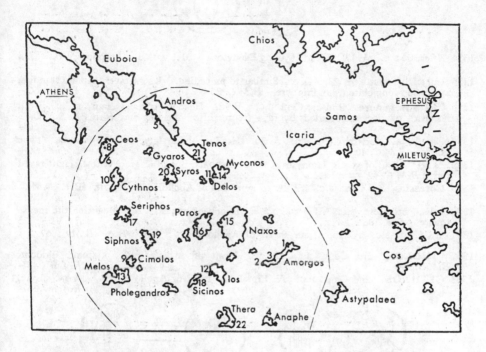

1 Aegiale, *Amorgos*	9 Cimolos	16 Paros
2 Arcesine, *Amorgos*	10 Cythnos	17 Seriphos
3 Minoa, *Amorgos*	11 Delos	18 Sicinos
4 Anaphe	12 Ios	19 Siphnos
5 Andros	13 Melos	20 Syros
6 Carthaea, *Ceos*	14 Myconos	21 Tenos
7 Coressia, *Ceos*	15 Naxos	22 Thera
8 Iulis, *Ceos*		

1348 **AMORGOS in genere.** *Before* 300 B.C. Æ 15. Head of Asklepios r. Ɍ. AMO. Bee. *B.M.C.—* .. .. *fair* 25/-

1349 **Aegiale.** 3rd Cent. B.C. Æ 15. Head of Athena r. Ɍ. ΑΙΓΙ. Owl standing r. *B.M.C.* 4 .. .. F 45/-

1350 **Arcesine.** 3rd Cent. B.C. Æ 14. Head of Athena. Ɍ. ΑΡΚΕ. Amphora. *B.M.C.—* R, *fair* 35/-

1351 **Minoa.** 3rd Cent. B.C. Æ 16. Head of Dionysos. Ɍ. ΜΙΝΩ. Kantharos. *B.M.C.—* R, *fair* 35/-

1352 **ANAPHE.** 3rd Cent. B.C. Æ 17. Full-face head of Apollo laur., slightly inclined to r. Ɍ. ANA. Two-handled vase; above, bee flying r. *B.M.C.* 2 R, *fair* 40/-

1353 **ANDROS.** 6th Cent. B.C. Æ *obol.* Amphora. ℞. Incuse square with irregular divisions. *Bab.* 1873 .. .. F £10

1354 *After* 300 B.C. Æ 17. Head of young Dionysos r. ℞. ANΔPI. Amphora. *B.M.C.* 3 F 45/-

1355 Imperial Times. Æ 23. *Obv.* Similar to preceding. ℞. ANΔPI. Apollo standing l., wearing long chiton, holding lyre. *B.M.C.* 23 .. .. .. F/*fair* 50/-

1356 **CEOS in genere.** 2nd-1st Cent. B.C. Æ 18. Head of Aristaeus, laur., r. ℞. KEI. Forepart of dog surrounded by rays (representing the dog-star Sirius). *B.M.C.* 8 F 50/-

1357 **Carthaea.** 2nd-1st Cent. B.C. Æ 20. Head of Apollo, laur., r. ℞. KAPΘA. Type as last. *B.M.C.* 40 .. .. *fair* 30/-

1358 Æ 18. Head of young Dionysos r. ℞. KAPΘA. Bunch of grapes; to l., eight-rayed star. *B.M.C.* 42 .. .. F 50/-

1359 **Coressia.** 3rd Cent. B.C. Æ 21. Laur. head of Apollo. ℞. KOPH. Bee. *B.M.C.* 66 .. .. *R, fair* 35/-

1360 **Iulis.** 6th Cent. B.C. Æ *hemidrachm.* Bunch of grapes. ℞. Quadripartite incuse square. *Bab.* 1888 .. .. *R, VF* £25

1361 3rd Cent. B.C. Æ 16. Laur. head of Apollo r. ℞. IOY. Bee. *B.M.C.* 67 F 45/-

1362 **CIMOLOS.** 3rd Cent. B.C. Æ 18. Head of Athena. ℞. KIMΩΛI. Trident. *B.M.C.* — .. .. *RR, fair* 45/-

1363 **CYTHNOS.** 2nd Cent. B.C. Æ 17. Laur. head of Apollo r. ℞. KYΘN. Lyre. *B.M.C.* 3 .. .. *R, fair* 35/-

1363   1365

1364 **DELOS.** 6th Cent. B.C. Æ *tritemorion.* Lyre. ℞. ΔHLI retrograde between spokes of wheel. *Bab.* 1936 .. .. *RR, F* £17

1365 200-87 B.C. Æ 15. Head of Apollo, laur., l. ℞. ΔH. Lyre. *B.M.C.* 4 VF 65/-

1366 Æ 10. Type as preceding. *B.M.C.* 6 .. .. F 30/-

1367 **GYAROS.** 1st Cent. B.C. or A.D. Æ 13. Head of Artemis with quiver. ℞. ΓYAPIΩN. Quiver with strap. *B.M.C.* 1 .. .. *R, fair* 45/-

1368 **IOS.** 2nd Cent. B.C. Æ 15. OMHPOY. Head of Homer r. ℞. IHTΩN. Athena standing l. *B.M.C.* 9 .. .. F 50/-

1369 **MELOS.** 500-416 B.C. Æ *stater.* Pomegranate. ℞. Square divided into eight triangles, four in relief; on the others, MAΛI. *Bab.* 1354 .. .. *RR, F* £100

1370 300-200 B.C. Æ 21. Pomegranate. ℞. MA. Beardless male head, helmeted, r. *B.M.C.* 26 .. .. F 50/-

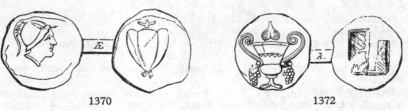

1370   1372

1371 **MYCONOS.** 3rd-2nd Cent. B.C. Æ 14. Head of Dionysos, bearded, r. ℞. ΜΥΚΟ. Grain of corn and bunch of grapes *B.M.C.* 4 .. .. .. R, F 55/-

1372 **NAXOS.** 6th Cent. B.C. Æ *stater.* Kantharos wreathed with ivy-leaves, ivy-leaf above; bunch of grapes tied to each handle. ℞. Incuse square irregularly divided. *B.M.C.* 2. *Illustrated at foot of page before* .. .. R, F £60

1373 4th Cent. B.C. Æ 11. *Obv.* as 1371, but to l. ℞. ΝΑ. Kantharos. *B.M.C.* 8 F 35/-

1374 1st Cent. B.C. Æ 17. Head of Apollo, laur., r. ℞. Nike r., holding wreath and palm: in field, r., kantharos. *B.M.C.*— .. .. VF 90/-

1375 **PAROS.** *c.* 350 B.C. Æ *hemidrachm.* Goat walking r. ℞. ΠΑ. Ear of corn. *B.M.C.* 3 .. .. RR, fair £14

1376 Æ 10. Goat standing r. ℞. ΠΑΡΙ. Similar. *B.M.C.* 7 .. fair/F 30/-

1377 *After* 308 B.C. Æ *didrachm.* Head of Artemis (?) to r., hair bound with three bands of ribbon. ℞. ΑΝΑΞΙΚ/ΠΑΡΙ. Goat r. *B.M.C.* 11 .. .. RR, VF £175

1377A — Head of Demeter r., veiled. ℞. ΠΑΡΙ within ivy-wreath. *B.M.C.* 13 RR, F £75

1378 Æ 12. Similar, but without veil. ℞. ΠΑΡΙ. Ears of wheat. *B.M.C.* 24 F 45/-

1379 **PHOLEGANDROS.** 2nd-1st Cent. B.C. Æ 18. Young male head. ℞. ΦΟΛΕ. Rushing bull. *B.M.C.* 1 .. .. R, fair 40/-

1380 **SERIPHOS.** 2nd-1st Cent. B.C. Æ 16. Head of Perseus r. ℞. ΣΕΡΙ. Gorgon-head facing. *B.M.C.* 6 .. .. fair 25/-

1381 Æ 16. *Obv.* as preceding. ℞. [ϹΕΡΕΙΦΙⲰΝ]. Harpa l. *B.M.C.* 11 F/fair 35/-

1382 **SICINOS.** 3rd Cent. B.C. Æ 19. Young male head. ℞. ΣΙΚΙ. Grapes. *Hunter,* pl. xliv, 2 .. .. RR, F £5

1383 **SIPHNOS.** Early 5th Cent. B.C. Æ *stater.* Head of Apollo of archaic style r., hair rolled and bound with plain cord. ℞. ΦΙΖ. Eagle flying r.; above head, barley-corn. *B.M.C.* 4 .. .. RRR, fair/F £60

| 1383 | 1385A |

1384 **SYROS.** 3rd-1st Cent. B.C. Æ 16. Bearded head of Pan r., horned. ℞. [ΣΥΡΙ]. Goat walking l. *B.M.C.* 1 .. .. fair 40/-

1385 **TENOS.** 6th Cent. B.C. Æ *triobol.* Bunch of grapes formed of three pendants. ℞. Quartered incuse square. *Bab.* 1925 .. .. R, F £20

1385A 4th Cent. B.C. Æ *tetradrachm.* Laur. head of Zeus Ammon r. ℞. ΤΗ. Poseidon enthroned l., holding dolphin and trident. *B.M.C.* 1 .. RRR, F £250

1386 3rd-2nd Cent. B.C. Æ 19. Head of young Zeus Ammon r. ℞. ΤΗΝΙ. Bunch of grapes; to l., trident. *B.M.C.* 10 .. .. VF 85/-

1387 **THERA** (Santorin). 600-450 B.C. Æ *stater.* Two dolphins, one to r., the other to l. ℞. Incuse divided into eight triangular compartments, five of which are deeply depressed. *B.M.C.*—; *Bab.* 1964 .. .. RR, fair/F £50

1388 3rd-2nd Cent. B.C. Æ 14. Head of Apollo r. ℞. ΘΗ below bull butting l. *B.M.C.* 2 .. .. R, fair 37/6

ASIA MINOR, ETC.

BOSPORUS.

1389 Gorgippia (now Anapa). 1st Cent. B.C. Æ 22. Laur. head of Apollo r. ℞. ΓΟΡΓΙΠΠΕΩΝ.   Stag running r.; thyrsos behind.   *B.M.C.* 1 ..   .. *R, fair* 60/-

1390 Phanagoria. 1st Cent. B.C. Æ *triobol.* Head of Apollo r. ℞. ΦΑΝΑΓΟΡΙΤΩΝ. Filleted thyrsos.   *B.M.C.*—; *Zograf* 43, 10   ..   .. *R,* F £20

1391 Æ 24. Similar. ℞. ΦΑΝΑΓΟΡΙΤΩΝ. Tripod; behind it, thyrsos filleted. *B.M.C.* 7   ..   .. *fair* 45/-

1392 — as Agrippias Caesareia. *Augustus.* Æ 22. Veiled bust of Livia r. ℞. ΑΓΡΙΠΠΕΩΝ. Prow l. *B.M.C.* 1   ..   .. *fair* 75/-

1393 Sinde. 4th Cent. B.C. Æ *diobol.* Head of Herakles r. ℞. ΣΙΝΔΩΝ. Horse's head r., all within incuse square. *B.M.C.* 1 ..   .. *RR,* F £20

For Kings of Bosporus see under Pontus.

COLCHIS.

1394 **Colchis in genere.** 4th Cent. B.C. Æ *hemidrachm.* Head of archaistic style, r.
℞. Bull's head r. *B.M.C.* 1 .. .. F 85/–; VF £10

1395 **Dioscurias.** 2nd-1st Cent. B.C. Æ 16. The caps of the Dioskuri, surmounted by
stars. ℞. ΔΙΟΣΚΟΥΡΙΑΔΟΣ. Thyrsos. *B.M.C.* 1 .. .. .. R, *fair* 50/–

PONTUS.

1396 **Amasia.** 120-63 B.C. Æ 20. Head of young Ares r., wearing helmet. ℞. ΑΜΑΣΣΕΙΑΣ.
Sword in sheath with strap. *B.M.C.* 1 .. .. *scarce, nearly* F 50/–

1397 *Commodus.* Æ 32. Greek legend. His bust r. ℞. ΑΔΡΑΜΑΣΙΜΗΤΡ ΝΕΩΚΠΡΤΠΟΝΤ.
Tyche l. holding rudder and cornucopiae. *B.M.C.*—; *Waddington* 36 *good* F/F £7

1398 *Caracalla.* Æ 30. Greek legend. His laur. bust dr. r. ℞. ΑΔΡCΕΥΑΝΤΑΜΑCΙ
ΜΗΝΕ ΤΡ and in ex., ΕΤCΗ (=208=215 A.D.). Altar of two stages; to l., tree. *B.M.C.* 32
F £5

1399 **Amisus,** also known for a time as **Peiraeeus** (Eski Samsun). 4th Cent. B.C. Æ *drachm.*
Head of the Tyche of the city r., wearing turreted stephanos. ℞. ΠΕΙΡΑ. Owl facing
on shield, wings open; ΔΙΟΓ beneath. *B.M.C.* 7 .. .. .. VF/F £14

1400 300-250 B.C. Æ *hemidrachm.* Similar, but legend on *rev.* ΑΣΚΛΕΟΥΣ and A beneath wing.
B.M.C. 14 .. .. *nearly* VF £7

1401 2nd-1st Cent. B.C. Æ 28. Head of Athena, helmeted, r. ℞. ΑΜΙΣΟΥ. Perseus
standing facing, holding harpa and the head of Medusa, whose decapitated body lies at
his feet: to l. and r., monogram. *Cf. B.M.C.* 32 .. .. .. F/*fair* 45/–

1401A Æ 20. Laur. head of Zeus r. ℞. ΑΜΙΣΟΥ in ex. Eagle on thunderbolt l., looking
back: on l. mon. *B.M.C.* 27 .. .. *nearly* VF 65/–

1401B Æ 20. Type as 1396 but ΑΜΙΣΟΥ. *B.M.C.* 40 .. .. F 40/–

1402 Æ 20. Head of young Dionysos r. ℞. ΑΜΙΣΟΥ. *Cista mystica* and thyrsos. *B.M.C.*
51 .. .. F 40/–

1403 Æ 22. Head of Perseus, helmeted, r. ℞. ΑΜΙΣΟΥ. Pegasos l., drinking: in ex.,
monograms. *B.M.C.* 60 .. .. F 50/–

1404 Æ 20. Aegis with Gorgon's head in centre. ℞. ΑΜΙΣΟΥ. Nike r., holding filleted
palm-branch: to l. and r., monograms. *B.M.C.* 69-77 .. .. .. F 35/–

1401B   1407

1405 **Cabeira** (Niksar). 120-63 B.C. Æ 21. Type as last but legend ΚΑΒΗΡΩΝ. *B.M.C.* 4
nearly F 45/–

1405A — as **Neocaesareia.** *Severus Alexander.* Æ 31. Greek legend. Laur. bust dr. and
cuir. r. ℞. ΚΟΙΝΠΟΝΣΕΟΚΑΙCΑΡΙΑC. Two agonistic urns on table, one underneath; in
ex., ΕΤΡΟΑ (=170=233 A.D.) *B.M.C.*— .. .. .. *good* VF/VF £18

1405B **Cerasus** (Keresoun). *Elagabalus.* Æ 28. As last. ℞. ΚΕΡΑCΟΥΝΤΙΩΝ. Herakles
facing *B.M.C.* 1 .. .. RR, *fair* 60/–

1406 **Chabacta.** 120-63 B.C. Æ 21. Type as No. 1396, but ΧΑΒΑΚΤΩΝ. *B.M.C.* 1
F 60/–

1407 **Comana.** 120-63 B.C. Æ 26. Type as 1401, but ΚΟΜΑΝΩΝ. *B.M.C.* 1 F 65/–

1407A Æ 22. Type as No. 1404, but ΚΟΜΑΝΩΝ. *B.M.C.* 2 .. .. F 45/–

1408 **Gaziura** (Turkhal). 120-63 B.C. Æ 21. Type as No. 1396, but ΓΑΖΙΟΥΡΩΝ. *B.M.C.* 2
R, F 70/–

1408A **Laodiceia.** Æ 20. Type as 1404, but ΛΑΟΔΙΚΕΩΝ. *B.M.C.* 1 R, *fair* 32/6

1409 **Pharnaceia.** 2nd Cent. B.C. Æ 20. Laur. head of Zeus r. ℞. ΦΑΡΝΑΚΕΩΝ.
Humped bull r. *B.M.C.* 1 .. .. *fair* 30/–

1410 120-63 B.C. Æ 20. Similar. ℞. ΦΑΡΝΑΚΕΙΑΣ. Eagle on thunderbolt. *B.M.C.* 2
good F 60/–

1411 **Taulara.** 120-63 B.C. Æ 28. As last, but ΤΑΥΛΑΡΩΝ. *Grose* 7388 *R, fair* 45/–

1411A **Trapezus.** 4th Cent. B.C. Æ *drachm.* Bearded head l. ℞. ΤΡΑ. Bunch of grapes on table. *B.M.C.* 1 .. .. *RR*, VF £250

1411B **Zela** (Zilleh). Æ 30. *Septimius Severus.* Greek legend. Laur. hd. r. ℞. ΖΗΛΙΤ-ѠΤΟΥΠΟΝ. Flaming altar within tetrastyle temple of Anaitis: in ex., ЄΤΡΜΒ (=142= 205 A.D.) *B.M.C.* 2 .. .. *R, fair* 75/–

1412 **KINGS OF PONTUS AND BOSPORUS : Mithradates VI.** 120-63 B.C. Æ *tetradrachm.* Head of Mithradates, diademed and with flowing hair, r. ℞. ΒΑΣΙΛΕΩΣ ΜΙΘΡΑΔΑΤΟΥ ΕΥΠΑΤΟΡΟΣ. Pegasos l., drinking : to l., star and crescent; to r. ΘΣ (=209= 89/8 B.C.). *Waddington* 15. *Style similar to illustration* .. .. *R*, VF £100

1413 Æ 22. Radiate bust r. ℞. Crescent and star. *B.M.C.*—; *Zograf* 44, 20 *fair* 45/–

1414 Æ 16. Bust of Perseus ? r. ℞. Lion seated r., looking back. *B.M.C.*—; *Zog.*— *RR, fair*/F 55/–

1415 **Polemo II.** 38-65 A.D. Æ *drachm.* ΒΑΣΙΛΕѠΣ ΠΟΛΕΜѠΝΟΣ. His diad. head r. ℞. ΕΤΟΥΣ Κ (=20=57/8 B.C.). Head of Nero r. *B.M.C.* 7. **Plate V** .. *R*, F £15

1416 **KINGS OF THE CIMMERIAN BOSPORUS. Asander.** 47-16 B.C. Æ 20. Head of Nike r. ℞. ΑΡΧΟΝΤΟΣ ΑΣΑΝΔΡΟΥ. Prow l. *B.M.C.* 1 .. .. *fair* £6

1417 **Rhescuporis I.** 14-42 A.D. Æ 22. ΤΙΒΕΡΙΟΥ ΚΑΙΣΑΡΟΣ. Head of the Roman emperor Tiberius r. ℞. Head of Rhescuporis I r. *B.M.C.* 6 .. .. F/*fair* 75/–

1418 **Mithradates.** 42-46 A.D. Æ 21. ΒΑΣΙΛΕΩΣ ΜΙΘΡΑΔΑΤΟΥ. Head of king r. ℞. ΒΑΣΙΛΙΣΣΗΣ ΓΗΠΑΙΠΥΡΕѠΣ. Head of Queen Gepaepyris r. *B.M C.* 5 .. *fair* 75/–

1419 Æ 23. Similar. ℞. Bow in case, lion's skin on club, trident. *B.M.C.* *fair*/F 55/–

1420 **Gepaepyris,** wife of last. Æ 20. ΒΑΣΙΛΙΣΣΗΣ ΓΗΠΑΙΠΥΡΕѠΣ. Her bust r. ℞. Female bust draped r. *B.M.C.* 1 .. .. *fair* £5

1421 **Rhescuporis II.** 78-92 A.D. Æ 22. His bust r. ℞. Female bust r. wearing kalathos and veil. *B.M.C.* 2 .. .. *fair* 32/6

1422 Æ 28. Similar. ℞. Nike advancing l. *B.M.C.* 6 .. .. .. *fair* 37/6

1423 Æ 32. King enthroned r. ℞. Sarmatian arms. *B.M.C.*—; *Zog.* 46, 16 *fair* 75/–

1424 **Sauromates I.** 93/4-123/4 A.D. *N stater.* ΒΑΣΙΛΕ ѠΣ ΣΑΥΡΟΜΑΤΟΥ. His diad. bust dr. r. ℞. Laur. head of Hadrian r.; below, ΗΙΥ (=418=124 A.D.). **Plate V** *RR, good* VF/*nearly* EF £50

1425 Æ 26. Similar. ℞. ΜΗ in wreath. *B.M.C.* 18-21 .. .. .. F 50/–

1426 Æ 21. Chair with crown on it, sceptre, shield and spear. ℞. ΜΗ in wreath. *B.M.C.* 25 F 50/–

1427 **Cotys II.** 123/4-131/2 A.D. Æ 23. ΒΑΣΙΛΕ ѠΣ ΚΟΤΥΟΣ. Bust r. ℞. King on horseback galloping r. *B.M.C.* 3 .. .. *fair* 45/–

1428 Æ 23. Similar. ℞. ΜΗ in wreath. *B.M.C.* 6 .. .. *fair* 40/–

1429 **Rhoemetalces.** 131/2-153/4 A.D. Pale gold or electrum *stater.* ΒΑΣΙΛΕ ѠΣ ΡΟΙΜ-ΗΤΑΛΚΟΥ. His diad. bust dr. r. ℞. Laur. head of Antoninus Pius r.; below, ΖΜΥ (=447=150 A.D.). *B.M.C.* 4 .. .. VF £35

1430 Æ 26. Similar. ℞. ΜΗ within wreath. *B.M.C.* 8 .. .. .. *fair* 40/–

1431 **Eupator.** 154/5-170/1 A.D. Æ 24. Monogram within wreath. ℞. ΚΑΠΕ. Temple of five columns. *B.M.C.* 9 .. .. *fair* 40/–

1432 **Sauromates II.** 172 (or 174/5)-210/11 A.D. Electrum *stater.* ΒΑΣΙΛΕѠΣ ΣΑΥΡΟΜΑΤΟΥ. His diad. bust dr. r. ℞. Laur. head of Septimius Severus, below ΔϘΥ (=494=197 A.D.) .. .. F/VF £20

1433 — Another. Similar. ℞. Laur. head of Septimius Severus r. facing that of his son Caracalla laur. and dr. l.; below, Φ (=500=203 A.D.) and sceptre .. VF £32/10/–

1434 Æ 27. Similar. ℞. King on horseback l., B to r. below. *B.M.C.* 18 .. *fair* 40/-
1435 Æ 30. Similar, but head of Sept. Severus r. countermarked on *rev.* *B.M.C.* 20
                                                         nearly F 50/-
1436 Æ 29. Similar. ℞. Poseidon standing l. *B.M.C.*— .. ℞, F/*fair* 65/-
1437 **Rhescuporis III.** 212-229 A.D. Electrum *stater.* ΒΑCΙΛΕWC PHCΚΟΥΠΟΡΙΔΟC. His diad. bust dr. r.; to r. trident. ℞. Laur. bust of Severus Alexander dr. r.; below, ΒΚΦ (=522=225 A.D.) .. .. VF £20
1438 Æ 24. Bust r. ℞. Aphrodite seated l. holding patera. *B.M.C.* 15 .. *fair* 40/-
1439 **Sauromates III.** 230-233 A.D. Æ 26. Bust r. ℞. As last *B M.C.*— *fair* 45/-
1440 **Ininthimeus.** 235-239 A.D. Billon *stater.* Diad. and dr. bust of king r. ℞. Laur. hd. of Gordian III r., club before; below, ΕΛΦ (=535=238 A.D.). *B.M.C.* 2. **Plate V**
                                                 good VF £15
1441 Æ 22. His bust r. facing bust of Aphrodite l. ℞. Aphrodite enthroned. *B.M.C.* 5
                                                 F 85/-
1442 **Rhescuporis V.** 240-276 A.D. Æ *stater.* Bust r. ℞. Busts of Valerian and Gallienus face to face; date, ΗΝΦ (=558=261 A.D.) .. .. *fair* 32/6
1443 Æ 20. ΒΑCΙΛΕWC PHCΚΟΥΠΟΡΙΔΟC. Diad. bust dr. r.; to r., trident. ℞. As No. 1438. *B.M.C.* 10 .. .. *fair* 32/6
1444 **Thothorses.** 279-309 A.D. Æ *stater.* ΒΑCΙΛΕWC ΘΟΘΟΡCΟΥ. His bust r. ℞. Bust of emperor r., ΔqΦ (=594=297 A.D.) below. *B.M.C.* 6 .. .. *fair* 40/-
1445 **Rhescuporis VI.** 304-342 A.D. Æ *stater.* His bust r., trident in front. ℞. Bust of emperor r., ΒΚΧ (=622=325 A.D.) below. *B.M.C.*— .. F/*good* F 47/6
To save space we have not given the legends in many cases in the foregoing pieces.

PAPHLAGONIA.

1445A **Abonuteichus**, later **Ionopolis** (Ineboli). *Antoninus.* Æ 28. Greek legend. Bare hd. r. ℞. ΑΒWΝΟΤΕΙΧΕΙΤWΝ ΓΛΥΚWΝ. The serpent Glycon. *B.M.C.* 1 ℞, *fair* 60/-
1445B **Geta.** Æ 17. Similar. ℞. ΙWΝΟΠΟΛΕΙΤW. Asklepios r. *B.M.C.* 2 ℞, *fair* 40/-
1446 **Amastris** (Amasra). *c.* 300 B.C. Æ *stater.* Young male head r. in laur. Phrygian cap, the flap of which is decorated with a large eight-rayed star. ℞. ΑΜΑCΤΡΙΕΩΝ. Tyche of the city seated l., holding sceptre and Nike; to l., large flower. *B.M.C.* 2 EF £75
1447 120-63 B.C. Æ 22. Aegis with Gorgonion in centre. ℞. ΑΜΑCΤΡΕΩΝ. Nike advancing r., two mon. *B.M.C.* 9 .. .. F 37/6

1446   1447A

1447A Time of *Antoninus Pius.* Æ 20. ΟΜΗΡΟC. Bust of Homer r. ℞. ΑΜΑCΤΡΙC. Bust of city, resembling Faustina I, turreted and veiled. *B.M.C.* 17 .. .. F 65/-
1448 *Lucius Verus.* Æ 26. Greek legends. His head r. ℞. ΑΜΑCΤΡΙΑΝWΝ. Galley l. *B.M.C.* 32 .. .. F 85/-
1449 **Cromna.** 4th Cent. B.C. Æ *drachm.* Head of Zeus, laur., l. ℞. ΚΡWΜΝΑ. Female bust (? Hera or Tyche of the city) l., wearing turreted and ornamented stephanos: to l., monogram: to r., rose. *Cf. B.M.C.* 1 .. .. .. VF £20; EF £50
1450 **Germanicopolis** including the fortress of **Gangra** (Changra). *Septimius Severus.* Æ 27. ΑΚΑΙΛCΕ . CΕΟΥΗΡΟCΑ. His head r. ℞. ΓΕΡΜΑΝΙΚΟΠΟΛΕΩC. Winged Nemesis l. holding staff and bridle; wheel at her feet. *B.M.C.* 3 .. .. F £5
1451 **Pimolisa.** 121-63 B.C. Æ 20. Helmeted head of Ares r. ℞. ΠΙΜWΛΙCΕWΝ. Sword in sheath with strap. *B.M.C.* (Pontus) 1 .. .. ℞, *fair*/F 50/-
1452 **Pompeiopolis** (Tashkopri). 2nd or 1st Cent. B.C. Æ 20. Head of Zeus. ℞. ΠΟΜΠΗΙΟΠΟΛΙΤWΝ. Torch in wreath. *Waddington* 1 .. .. .. ℞, *fair* 50/-
1453 **Sebaste.** *M. Aurelius* and *L. Verus.* Æ 22. ΑΥΤΟΚΡΑΤΟΡWΝ CΕΒΑCΤWΝ. Their busts face to face. ℞. CΕΒΑCΤΗC ΜΗΤΡΟΠΟΠΑ ΦΛ. Winged Nike walking l. *Grose* 7416 .. .. F £7
1453A **Sesamus.** 340-300 B.C. Æ 15. Laur. head of Zeus l. ℞. CΗCΑ. Female head l. *B.M.C.* 1 .. .. ℞, *fair* 50/-

1454 **Sinope.** 500-443 B.C. Æ *drachm.* Head of eagle l., dolphin below. ℞. Quadripartite incuse square, alternate quarters deeper. *Cf. B.M.C.* 4. **Plate V** VF £45

1455 443-375 B.C. Æ *drachm.* Head of Sinope, the daughter of Asopus, l., wearing sphendone. ℞. ΣΙΝΩ. Sea-eagle on dolphin. *B.M.C.* 7 .. .. .. F £9

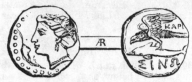

1456 375-350 B.C. Æ *drachm.* Similar, but with aplustre to l. ℞. Similar, with magistrate's name in field to r. *B.M.C.* 11-20 .. .. VF £21

1457 306-290 B.C. Æ *hemidrachm.* Head of Sinope l. wearing turreted crown. ℞. ΣΙΝΩ above prow l. on which star of seven rays; to l., mon. and aplustre. *B.M.C.* 26-29
VF £12

1458 290-250 B.C. Æ *didrachm.* Turreted head of Sinope l.; to r., large circular countermark containing radiate facing head of Helios with ΣΙΝΩΠΕΩΝ between the rays. ℞. ΣΙΝΩ. Poseidon seated l., holding dolphin and trident; countermark, head of Zeus l. *B.M.C.* 34 .. .. *good* F £45

1459 120-60 B.C. Æ 20. Head of Zeus, laur., r. ℞. ΣΙΝΩΠΗΣ. Eagle l. on thunderbolt, head r.: to l., monogram. *B.M.C.* 38 .. .. F 45/-

1460 Æ 21. Aegis with Gorgon's head in centre. ℞. ΣΙΝΩΠΗΣ. Nike r., holding palm: in field, r., monogram. *B.M.C.* 48 .. .. F 45/-

1461 *Augustus.* Æ 23. C.I.F.S. ANXXXVI (=9 B.C.). His bare head r. ℞. EX DD. Jugate heads of Cauis and Lucius r. *B.M.C.* 2 .. .. *fair* 42/-

1462 **KINGS OF PAPHLAGONIA.** **Pylaemenes II** or **III.** *c.* 120 B.C. Æ 23. Head of young Herakles r. ℞. ΒΑΣΙΛΕΩΣ ΠΥΛΑΙΜΕΝΟΥ ΕΥΕΡΓΕΤΟΥ. Nike advancing l. *B.M.C.* 1 .. .. R, F £6

1463 **Deiotarus Philadelphus** and **Deiotarus Philopator.** 31-5 B.C. Æ 24. ΒΑΣΙΛΕΩΣ ΔΗΙΟΤΑΡΟΥ ΦΙΛΑΔΕΛΦΟΥ. His head r. ℞. ΒΑΣΙΛΕΩΣ ΑΗΙΟΤΑΡΟΥ ΦΙΛΟΠΑΤΟΡΟΣ. Caps of the Dioscuri. *Waddington* 5 .. .. *RR, fair* £6

BITHYNIA.

1464 **Koinon of Bithynia.** *Hadrian.* Æ 33. ΑΥΤ . ΚΑΙC . ΤΡΑΙ . ΑΔΡΙΑΝΟC CEB. His laur. head r. ℞. ΚΟΙΝΟΝ ΒΕΙΘΥΝΙΑC. Octastyle temple with Corinthian columns in which male figure sacrifices at altar. *B.M.C.* 12 *good* F/*nearly* VF £15

1465 **Apameia** (*before* 202 B.C., called **Myrlea,** and in Imperial Times, Colonia Julia Concordia Apamea Augusta). *Before* 202 B.C. Æ 14. Head of Demeter r. ℞. ΜΥΡΛΕΑ. Lyre. *B.M.C.* 12 .. .. *fair* 27/6

1466 *After* 203 B.C. Æ 23. ΑΠΑΜΕΩΝ. Head of Apollo r. ℞. ΤΩΝ ΜΥΡΛΕΑΝΩΝ. Lyre; beneath, CΛΣ (=236=47 B.C.). *B.M.C.* 17 .. .. F 52/6

1467 *Commodus.* Æ 20. IMP . CAES . COMMO . ANTONI . PF . AVG. His laur. bust r. ℞. C . I . C . A . D . D. Dried tunny fish r. *B.M.C.* 30 .. .. F 65/-

1467A *Valerian I.* Æ 24. His rad. bust r. ℞. COL. IVL. CONC. AVG. APAM. Dionysos standing l. holding kantharos and pole, round which is entwined a grape-vine. *B.M.C.* 42
F 75/-

1467A   1469A

1467B **Bithynium** or **Claudiopolis** (Eski-hissar, near Boli). *Julia Domna.* Æ 20. Her bust r. ℞. ΒΕΙΘΑΔΡΙΑΝΩΝ. Hermes standing l., holding purse and caduceus. *B.M.C.* 7 .. .. *fair*/F 65/-

1467c **Caesareia Germanica.** *Macrinus.* Æ 27. Greek legend. Laur. bust dr. r. ℞. ΚΑΙCΑΡƐΙΑC ΓΕΡΜΑΝΙΚΗC. Tyche stg. l. *B.M.C.* 4 .. .. .. *R, fair* 85/–

1468 **Calchedon** (Kadikeui). 411-394 B.C. Æ *hemidrachm.* ΚΑΛΧ. Bull standing l. on ear of corn. ℞. Incuse square of "mill-sail" pattern. *B.M.C.* 9 .. .. VF £7

1469 *After* 394 B.C. Æ *drachm.* Similar, but with caduceus to l. ℞. Incuse square, quartered, the surface granulated. *B.M.C.* 14 .. .. .. F £5

1469A *After* 280 B.C. Æ *octobol.* Head of Demeter r. ℞. ΚΑΛΧ in ex. Apollo seated r. on omphalos ; behind, Ε. *B.M.C.* 20. *Illustrated on page* 118 .. *RR, good* F £45

1470 *Tranquillina.* Æ 25. Greek legend. Her dr. bust r. ℞. ΚΑΛΧΑΔΟΝΙΩΝ. Apollo r., reclining on swan swimming l. *B.M.C.* 35 .. .. .. *fair* £5

1471 **Cius** (Gemlik). 321-300 B.C. Æ *hemidrachm.* ΚΙΑ. Head of Apollo laur. r. ℞. Prow of vessel l. and magistrate's name. *B.M.C.* 8 .. .. .. *nearly* VF/F £15

1472 2nd Cent. A.D. Æ 24. ΤΟΝ ΚΤΙCΤΗΝ. Head of young Herakles r. ℞. ΚΙΑΝΩΝ. Galley l. *B.M.C.* 33 .. .. VF/F 65/–

1472A **Creteia-Flaviopolis.** *Julia Domna.* Æ 26. Her bust r. ℞. ΚΡΗ/ΤΙΕΩΝ/ ΦΛΑΟΥΙΟ/ΠΟΛΕΙ/ΤΟΝ in wreath. *B.M.C.* 2 .. ..*R,* F £10

1473 **Dia.** 120-60 B.C. Æ 20. Head of Zeus, laur., r. ℞. ΔΙΑΣ. Eagle l., head r., on thunderbolt: to l. and r., monograms. *B.M.C.*— .. .. *R,* VF £6

1471   1474A

1474 **Heraclea Pontica** (Eregli). 394-352 B.C. Æ *trihemiobol.* Head of bearded Herakles l. ℞. ΗΡΑΚΛΕΙΑ. Club. *B.M.C.* 7 .. .. .. VF/*good* F £15

1474A Time of the tyrant Satyrus, 352-345 B.C. Æ *stater.* Head of young Herakles l. in lion's skin; below, club. ℞. ΗΡΑΚΛΕΙΑ. Turreted head of the City-goddess l. *B.M.C.* 16 .. .. *R, nearly* VF £60

1475 *Dionysius.* 337-305 B.C. Æ *stater.* Head of young Dionysos l., wearing wreath of ivy: behind head, thyrsos. ℞. ΔΙΟΝΥΣΙΟΥ. Herakles, standing l., attaching spear to trophy. *B.M.C.* 25 .. .. *RR,* VF/F £70

1476 Time of Lysimachus. 302-281 B.C. Æ *stater.* Head of young Herakles r. ℞. ΗΡΑΚΛΕΩΤΑΝ. Dionysos seated l. *B.M.C.* 30 .. .. VF £30; EF/VF £50

1477 3rd Cent. B.C. Æ 17. Similar, but *rev.* type, lion running r. *B.M.C.* 34 F 21/–

1478 *Geta.* Æ 22. Greek legend. His dr. bust r. ℞. ΗΡΑΚΛΗΑC ΕΝΠΟΝΤΩ. Asklepios standing l. *B.M.C.* 50 .. .. F £6

1475   1480A

1479 **Juliopolis.** *Gallienus.* Æ 16. Greek legend. His dr. bust r. ℞. ΙΟΥΛΙΟΠΟ ΛΕΙΤ. Legionary eagle between two standards. *Grose* 7479 .. .. .. F 52/6

1480 **Nicaea** (Isnik). *C. Papirius Carbo.* 62-59 B.C. Æ 23. ΝΙΚΑΙΕΩΝ. Head of young Dionysos r. ℞. ΕΠΙ ΓΑΙΟΥ ΠΑΠΙΡΙΟΥ ΚΑΡΒΩΝΟΣ. Roma seated l.: in ex., ΡΩΜΗ. *B.M.C.* 2 *fair* 32/6

1480A *C. Vibius Pansa.* 48-47 B.C. Æ 23. ΝΙΚΑΙΕΩΝ. Bare head of Julius Caesar r. ℞. ΕΠΙ ΓΑΙΟΥ ΟΥΙΒΙΟΥ ΠΑΝΣΑ. Nike standing r.: beneath, CΛΣ (=236=47 B.C.). *B.M.C.* 9 *R,* F £15

1481 **Nicaea.** *Caracalla.* Æ 22. Greek legend. His dr. bust r. Ŗ. ΝΙΚΑΙΕΩΝ. Tyche standing l. *B.M.C.* 78 .. .. F/*fair* 67/6

1482 *Severus Alexander.* Æ 28. Μ ΑVΡ CΕVΗ ΑΛΕΞΑΝΔΡΟC Laur bust r. Ŗ. ΝΙΚΑΙΕΩΝ. Asklepios reclining l., head r., on back of winged serpent r., and holding serpent-staff. *Not in B.M.C.* .. .. *green-brown patina,* VF £25

1483 *Gordian III.* Æ 19. Radiate bust of emperor r. Ŗ. ΝΙΚΑΙΕΩΝ. Four standards. *B.M.C.* 119 .. .. F 52/6

1484 *Valerian.* Æ 20. Laur. bust of emperor r. Ŗ. ΙΠΠΑΡΧ ΝΙΚΑΙΕΩΝ. Hipparchus the astronomer seated l.; before him, globe on pedestal. *B.M.C.*—; *Von Aulock* 717 R, F £5

1485 **Nicomedia** (Izmid). *C. Papirius Carbo.* 60-59 B.C. Æ 24. ΝΙΚΟΜΗΔΕΩΝ. Head of Zeus, laur., r. Ŗ. ΕΠΙ ΓΑΙΟV ΠΑΠΙΡΙΟV ΚΑΡΒΩΝΟΣ. Roma seated l. on pile of shields, holding Nike and spear. *B.M.C.* 1 .. .. F 75/-

1485A *Severus.* Æ 35. His rad. head r. Ŗ. ΝΙΚΟΜΗΔΕΩΝ ΔΙCΝΕΩΚΟΩΝ. Hades or Sarapis seated on throne l.; before him Kerberos. *B.M.C.* 38 .. .. F £15

1486 *Caracalla.* Æ 27. Greek legend. His bust r. Ŗ. ΝΙΚΟΜΗΔΕΩΝ ΔΙCΝΕΩΚΟΡΩΝ. Octastyle temple. *B.M.C.* 51 .. .. F 85/-

1487 **Prusa ad Olympum** (Brûsa). *Trajan.* Æ 27. Greek legend. His bust r. Ŗ. ΠΡΟVC-ΑΕΩΝ. Athena l. *B.M.C.* 3 .. .. F £5

1487A **Prusias ad Hypium** (Uskub). *M. Aurelius.* Æ 27. His bare-headed bust dr. and cuir. r. Ŗ. ΠΡΟVCΙΕΩΝ VΠΙΟC. River-god Hypius reclining l. holding branch and cornucopiae. *B.M.C.* 2 .. .. *fair* 50/-

1487B **Tium** (Filyas). *Antoninus.* Æ 18. His laur. head r. Ŗ. ΤΙΑΝΩΝ. Cista mystica. *B.M.C.* 7 .. .. F 45/-

1488 **KINGS OF BITHYNIA. Prusias I.** 238-183 B.C. Ŗ *tetradrachm.* His diad. head l., bearded. Ŗ. ΒΑΣΙΛΕΩΣ ΠΡΟVΣΙΟV. Zeus standing l.; two mon. *B.M.C.* 1 VF £60

1489 Æ 30. Laur. head of Apollo l. Ŗ. Similar legend. Winged figure of Athena standing l. *B.M.C.* 3 .. .. VF 80/-

1490 Æ 19. Similar, but r. Ŗ. Similar legend. Lyre. *B.M.C.* 8 .. *good* F 42/-

1491 Æ 18. As last but *rev.* type, quiver and bow. *B.M.C.* 9 .. .. F 30/-

1492 **Prusias II.** 183-149 B.C. Ŗ *tetradrachm.* As No. 1488, but head of Prusias II, unbearded or only faint beard, with diad. winged, and on *rev.* eagle on thunderbolt in field and only one mon. *B.M.C.* 1 .. .. VF £50

1493 Æ 16. Head of king r. Ŗ. ΒΑΣΙΛΕΩΣ ΠΡΟVΣΙΟV. Herakles l., holding club and lion-skin. *B.M.C.* 3 .. .. F 25/-

1494 Æ 22. Head of young Dionysos r., wreathed with ivy. Ŗ. Similar legend. The centaur Cheiron r., playing lyre. *B.M.C.* 10 .. .. F 35/-

1495 **Nicomedes II.** 149-120 (?) B.C. Æ *tetradrachm.* His diad. head r. ℞. ΒΑΣΙΛΕΩΣ ΕΠΙΦΑΝΟΥΣ ΝΙΚΟΜΗΔΟΥ. Zeus standing l.; in field, eagle on thunderbolt, mon. and date CΞΡ (=166=131 B.C.). *B.M.C.* 3 .. .. VF £27/10/-

1496   1497

1496 **Nicomedes III.** 120-92 (?) B.C. Æ *tetradrachm.* As before but for date ΠΡ. (=180=117 B.C.). *B.M.C.* 15 .. .. VF £27/10/-

1497 **Nicomedes IV.** 92 (?)-74 B.C. Æ *tetradrachm.* As before but for date ΓΣ. (=206= 91 B.C.). *B.M.C.* 2 .. .. VF £27/10/-

MYSIA.

1498 **Adramyteum.** 133-67 B.C. Æ *cistophorus.* Serpent issuing from *cista mystica*; all within wreath. ℞. Two serpents over quiver; on l., ΑΔΡ in mon.; above mon.; on r., eagle. *B.M.C.* 5 .. .. R, F £12

1499 Æ 20. Laur. head of Apollo l. ℞. ΑΔΡΑΜΥΤΗΝΩΝ. Cornucopiae between pilei; mon. below. *B.M.C.* 7 .. .. *fair* 35/-

1500 **Apollonia ad Rhyndacum** (Abulliont). 1st Cent. B.C. Æ 13. Head of Artemis. ℞. ΑΠΟΛΛΩΝΙΑΤΩΝ ΡΥΝΔΑ. Torch. *B.M.C.*— .. .. *fair* 30/-
N.B.—The *drachms* and *hemidrachms*, etc. given by the *B.M.C. Mysia* to this town are now attributed to Apollonia Pontica in Thracia, see nos. 672-3.

1501 **Atarneus** (Kaleh-Agili). 3rd Cent. B.C. Æ 12. Laur. head of Apollo r. ℞. ΑΤΑΡ. Forepart of horse r. *B.M.C.* 4 .. .. *fair* 30/-

1502 **Attaea.** *Septimius Severus.* Æ 24. Greek legend. His laur. head r. ℞. ΑΤΤΑΙΤΩΝ Asklepios standing facing, head l. *B.M.C.* 11 .. .. R, F 80/-

1502A **Came.** *Sept. Severus.* Æ 18. Greek legend. His laur. hd. r. ℞. ΚΑΜΗΝΩΝ Asklepios stg. l. *B.M.C.* (Aeolis) 4 .. .. R, *fair* 40/-

1502B **Cisthene.** 2nd Cent. B.C. Æ 27. Head of Demeter r., veiled and wreathed with corn. ℞. ΚΙΣ. Horseman r. ; beneath, dolphin r. *B.M.C.* 1 .. R, *fair* 40/-

1503 **Cyzicus.** 480-400 B.C. Electrum *stater.* Horseman r. on tunny. ℞. Incuse square of mill-sail pattern. *cf. Bab.*, pl. 175, 15. **Plate V** .. .. .. RR, VF £400

1504 Electrum *sixth.* Dog standing l. on tunny. ℞. Similar. *B.M.C.* 91 VF £50

1505 Æ *trihemiobol.* Forepart of boar l. ℞. Head of lion l. in incuse square. *B.M.C.* 108
good F £6

1506 4th Cent. B.C. Æ *tetradrachm.* ΣΩΤΕΙΡΑ. Head of Kore Soteira l. wearing corn-wreath and veil wound around head. ℞. ΚΥΙΙ. Lion's head l.; beneath, tunny l.; on r., bee. *B.M.C.* 128 *var.* .. .. RR, VF/EF £150

1506A Æ *drachm.* As before but Σ on r. *B.M.C.* 131. **Plate V** R, VF/*good* F £20

Mysia
1 Adramyteum
2 Apollonia ad
    Rhyndacum
3 Atarneus
4 Attaea
6 Cisthene
7 Cyzicus
8 Gambrium
10 Hadriani ad Olympum
13 Lampsacus
14 Miletopolis
15 Parium
16 Pergamum
17 Perperene
18 Pitane
19 Placia
20 Poemanenon
21 Priapus
22 Proconnesus

Troas
23 Abydus
24 Alexandria Troas
25 Antandrus
26 Assus
28 Cebren
29 Colone
30 Dardanus
31 Gargara
33 Gergis
34 Hamaxitus
35 Ilium
36 Lamponeia
37 Neandria
38 Ophrynium
39 Scamandria
40 Scepsis
41 Sigeium
42 Thymbra
43 Zeleia
Is. off Troas
44 Tenedos

Aeolis
45 Aegae
47 Cyme
48 Elaea
49 Grynium
50 Larissa Phriconis
51 Myrina
52 Temnus

Lesbos
53 Antissa
54 Eresus
55 Methymna

56 Mytilene
57 Pyrrha
Is. near Lesbos
58 Nesos
59 Pordosilene
Ionia
60 Clazomenae
61 Colophon
62 Ephesus
63 Erythrae
64 Heraclea ad Latmum
65 Larissa
66 Lebedus
67 Leuce
68 Magnesia ad
    Maeandrum
69 Metropolis
70 Miletus
71 Naulochus
72 Phocaea
73 Phygela
74 Priene
75 Smyrna
76 Teos
Is. of Ionia
77 Chios
78 Oenoe, *Icaria*
79 Samos
Caria
81 Alabanda
82 Alinda
83 Amyzon
84 Antiocheia ad
    Maeandrum
85 Aphrodisias
86 Apollonia Salbace
87 Astyra
88 Attuda
89 Bargasa?
90 Bargylia
91 Caunus
92 Ceramus
93 Cidramus
94 Cnidus
95 Euromus
96 Halicarnassus
97 Harpasa
98 Heraclea Salbace
99 Hydisus?
100 Hyllarima?
101 Iasus
102 Idyma
103 Mylasa
104 Myndus
105 Neapolis ad Harpasum

106 Orthosia
107 Plarasa
108 Sebastopolis
109 Stratoniceia
110 Tabae
111 Trapezopolis
Islands off Caria
112 Astypalaea
113 Calymna
114 Posidium, *Carpathos*
115 Cos
117 Nisyros
118 Camirus, *Rhodes*
119 Ialysus, *Rhodes*
120 Lindus, *Rhodes*
121 Rhodus, *Rhodes*
122 Telos

Lydia
123 Acrasus?
124 Aninetus
125 Apollonis
126 Apollonos-hieron
127 Attalea
128 Bagis?
129 Blaundus
130 Briula
132 Clannudda
133 Daldis
134 Dioshieron
135 Germe ad Caïcum
136 Gordus-Julia
137 Hermocapelia
138 Hieracome, later
    Hierocaesareia
139 Hypaepa
140 Hyrcanis
141 Maeonia
142 Magnesia ad Sipylum
143 Mastaura
144 Mostene
145 Nacrasa
146 Nysa
147 Philadelphia
148 Saïtta
149 Sala
150 Sardes
151 Silandus
152 Stratoniceia-
    Hadrianopolis
153 Tabala
154 Thyatira
155 Tmolus Aureliopolis
156 Tomaris
157 Tralles
158 Tripolis

MYSIA—*continued*.

1507 **Cyzicus.** 3rd Cent. B.C. Æ 17. Head of Kore Soteira r. ℞. KYZI. Tripod between caduceus and monogram. *B.M.C.* 143 *var*...   ..   ..   ..   F 53/-

1508 Æ 20. *Obv.* Similar to preceding. ℞. KYZI and monogram, all within wreath. *B.M.C.* 150   ..   ..   F 35/-

1509 1st Cent. B.C. Æ 28. Laur. head of Apollo r. ℞. KYZIKHNΩN. Tripod, two monograms and lighted torch. *B.M.C.* 165 ..   ..   ..   *good* F/VF 85/-

1510 Imperial Times: 98-211 A.D. Æ 29. KVZIKOC. Head of the founder Cyzicus r. ℞. KVZIKHNΩN NEOKOPΩN. Two flaming torches entwined by serpents: between them, small altar. *B.M.C.* 185 ..   ..   F/VF 75/-

1511 **Cyzicus.** 253-270 A.D. Æ 23. *Obv.* as preceding. ℞. CTPA BACIΛEΩC KVZIKHNΩN
NEOKOP. Type as preceding. *B.M.C.* 205 .. .. F 45/-

1512 *Commodus.* Æ 27. Greek legend. His laur. head r. ℞. KVI / IKHN / ΩNN / EΩ within
laurel wreath. *B.M.C.* 230 .. .. F 75/-

1513 **Gambrium.** 3rd Cent. B.C. Æ 16. Laur. head of Apollo r. ℞. ΓAM. Star.
B.M.C. 11 .. .. F 40/-

1514 **Hadrianeia.** *Septimius Severus.* Æ 18. Greek legend. His laur. head r. ℞.
AΔPIANEΩN. Asklepios moving r., head turned l. *Grose* 7622 .. .. *fair* 45/-

1515 **Hadriani ad Olympum.** *Plautilla.* Æ 22. Greek legend. Her dr. bust r. ℞.
AΔPIANΩN ΠPOC OΛY. Tyche standing l. *Grose* 7623.. .. .. .. F £7

1516 **Hadrianothera.** *Julia Domna.* Æ 27. Greek legend. Her bust r.; two countermarks. ℞. CTP . ΔIOΓENOVC AΔPIANOΘHPITΩN. Sept. Severus on horseback galloping
r. *B.M.C.* 6 .. .. F/*fair* £5

1516A **Iolla.** 4th Cent. B.C. Æ 15. Laur. head of Zeus r. ℞. IOΛΛA. Forepart of
winged horse r, ear of corn below. *B.M.C.* 2 .. .. R, F 60/-

1517 **Lampsacus** (Lapseki). 4th Cent. B.C. *N stater.* Laur. head of Zeus l., thunderbolt
behind. ℞. Forepart of winged horse r. *B.M.C.* 28 .. .. RR, VF £850

1517A Æ *triobol.* Janiform¹ female head. ℞. ΛAM. Head of Athena r. *Grose* 7631
nearly F 65/-

1518 Æ *trihemiobol.* Similar. *Grose* 7634 .. .. F 65/-

1519 4th-3rd Cent. B.C. Æ 15. ΛAM, as preceding. ℞. Forepart of Pegasos r. *B.M.C.*
50 .. .. F 27/6

1520

1525

1520 190-85 B.C. Æ *tetradrachm.* Head of Priapos, ivy-crowned and horned, r. ℞.
ΛAMΨAKHΩN. Apollo Kitharoedos standing r., holding lyre and plectrum; on l., mon. ;
on r., palm ; in ex., magistrate's name with patronomic. *B.M.C.* 68
RRR, good F £100

1520A Æ 20. As last. ℞. ΛAMΨA KHNΩN. Forepart of Pegasos r. *B.M.C.* 69 F 40/-

1521 Æ 20. Head of Apollo, laur., r. ℞. Legend as preceding: Athena standing l.,
holding Nike. *B.M.C.* 73 .. .. F/*fair* 27/6

1522 *Caracalla.* Æ 22. Greek legend. Laur. bust dr. r. ℞. ΛAMΨAKHNΩN. Homonoia
standing l. *B.M.C.* 87 .. .. *fair*/F 50/-

1523 **Miletopolis.** 2nd-1st Cent. B.C. Æ 19. Head of Athena r. ℞. MIΛHTOΠOΛITΩN.
Owl with double-body facing. *B.M.C.* 6 .. .. F 40/-

1524 **Parium.** 500-400 B.C. Æ *drachm.* Crude Gorgon-head. ℞. Incuse square
containing cruciform pattern. *B.M.C.* 1 .. .. R, F £12

1525 350-300 B.C. Æ *hemidrachm.* Gorgon-head. ℞. ΠAPI. Bull standing l., looking
back. *B.M.C.* 14 .. .. VF £5

1526 Imperial Times. Æ 11. C.G.I.P. Female head r. ℞. D.D. Ewer. *B.M.C.* 80
fair/F 20/-

1527 *Augustus.* Æ 20. AVG. His head r. ℞. Two colonists ploughing with yoke of
oxen. *B.M.C.* 86 .. .. F 45/-

1527A *Commodus.* Æ 24. His laur. bust dr. r. ℞. DEO AESC SVB above, C.G.I.H.P. in ex.
Asklepios seated r. with bull before him placing right fore-foot on his lap (to be
examined ?). *B.M.C.* 104 .. .. R, *fair* 60/-

1528 **Pergamum** (Bergama). 310-283 B.C. Æ *diobol*. Head of young Herakles, wearing lion-skin, r. ℞. ΠΕΡΓΑΜΗ. The Palladium, facing. *B.M.C.* 9 .. .. .. VF £6

1529 Æ 17. Head of Athena, helmeted, l. ℞. ΠΕΡΓΑ. Two bull's heads facing one another. *B.M.C.* 11 .. .. F 42/–

1530 Æ 10. Head of Athena, helmeted, r. ℞. Two stars. *B.M.C.* 24 .. *fair* 17/6

1531 Philetaerus, 284-263 B.C. Æ *tetradrachm*. Head of Seleucus I Nicator, divinized. ℞. ΦΙΛΕΤΑΙΡΟΥ. Athena seated l. with spear and shield; to r. bow; above r. arm, ivy leaf. *B.M.C.* 28 .. .. R, F £150

1532 281-197 B.C. Æ 14. Head of Athena, helmeted, r. ℞. ΦΙΛΕΤΑΙΡΟΥ. Bow. *B.M.C.* 54 .. .. F 30/–

1532A Eumenes I, 263-241 B.C. Æ *tetradrachm*. Diad. head of Philetaerus r. (also with diadem and laurel-wreath entwined). ℞. As last but ivy leaf below r. arm and A on throne. *B.M.C.* 30. *See illustration on page* 11 .. .. VF £75

1527A   1532B

1532B Attalus I. 241-197 B.C. Æ *tetradrachm*. As before but A below arm and ivy leaf or bunch of grapes on l. *B.M.C.* 35-7 .. .. VF £50

1532C Eumenes II, 197-159 B.C. Æ *tetradrachm*. As before but E M or other mon. below arm and various symbols on l. *B.M.C.* 39-46. **Plate VI** .. .. VF £50

1532D Attalus II. 159-138 B.C. Æ *tetradrachm*. Similar but different mon. and symbols, spread fabric. *B.M.C.* 48-53 .. .. VF £50

1533 133-67 B.C. Æ *cistophoric tetradrachm*. *Cista mystica* from which serpent issues l.: all within wreath of ivy. ℞. ΠΕΡ (in monogram). Bow-case between two coiled serpents: to r., snake-entwined thyrsos. *B.M.C.* 94-125. **Plate VI** .. VF £12

1534 Æ 16. Head of Asklepios, laur., r. ℞. ΑΣΚΛΗΠΙΟΥ ΣΩΤΗΡΟΣ. Snake-entwined staff of Asklepios. *B.M.C.* 155 .. .. F 27/6

1535 Æ 19. Similar. ℞. Legend as preceding: serpent coiled round omphalos. *B.M.C.* 158 .. .. F 25/–

1536 Æ 19. Helmeted head of Athena r. ℞. ΑΘΗΝΑΣ ΝΙΚΗΦΟΡΟΥ. Trophy. *B.M.C.* 180 .. .. F 25/–

1537 Æ 15. As before but *rev*. type, owl on palm-branch. *B.M.C.* 196 .. F 30/–

1538 Imperial Times. Æ 17. ΘΕΟΝ ϹΥΝΚΛΗΤΟΝ. Youthful bust of the Senate r. ℞. ΘΕΑΝ ΡΩΜΗΝ. Turreted bust of Roma r. *B.M.C.* 205 .. ..F 27/6; VF 60/–

1539 Æ 15. Bust of Asklepios l.: in front, serpent. ℞. ΠΕΡΓΑΜΗΝΩΝ. Serpent-staff. *Cf. B.M.C.* 233 .. .. *fair*/F 30/–

1540 *Tiberius and Livia*. Æ 20. ϹΕΒΑΣΤΟΙ ΕΠΙ ΠΕΤΡΩΝΙΟΥ ΤΟϹ. Bust of Livia r. facing bust of Tiberius l. ℞. ΘΕΟΝ ϹΕΒΑϹΤΟΝ ΠΕΡΓΑΜΗΝΟΙ. Tetrastyle temple containing statue of Augustus. *B.M.C.* 253 .. .. F/VF £8

1541 **Pergamum and Ephesus in alliance.** *Commodus*. Æ 42. ΑΥ . ΚΑΙ . Μ . ΑΥΡΗ . ΚΟΜΟΔΟϹ. His laur. bust dr. r. ℞. ΕΠΙϹΤΡΠΑΙΠΙΟΥ ΚΟΙΝΟΝ ΟΜΟΝΟΙΑ, Asklepios standing facing, head turned l., facing figure of the Ephesian Artemis; Nike flies down to crown each figure; in ex. ΠΕΡΓΑΜΗΝΩΝ ΚΑΙ ΕΦΕϹΙΩΝ. *B.M.C.* 354 RR, F £25

1542 **Perperene.** *Septimius Severus*. Æ 18. Greek legend. His laur. head r. ℞. ΠΕΡΠΕΡΗΝΙΩΝ. Asklepios standing l. *B.M.C.* 10 .. .. F 85/–

1543 **Pitane.** 4th Cent. B.C. Æ 11. Head of Zeus Ammon r. ℞. ΠΙΤΑΝ around pentagram. *B.M.C.* 9 .. .. F 50/–

1544 Imperial Times. Æ 12. ΑΜΜΩΝ. Head of Zeus Ammon r. ℞. ΠΙΤΑΝΑΙΩΝ. Round shield ornamented with pentagram. *B.M.C.* 17 .. .. *fair* 30/–

1545 **Placia.** 4th Cent. B.C. Æ 12. Female head, turreted, r. ℞. ΠΛΑΚΙΑ. Lion r., devouring prey: beneath, ear of corn. *B.M.C.* 5 .. .. F 45/–

1545A **Poemanenon.** 1st Cent. B.C. Æ 21. Laur. head of Zeus r. ℞. ΠΟΙΜΑΝΗΝΩΝ. Thunderbolt; beneath B I. *B.M.C.* 1 .. .. R, F 85/–

1546 **Priapus.** 3rd Cent. B.C. Æ 19. Laur. head of Apollo r. ℞. ΠΡΙΑΠΗΝΩΝ. Shrimp r., symbol below. *B.M.C.* 3-5 .. .. F 55/-

1547 1st Cent. B.C. Æ 15. Head of Dionysos r. ℞. ΠΡΙΑΠ and bunch of grapes. *B.M.C.* 10 .. .. *R, fair* 35/-

1548 Æ 18. Head of Demeter r. ℞. ΠΡΙΑΠΗΝΩΝ. Bull's head and monogram all within wreath. *B.M.C.* 15 .. .. *R, F* 60/-

1549 **Proconnesus.** 330-280 B.C. Æ 17. Female head r.: above, magistrate's name. ℞. ΠΡΟ. Oenochoe r. *B.M.C.* 4 .. .. *F/fair* 35/-

1550 Æ 10. Female head r. ℞. ΠΡΟΚΟΝ. Type as preceding. *B.M.C.* 5 *fair* 21/-

TROAS.

1551 **Abydus.** Late 4th Cent. B.C. Æ *hemidrachm.* Laur. head of Apollo r. ℞. ΑΒΥ. Eagle standing l., also magistrate's name and symbol. *B.M.C.* 12-24 VF/F £12

1552 *After* 196 B.C. Æ *tetradrachm.* Dr. bust of Artemis r. ℞. ΑΒΥΔΗΝΩΝ. Eagle standing r.; before, symbol; in ex., magistrate's name. *B.M.C.* 49-57 *R*, VF £90

1553 *Septimius Severus.* Æ 38. Greek legend: bust of Severus r. ℞. ΕΠΙ . ΑΡΧ . ΦΑΒΑ . ΠΡΟΚΛΟΥ ΑΒΥΔΗ. Leander amid waves swimming r. towards tower (the lighthouse of Sestus) in which stands Hero l., holding lighted lamp. *B.M.C.* 60 *RR, fair* £10

1552   1556A

1554 **Alexandria Troas** (Eski Stambul). 3rd-2nd Cent. B.C. Æ 12. Head of Apollo, laur., r. ℞. ΑΛΕ. Horse feeding r. *B.M.C.* 10 .. .. F 25/-

1555 Imperial Times. Æ 22. COL ALEX TRO. Turreted bust of Alexandria Troas r.: behind shoulder, vexillum. ℞. COL AVG TRO. Herdsman, holding pedum, standing l.: to l., statue of Apollo Smintheus: to r., bull r. *B.M.C.* 41 .. VF/F 65/-

1556 *Commodus.* Æ 25. IMP CAI M AVR COMMOD AVG. Bust, laur., r. ℞. COL AVG TROAD. Apollo standing l., r. foot on pedestal, holding branch. *Not in B.M.C.* .. F £5

1556A *Crispina.* Æ 25. Her bust r. ℞. COL AVG TROAD. Emperor in military dress sacrificing before tripod l., in front of a statue of Apollo on pedestal; above, eagle holding head of bull. *Vallient* p. 223 .. .. *R, fair* £5

1556B *Caracalla.* Æ 24. His laur. head r. ℞. COL AVG TR. Horse feeding r.; behind tree; beyond horse, rustic holding pedum. *B.M.C.* 95 .. .. .. F 75/-

1556C — — ℞. COL ALEXAND AVG. Emperor galloping l.; before, statue of Apollo Smintheus. *B.M.C.* 84 .. .. F 75/-

1556B   1556C   1559

1557 *Gallienus.* Æ 19. IMP C P LIC GALLIEN. Laur. bust r. ℞. COL AVG TRO. Wolf and twins. *B.M.C.* 184 .. .. F 65/-

1558 **Antandrus.** *c.* 400 B.C. Æ *hemidrachm.* Head of Artemis Astyrene r. ℞. ΑΝΤΑΝ. Goat standing r. in front of tree. *B.M.C.* 1 .. .. *RR, F* £30

1559 **Assus.** 400-241 B.C. Æ *drachm* (?, 45 grs.). Head of Athena r. ℞. ΑΣΣΙΟΝ. Bull's head facing. *B.M.C.* 6 .. .. *RR, F/VF* £60

1559A Æ 10. Helmeted head of Athena r. ℞. ΑΣΣΙ. Bull's head facing. *B.M.C.* 9
nearly VF/F 40/-

1560 Æ 11. *Obv.* type as preceding. ℞. ΑΣΣΙ. Griffin l. *B.M.C.* 13 VF 65/-

1561 **Birytis.** 4th Cent. B.C. Æ 18. Head of Kabeiros l., wearing pileus. ℞. ΒΙΡΥ.
Club: all in laurel-wreath. *B.M.C.* 1 .. .. F 35/-; VF 75/-

1562 **Cebren.** 5th Cent. B.C. Æ *diobol* (?, 19 grs.) ΚΕΒΡΕ. Head of ram r. ℞. Quadripartite incuse square. *B.M.C.* 7 .. .. *fair* £10

1562A 400-310 B.C. Æ 11. Head of Apollo, laur., r. ℞. Κ. Head of ram r. *B.M.C.* 23
F 32/6; VF 65/-

1562B 310-280 B.C. as **Antiocheia.** Æ 16. As last but ΑΝΤΙΟΧΕΩΝ and symbol below ram's
head. *B.M.C.* 37 .. .. *fair* 30/-

1563 **Colone.** 4th Cent. B.C. Æ 16. Head of Athena r. ℞. ΚΟΛΩΝΑΩΝ between rays
of eight-rayed star. *B.M.C.* 2 .. .. *fair* 27/6

1564 **Dardanus** (Maltepé). 4th Cent. B.C. Æ 17. Horseman galloping r. ℞. ΔΑΡ. Cock
standing r. *B.M.C.* 18 .. .. *fair* 22/6

1565 2nd Cent. B.C. Æ 16. Bearded male head r. ℞. ΔΑΡ. Horseman galloping r.
B.M.C. 23 .. .. *fair* 22/6

1566 **Gargara.** 4th Cent. B.C. Æ 17. Laur. head of Apollo r. ℞. ΓΑΡ above horse
prancing r., raised foreleg, thunderbolt below. *B.M.C.* 5 .. .. .. *fair* 22/6

1567 **Gentinus.** 4th Cent. B.C. Æ 14. Female head r., hair rolled. ΓΕΝ. Bee; in field,
palm-tree. *B.M.C.* 1 .. .. *fair* 27/6

1568 **Gergis.** 400-350 B.C. Æ 9. Head of Sibyl Herophile three-quarter face to r.,
laur. ℞. ΓΕΡ. Sphinx seated r. *B.M.C.* 2 .. .. F 42/-

1569 **Hamaxitus.** 4th Cent. B.C. Æ 17. Laur. head of Apollo l. ℞. ΑΜΑΞΙ. Lyre;
B.M.C. 1 .. .. R, F 55/-

1570 **Ilium** (Hissarlik: the site of ancient Troy). 300-250 B.C. Æ 13. Helmeted head of
Athena l. ℞. ΙΛΙ. Athena Ilias standing l., holding distaff and spear. *B.M.C.* 4
F 35/-

1571 *After* B.C. 189. Æ *tetradrachm.* Head of Athena r. wearing laur. helmet. ℞. ΑΘΗΑΣ
ΙΛΙΑΔΟΣ. Athena Ilias stg. r. holding distaff and spear on shoulder; in field l., mon.;
on r.; Pegasos drinking l. *B.M.C.* 12 .. .. RR, F £125

1572 Imperial Times. Æ 20. ΙΛΙ. Helmeted bust of Athena l. ℞. Aeneas adv. r.,
leading Ascanius with r. hand and carrying Anchises on l. arm. *B.M.C.* 20
R, F/VF £6

1573 Æ 19. ΙΛΙ. Wolf l., suckling twins. ℞. ΕΚΚΤΩΡ. Hector, armed, adv. l., with
spear and shield. *B.M.C.* 24 .. .. F/VF £5

1574 Æ 17. ΘΕΑ ΡΩΩΜΗ. Turreted bust of Roma, r. ℞. ΙΛΙ. Ganymede being carried
off by eagle flying l. *B.M.C.* 27 .. .. F 75/-

1575 *Crispina.* Æ 26. ΚΡΙCΠΕΙΝΑ CΕΒΑCΤΗ. Bust r. ℞. ΙΛΙΕΩΝ. Ilos l., sacrificing
bull before statue of Athena Ilias. *B.M.C.* 68 .. .. F £6

1576 *Caracalla.* Æ 26. ΑΥ Κ Μ ΑΥ ΑΝΤΩΝΙΝΟC. Bust, laur., r. ℞. ΙΛΙΕΩΝ ΙΛΟC. Ilos
l., sacrificing before statue of Athena Ilias on pedestal. *B.M.C.* 87 *var.* R, *fair* 65/-

1576A **Lamponia.** 400-350 B.C. Æ 12. Head of Dionysos r. ℞. ΛΑΜ around bull's
head facing; symbol above. *B.M.C.* 3 .. .. RR, F 60/-

1577 **Neandria.** 4th Cent. B.C. Æ 20. Laur. head of Apollo r. ℞. ΝΕΑΝ. Horse
feeding r.; in ex., corn-grain. *B.M.C.* 8 .. .. *fair* 24/-

1578 **Ophrynium** (Erenkoy). 350-300 B.C. Æ 13. Bearded male head, helmeted, three-
quarter r. ℞. ΟΦΡΥ. Infant Dionysos kneeling r. *B.M.C.* 4 .. .. F 40/-

1578A **Scamandria.** 4th Cent. B.C. Æ 18. Head of nymph Ide r. ℞. ΣΚΑ. Fir-tree.
B.M.C. 1 .. .. RR, *fair* 45/-

1579 **Scepsis.** 400-310 B.C. Æ 16. Forepart of Pegasos l. ℞. ΣΚΗ. Fir-tree within
linear square. *B.M.C.* 10 .. .. *fair* 30/-

1580 Sigeium. 4th Cent. B.C. Æ 18. Head of Athena, helmeted, three-quarter r. ℞. ΣΙΓΕ. Owl r., head facing. *B.M.C.* 2 .. .. F 40/–

1581 Æ 20. *Obv.* as preceding. ℞. ΣΙΓΕ. Double-bodied owl: to r., crescent. *B.M.C.* 14 .. .. *fair*/F 27/6

1582 Thymbra. 4th Cent. B.C. Æ 17. Head of Zeus Ammon l. ℞. ΦΥ. Star below, monogram н р. *B.M.C.* 4 .. .. F 35/–

1582A Zeleia. 350-300 B.C. Æ 12. Head of Artemis r., wearing stephanos. ℞. ΙΕΛΕ. Stag stg. r. *B.M.C.* 2 .. .. *R*, F 42/–

1580   1589

1583 ISLANDS OFF TROAS: Tenedos. 550-470 B.C. *Æ hemidrachm.* Janiform head of archaic style (bearded male head l., female head r.). ℞. ΤΕΝΕ ΔΙΟΝ. Double-axe: all in linear square within incuse square. *B.M.C.* 4 .. .. .. F/VF £15

1584 *Æ hemiobol.* Janiform head. ℞. Double-axe in linear square within incuse square. *B.M.C.* 7 .. .. *fair* £6

1585 450-387 B.C. *Æ tetradrachm.* Janiform head of fine style (bearded male head l., female head r.). ℞. ΤΕΝΕΔΙΟΝ. Double-axe between bunch of grapes and lyre, all in incuse square. *B.M.C.* 11 .. .. *R*, F £50

1586 *Æ drachm.* Similar. *B.M.C.* 15 .. .. F £13

1587 *Æ diobol.* Similar. ℞. Head of Athena r. *B.M.C.*— .. .. F 75/–

1588 Æ 8. Janiform head. ℞. Double-axe. *B.M.C.*— .. .. .. *fair* 32/6

1589 *After* 189 B.C. *Æ tetradrachm.* Janiform head of later style. ℞. ΤΕΝΕΔΙΩΝ above double-axe; to l., mon. and bunch of grapes; to r., owl; all within laurel wreath. *B.M.C.* 28 .. .. VF £225

AEOLIS.

1590 Aegae (Nemrud Kalessi). 3rd Cent. B.C. Æ 16. Head of Apollo, laur., r. ℞. ΑΙΓΑΕ. Goat's head r. *B.M.C.* 2 .. .. VF/F 50/–

1590A 2nd-1st Cent. B.C. *Æ tetradrachm.* Similar but with bow and quiver at neck. ℞. ΑΙΓΑΙΕΩΝ. Zeus standing l.; on l., mon.: all in wreath. *B.M.C.* 9. **Plate VI** *RRR, nearly* VF/VF £120

1591 Æ 18. *Messalina.* ϹΕΒΑϹΤΗ ΜΕϹΑΛΕΙΝΑ. Her dr. bust r. ℞. ΑΙΓΑΕ ШΝ. Zeus standing l.' *Grose* 7875 .. .. *R, fair* £10

1591A Boeone. 4th cent. B.C. Æ 10. Female head l. ℞. ΒΟΙΩΝΙΤΙΚΟΝ. Bull stg. r. *B.M.C.* 1 .. .. *fair* 27/6

1592 Cyme (Namourt). 480-450 B.C. *Æ hemiobol.* ΚΥ. Head of eagle l. ℞. Mill-sail pattern incuse square. *B.M.C.* 11 .. .. F £6

1593 320-250 B.C. *Æ hemidrachm.* ΚΥ. Eagle standing r., head turned back. ℞ Forepart of horse r.; above, vase with one handle. *B.M.C.* 21 *nearly* VF £12

1594 Æ 17. ΚΥ. Forepart of horse r.: below, magistrate's name. ℞. One-handled vase: to l., monogram. *B.M.C.* 40-52 .. .. F 30/–

1595 *About* 250 B.C. Æ 15. Head of the Amazon Cyme r. ℞. ΚΥ. Forepart of horse r.: to r., one-handled vase: beneath, magistrate's name. *B.M.C.* 54 .. .. F 25/–

1596 250-190 B.C. Æ 22. Similar; countermarked with small head of Artemis. ℞. ΚΥ above horse walking r.; vase below raised leg; ΠΥΘΙΩΝ in ex. *B.M.C.* 71 F/*fair* 30/–

1597 — Another, without countermark and legend ΚΥΜΑΙΩΝ. *B.M.C.* 66 .. F 27/6

1598   1600

1598 *After* 190 B.C. *Æ tetradrachm.* Head of the Amazon Cyme r. ℞. KYMAIΩN. Horse
walking r.: beneath one-handled vase: in ex., ΣEYOHΣ: all within wreath of laurel. *B.M.C.*
78 .. .. EF £120

1599 Imperial Times. Æ 18. KYMH. Turreted female bust l. ℞. KYMAIΩN. Isis
standing l. *B.M.C.* 121 .. .. F 32/6

1600 **Elaea.** 4th-3rd Cent. B.C. Æ 18. Head of Athena l. ℞. EΛ. Corn-grain;
all within olive-wreath. *B.M.C.* 7 .. .. F 30/-

1601 **Grynium.** 3rd Cent. B.C. Æ 18. Laur. head of Apollo three-quarter face to l.
℞. ΓΥΡΝΗΩΝ. Mussel-shell. *B.M.C.* 1 .. .. R, F 50/-

1601A **Larissa Phriconis** (Bourounjik). 4th Cent. B.C. Æ 11. Female head l. ℞. ΛΑΡΙ.
Amphora surrounded by grapes, caduceus and ear of corn. *B.M.C.* 4 .. *fair* 30/-

1602   1605

1602 **Myrina** (Kalabassary). 2nd-1st Cent. B.C. *Æ tetradrachm.* Head of Apollo of Grynium,
laur., r. ℞. MYPINAIΩN. Apollo standing r., holding patera and filleted laurel-branch;
before him, omphalos and amphora: in field l., monogram. *B.M.C.* 1
                                                              VF/F £62/10/-

1603 Æ 16. Laur. head of Apollo r. ℞. MYPI. Amphora; to r., lyre. *B.M.C.* 27
                                                              F 40/-

1604 **Temnus.** 2nd-1st Cent. B.C. Æ 9. Head of Dionysos l. ℞. TA. Bunch of
grapes. *B.M.C.* 9 .. .. *fair* 17/6

1605 Late Imperial Times. Æ 20. ΘΗΜΝΟC. Turreted female bust r. ℞. ΘΗΜΝΕΙΤΩΝ.
Tyche standing l. *B.M.C.* 18 .. .. F 50/-

LESBOS.

1606 550-440 B.C. Billon *stater* (224 grs.). Gorgon-head. ℞. Rude incuse square.
B.M.C. 6 .. .. R, VF/F £75

1607 Billon *quarter-stater* (48 grs.). Two boars' heads facing each other. ℞. Incuse square
                                                              F £10

1608 Billon *hemiobol.* Two eyes. ℞. Incuse of swastika form. *B.M.C.* 26   F £9

1609 Billon *obol.* Negro's head r. ℞. Incuse square. *B.M.C.* 42 .. .. F £12/10/-

1610 Billon *stater.* Olive-tree between two calves heads facing one another. ℞. Small
incuse square. *B.M.C.* 46 .. .. *nearly* VF £20

1610A 480-440 B.C. Electrum *hecte.* Forepart of winged boar r. ℞. Incuse lion's head r.:
behind, two incuse rectangles. *B.M.C.* 3. **Plate VI.** .. .. *nearly* EF £82/10/-

1610B 440-350 B.C. Electrum *hecte*. Forepart of winged lion l. ℞. Sphinx seated r. *B.M.C.* 35. **Plate VI** .. .. VF/*good* F £67/10/-

1611 — Another. Laur. head of Apollo r. ℞. Female head r., hair in sphendone; behind, a serpent. *B.M.C.* 85 .. .. VF/*good* F £32/10/-

1612 — Another. Veiled head of Demeter r. ℞. Tripod within linear square. *B.M.C.* 118 .. .. VF £45

1613 **Koinon of Lesbos.** 330-280 B.C. Æ 16. Head of Hera r. wearing stephane. ℞. ΑΙΟΛΕ above thunderbolt; below, caduceus r. *B.M.C.* 7 .. .. .. F 40/-

1613A **Antissa.** 300-167 B.C. Æ 16. Female head r., hair rolled and bound with taenia. ℞. ΑΝΤΙΣ. Male head r. with pointed beard and long hair, wears tall headdress with veil; in front, caduceus. *B.M.C.* 2 .. .. *fair* 32/6

1613B **Eresus.** 3rd cent. B.C. or later. Æ 17. Head of Hermes r. wearing petasos. ℞. ΕΡΕΣΙ. Ear of corn. *B.M.C.* 2 .. .. R, *fair* 40/-

1614 **Methymna.** 500-450 B.C. Æ *tetrobol*. Warrior kneeling l., holding spear and round shield. ℞. Horseman r. on fore-part of horse, within dotted border; all in incuse square. *B.M.C.* 7 .. .. R, VF/F £30

1614A 420-377 B.C. Æ *didrachm*? (99 grains). Hd. of Athena l., helmet ornate with vine-tendrils, ivy-leaf and crescent. ℞. ΜΑΘΥΜΝΑΙΟΝ. Lyre in square: all within incuse square. *B.M.C.* 10 .. .. RR, F £100

1614A   1618A

1615 330-240 B.C. Æ *hemidrachm*. Head of young Herakles r. ℞. ΜΑΘΥ. Arion seated on dolphin r., holding lyre. *B.M.C.* 16   R, *nearly* VF/*good* F £22/10/-

1616 Æ 16. Helmeted head of Athena r. ℞. ΜΑΘΥ. Kantharos. *B.M.C.* 23   F 32/6

1617 **Mytilene.** 440-400 B.C. Æ 9. Laur. head of Apollo r. ℞. ΜΥΤ. Calf's head. *B.M.C.* 6 .. .. F 40/-

1618 400-350 B.C. Æ *trihemiobol*. Similar. ℞. Head of nymph, Mytilene r. *B.M.C.* 14 *nearly* F 75/-

1618A 350-250 B.C. Æ *stater*. Laur. head of Apollo r. ℞. ΜΥΤΙ. Lyre: to l., symbol: the whole in linear compartment. *B.M.C.* 28 etc. .. .. .. R, F £45

1619 2nd-1st Cent. B.C. Æ 16. Head of Zeus Ammon, beardless, r. ℞. ΜΥΤΙ. Terminal figure of Dionysos, facing. *B.M.C.* 106 .. .. *good* F 40/-

1620 Æ 19. Head of Zeus Ammon, bearded, r. ℞. Similar to preceding. *B.M.C.* 137 F 32/6

1621 Imperial Times, 138-198 A.D. Æ 20. ΨΑΠΦΩ. Draped bust of Sappho r. ℞. ΜΥΤΙΛΗΝΑΙΩΝ. Lyre. *B.M.C.* 169 .. .. F 52/6

1622 *Antinous.* Æ 16. Head of Antinous r. ℞. ΜΥΤΙΛΗΝΑΙΩΝ. Bull r. *B.M.C.* 199 F £25

1622A **Pyrrha.** 4th cent. B.C. Æ 11. Head of nymph, Pyrrha, in sphendone l. ℞. ΠΥΡ. Goat. *B.M.C.* 1 .. .. R, F 52/6

1623 **ISLANDS NEAR LESBOS : Nesos.** 3rd Cent. B.C. Æ 19. Head of Apollo r. ℞. ΝΑΣΙ. Lyre. *B.M.C.* 9 .. .. R, *fair* 40/-

1624 **Pordosilene** (later Poroselene, now Pyrgos). Time of Septimius Severus. Æ 15. Head of Athena r. ℞. ΠΩΡΟΣΕΛΗΝΕΙΤΩΝ. Telesphoros standing facing. *B.M.C.* 4 R, F 65/-

IONIA.

1625 **Clazomenae.** *c.* 500 B.C. Æ *stater.* Forepart of winged boar r. ℞. Quadripartite incuse square. *B.M.C.* 3. **Plate VI** .. .. VF £40

1626 387-301 B.C. Æ *tetradrachm.* Head of Apollo facing three-quarters l. ℞. ΚΛΑΙΟ. Swan standing l., flapping its wings, head turned back: magistrate's name below. *B.M.C.* 18 .. .. *RRR*, F £700

1626A Æ *drachm.* Somewhat similar; magistrate's name above, ΚΛΑ below. *B.M.C.* 20 *R*, VF £75

1626B Æ *hemidrachm.* Similar. *B.M.C.* 23 .. .. *nearly* VF £35

1626   1633

1627 Æ 17. Head of Athena r. ℞. Ram walking r. *B.M.C.* 48 .. .. *fair* 21/–

1628 Æ 9. Similar, with ΚΛΑ on *rev.* *B.M.C.* 54 .. .. *fair*/F 21/–

1629 Æ 12. Head of Athena, three-quarter r. ℞. Similar. *B.M.C.* 56 .. *fair* 21/–

1630 Æ 18. As last. ℞. ΚΛΑΙΟΜΕΝΙΩΝ. Forepart of ram r. *B.M.C.* 73 .. F 40/–

1631 *After* 300 B.C. Æ 9. Forepart of winged boar r. ℞. Κ Λ in quadripartite shallow incuse square. *B.M.C.* 99 .. .. *fair* 17/6

1632 **Colophon.** 5th Cent. B.C. Æ *tetartemorion.* Head of Apollo Clarios facing. ℞. ΤΕ in monogram, in incuse square. *Bab.* 1908.. .. .. .. *RR, fair*/F £7

1633 440-400 B.C. Æ *drachm.* Laur. head of Apollo l. ℞. ΚΟΛΟΦΩ to l. of lyre, ΝΙΚΙΑΣ to r. *B.M.C.* 6 .. .. F £20

1634 400-350 B.C. Æ 10. Head of Apollo r. ℞. ΚΟΛ. Lyre. *B.M.C.* 14 .. *fair* 17/6

1635 *After* 300 B.C. Æ 19. ΚΟΛΟΦΩΝΙΩΝ. Apollo standing r., holding patera and lyre. ℞. ΑΠΟΛΛΑΣ. Homer seated l. *B.M.C.* 42 .. .. F 40/–

1636 *Otacilia.* Æ 29. Μ . ΩΤΑΚ . СΕΒΗΡΑ. Her dr. bust r. ℞. ΚΟΛΟΦΩΝΙΩΝ. Homer seated r. *B.M.C.* 54 .. .. *fair* 50/–

1637 **Ephesus.** 387-295 B.C. Æ *tetradrachm.* ΕΦ. Bee with straight wings. ℞. Forepart of kneeling stag r., looking back: behind, date-palm; before, magistrate's name. *Cf. B.M.C.* 30-52 .. .. *nearly* F/F £12; VF £50

1638 Æ *diobol.* *Obv.* as preceding. ℞. ΕΦ. Two stags' heads face to face. *B.M.C.* 53 VF £13

1639 305-288 B.C. Æ 10. Female head l. ℞. ΕΦ. Bee. *B.M.C.* 68 .. F 25/–

1640 280-258 B.C. Æ 16. ΕΦ. Bee. ℞. Stag standing r.: above, quiver. *Cf. B.M.C.* 80-1 .. .. F 35/–

1641 Æ 16. ΕΦ. Bee: all in laurel-wreath. ℞. Stag feeding r.: above, quiver. *B.M.C.* 83-5 .. .. *nearly* F 27/6

1642 258-202 B.C. Æ *didrachm.* Head of Artemis r., wearing stephanos. ℞. ΕΦ. Forepart of kneeling stag r., looking back; behind, magistrate's name. *B.M.C.* 86-117 VF £50

1643 202-133 B.C. Æ *drachm.* ΕΦ. Bee. ℞. Stag standing r. in front of date-palm; to r., magistrate's name. *B.M.C.* 121-133 .. .. .. *fair* 75/–; VF £14

1644 Æ 19. *Obv.* as No. 1641. ℞. As last, but name in ex. *B.M.C.* 134/42 *fair* 21/–

1645 **Ephesus.** 133-67 B.C. Æ *cistophoric tetradrachm.* Cista mystica, from which a serpent issues: all in ivy-wreath. R. ΕΦΕ. Bow-case between coiled serpents: in field l., ΞΕ: above, ear of corn between two cornuacopiae: to r., torch. *B.M.C.* 168 VF £16

1646 48-27 B.C. Æ 20. Bust of Artemis r. R. Long torch between two stags facing each other: in field, magistrate's name. *B.M.C.* 182 .. .. .. *fair* 22/6

1647 Imperial Times. Æ *tessera.* 19 *mm.* ΕΦ. Stag kneeling l., looking back: in ex. CΚ ШΠΙ. R. ΚΗΡΙΛΙCΙϽΔΕΙΡΟC ΠΑΛΥΡΙΝ. Bee. *The meaning of this legend is not clear, but it may be a magical formula against disease.* *B.M.C.* 186 F £5; VF £10

1648 *Septimius Severus.* Æ 22. Laur. head of emperor r. R. ΕΦΕCΙΩΝ Β ΝΕΟΚΟΡΩΝ. Cultus-statue of Artemis between two seated children .. .. .. F 55/-

1649 *Caracalla.* Æ 17. Laur. head of emperor r. R. ΕΦΕCΙΩΝ. Boar running r. *B.M.C.* 280 .. .. *fair* 35/-

1650 *Geta.* Æ 17. ΑΥΤΚΠΟCΕ ΓΕΤΑC. Laur. head r. R. ΕΦΕCΙΩΝ. Type as No. 1648. *B.M.C.* 283 .. .. VF/F £7

1651 *Herennia Etruscilla.* Æ 26. ΕΡΕΝ ΕΤΡΟVCΚΙΛΛΑ CΕ. Bust r. R IΕΡΑ ΕΦΕCΙΩΝ. Car with canopy drawn by two horses r. *Not in B.M.C.* .. .. R, F £7

1652 *Gallienus.* Æ 26. ΑΥΤ ΠΟ ΛΙΚ ΓΑΛΛΙΗΝΟC. Laur. bust r. R. ΕΦΕCΙΩΝ Γ ΝΕΟΚΟ-ΡΩΝ. Leto running r., looking l., carrying her children Apollo and Artemis. *B.M.C.* 374 .. .. R, F/VF £9

1653 **Ephesus in alliance with Smyrna.** *Domitia.* Æ 20. ΔΟΜΙΤΙΑ CΕΒΑCΤΗ. Her bust r. R. ΑΝΘΥ ΚΑΙ CΕΝ ΠΑΙΤΟΥ ΟΜΟΝΟΙΑ: in field, SMYP and ΕΦΕ. Two Nemeses face to face. *B.M.C.* 411 .. .. RR, F £12

1654 **Erythrae.** 5th Cent. B.C. Æ *drachm.* Naked man holding prancing horse by the rein. R. ΕΡΥΘ. Flower of twelve petals: all in incuse square. *B.M.C.* 19 *almost* VF £30

1655 387-300 B.C. Æ *tetradrachm.* Hd. of Herakles in lion's skin r. R. ΕΡΥ, owl / club / ΜΟΛΙΩΝ / bow in case / mon. *B.M.C.* 42 .. .. *good* F/*nearly* VF £47/10/-

1655A Æ 15. Very similar. *B.M.C.* 66-80 .. .. F 27/6

1655   1661

1656 300-200 B.C. Æ 15. *Obv.* as preceding. R. ΕΡΥ and magistrate's name. *B.M.C.* 102-116 .. .. F 27/6

1657 Æ 13. Head of Apollo, r. R. as preceding but also bow. *B.M.C.* 145 *fair* 17/6

1658 200-133 B.C. Æ 19. Head of young Herakles wearing lion-skin, r. R. ΕΡΥ. Bow in case, club, magistrate's name, etc. *B.M.C.* 153-196 .. .. .. F 27/6

1659 Imperial Times. Æ 15. ΕΡΥΘΡΑΙΩΝ. Helmeted head of Athena l. R. Corn-ears and poppies tied together. *B.M.C.* 231 .. .. *fair* 20/-

1660 Æ 18. ΕΡΥΘΡΑΙ. Turreted bust of Tyche r. R. ΕΡΥΘΡΑΙΩΝ. Fire-beacon. *B.M.C.* 239 .. .. F 40/-

1661 **Heraclea ad Latmum.** After 190 B.C. Æ *tetradrachm.* Head of Athena r., helmet adorned with Pegasos and foreparts of five horses. R. ΗΡΑΚΛΕΩΤΩΝ above club; below, Nike between two mon.; all in wreath. *B.M.C.* 1 .. .. R, VF £150

1661A Æ 9. Owl r., wings closed. R. Crest of helmet. *B.M.C.* 13 .. R, *fair* 30/-

1661B **Larissa.** *Circa* 300 B.C. or later. Æ 17. Laur. head of Apollo r. R. ΛΑ. Horseman prancing r. *B.M.C.* 1 .. .. R, *fair* 42/-

1662 **Lebedus.** *After* 190 B.C. Æ 18. Head of Athena three-quarter l. R. ΛΕ. Prow. *B.M.C.* 6 .. .. F 42/-

1662A **Leuce.** 350-300 B.C. Æ 15. Laur. head of Apollo l. R. ΛΕΟ. Swan stg. l. with flapping wings. *B.M.C.* 3 .. .. F 50/-

1663 **Magnesia ad Maeandrum.** 350-190 B.C.   Æ 17.   Horseman with lance galloping
r.   Ŗ.   MAΓ.   Humped bull butting r.; magistrate's name beneath; all in circular
maeander pattern.   *B.M.C.* 19 .. .. F 42/–

1664 *After* 190 B.C.   Æ *tetradrachm.*   Bust of Artemis r., wearing stephanos, bow and
quiver at shoulder.   Ŗ.   MAΓNHTΩN.   Apollo standing l. on maeander pattern, holding
filleted branch and resting l. elbow on tripod; in field r., magistrate's name; all within
laurel-wreath.   *Cf. B.M.C.* 36-38 .. .. R, VF £90

1664   1672

1665 Æ 16.   MAΓNHT.   Stag standing r.   Ŗ.   Cultus-statue of Artemis Leukophryene.
B.M.C. 47 .. .. F 35/–

1666 *Severus Alexander.*   Æ 22.   Greek legend.   His laur. bust dr. r.   Ŗ.   MAΓNHTΩN.
Eagle standing r.   *B.M.C.* 71 .. .. *fair* 30/–

1667 **Metropolis.**   1st Cent. B.C.   Æ 17.   Head of Athena r.   Ŗ.   MHTPOΠOΛITΩN.
Thunderbolt.   *B.M.C.* 1 .. .. R, F 52/6

1668 **Miletus.**   478-390 B.C.   Æ *diobol.*   Forepart of lion r., looking back.   Ŗ.   Ornamental star in incuse square.   *B.M.C.* 14 .. .. VF 75/–

1669 As preceding, but *obv.* type to l., head r.   *B.M.C.* 34 .. R, *nearly* VF 90/–

1670 390-350 B.C.   Æ 13.   Lion walking l., head r.   Ŗ.   Ornamental star.   *B.M.C.* 44
F 25/–

1671 350-300 B.C.   Æ *hemidrachm.*   Laur. head of Apollo l.   Ŗ.   MI mon.   Lion standing
l., head turned back, magistrate's name below.   *B.M.C.* 68-73 .. .. VF £14

1672 300-250 B.C.   Æ *didrachm.*   Similar.   *B.M.C.* 84-90 .. .. VF £32/10/–

1673 250-190 B.C.   Æ 10.   Similar, but types to r.   *B.M.C.* 102 .. VF/F 42/–

1674 *After* 190 B.C.   Æ 1½ *drachm.*   Similar, but lion l.   *B.M.C.* 115 .. VF £20

1675 Æ 18.   Statue of Apollo r., holding stag and bow.   Ŗ.   Lion recumbent r., looking
back at star: in ex., magistrate's name.   *Cf. B.M.C.* 134/7 *fair* 22/6; F/VF 60/–

1676 *Claudius.*   Æ 20.   Greek legend.   His laur. head l.; to l., star.   Ŗ.   MIΛHΣIΩN
ΔIΔYMEYΣ.   Cultus-statue of Apollo r.   *B.M.C.* 146 .. .. F 65/–

1676A **Naulochus.**   *Circa* 350 B.C.   Æ 11.   Head of Athena r.   Ŗ.   NAY.   Dolphin r.;
all within circle of Maeander pattern.   *B.M.C.* 1 .. .. .. R, *fair* 30/–

1677 **Phocaea.**   5th-4th Cent. B.C.   Æ *obol.*   Head of seal r.   Ŗ.   Incuse square.   *B.M.C.*
79 *var.* .. .. RR, F £10

1678 Æ *hemidrachm.*   Head and neck of griffin l.   Ŗ.   Incuse square with checked border
enclosing star.   *B.M.C.* 81 .. .. *nearly* VF £6

1679 3rd-2nd Cent. B.C.   Æ 17.   Bust of Hermes r.   Ŗ.   ΦΩ.   Forepart of griffin r.;
magistrate's name below.   *B.M.C.* 105 .. .. F 35/–

1680 Æ 20.   Helmeted head of Athena r.   Ŗ.   Griffin walking r.: in ex., ΦΩKAIEΩN.   *B.M.C.*
109 .. .. *fair*/F 30/–

1681 **Phygela.**   350-300 B.C.   Æ 10.   Head of Artemis r.   Ŗ.   ΦY.   Bull r.   *B.M.C.* 1
F 40/–

1682 **Priene.**   3rd Cent. B.C.   Æ *drachm.*   Head of Athena l.   Ŗ.   ΠPIH.   Trident head:
on r., magistrate's name: all within circle of Maeander pattern.   *B.M.C.* 5.   *Illustrated
at top of next page* .. .. RR, F £35

1682A Æ 17.   Head of Athena r.   Ŗ.   ΠPIHNEΩN.   Tripod.   *B.M.C.* 8 .. *fair* 21/–

1683 2nd-1st Cent. B.C.   Æ 22.   *Obv.* as preceding.   Ŗ.   ΠPIH.   Owl on amphora: in ex.,
AXIΛΛEIΔHΣ.   *B.M.C.* 44 .. .. *fair*/F 30/–

1682   1684

1684 **Smyrna** (Izmir). 190-133 B.C. Æ *tetradrachm.* Turreted head of Kybele r. Ɍ.
ΙΜΥΡΝΑΙΩΝ above lion standing r.; in ex., magistrate's name; all in oak-wreath. *B.M.C.* 6
VF £120

1685 2nd-1st cent. B.C. Æ 15. Head of Kybele, turreted, r. Ɍ. ΙΜΥΡΝΑΙΩΝ. Statue
of Aphrodite r.; before her, Nike l. on column. *B.M.C.* 22-33 .. .. F 25/–

1686 Æ 16. Similar, but statue standing facing, Nike on l. hand. *B.M.C.* 34 F 25/–

1687 Æ 18. As last, but with head of Kybele within wreath. *B.M.C.* 35-46 .. F 30/–

1688 Æ 14. Head of Apollo r. Ɍ. ΙΜΥΡΝΑΙΩΝ. Hand in *caestus. B.M.C.* 47-60
F 30/–

1689 Æ 11. Head of Kybele, turreted, r. Ɍ. Legend as preceding: portable altar. *B.M.C.*
65-70 .. .. F 25/–

1690 Æ 11. Head of Apollo r. Ɍ. Legend as preceding: lyre. *B.M.C.* 73 F 25/–

1691 Æ 23. *Obv.* as preceding. Ɍ. ΙΜΥΡΝΑΙΩΝ. Homer seated l.: in field, ΜΗΤΡΟ-
ΔΟΡΟΣ. *B.M.C.* 111 .. .. F 40/–

1692 Imperial Times: Æ 25. CTPA TI, etc. Zeus seated l. Ɍ. ΕΠΙ ΤΙ ΚΛΑΥΔΙΟΥ
ΙΕΡΟΝΥΜΟΥ in wreath. *B.M.C.* 120 .. .. R, M/fair 32/6

1693 Æ 20. *Obv.* legend as *rev.* of preceding: Nemesis standing r. Ɍ. River-god reclining l., etc. *B.M.C.* 124-8 .. .. F 50/–

1694 Æ 21. ΑΝΘΥΦΡΟΝΤΕΙΝΩ ΣΜΥΡ. Turreted bust of Kybele r. Ɍ. ΕΠΙ ΜΥΡΤΟΥ CTPA
ΡΗΓΕΙΝΟC. Amazon Smyrna standing l., holding spear and bipennis. *B.M.C.* 134
F 50/–

1695 Æ 19. ΑΝΘΥ ΦΡΟΝΤΕΙΝΩ. Head of Herakles r. Ɍ. ΕΠΙ ΜΥΡΤΟΥ ΡΗΓΕΙΝΟC. ΖΜΥΡ.
River-god reclining l. *B.M.C.* 135 .. .. F 42/–

1696 Æ 14. ΣΜΥΡΝΑΙΩΝ. Bee. Ɍ. Legend as preceding: dolphin r. *B.M.C.* 141
fair 21/–

1697 2nd Cent. A.D. Æ 21. ΖΕΥC ΑΚΡΑΙΟC. Head of Zeus r. Ɍ. ΣΜΥΡ ΠΑΝΙΩΝΙΟC.
Artemis Panionios standing l., holding branch and bow. *B.M.C.* 157 .. *fair* 17/6

1698 Æ 18. CΙΠΥΛΗΝΗ. Head of Kybele Sipylene, turreted, r. Ɍ. ΣΜΥΡΝΑΙΩΝ.
Homonoia standing l. *B.M.C.* 162 .. .. F 30/–

1699 Æ 20. ΣΜΥΡΝΑΙΩΝ. Bust of Amazon Smyrna, turreted, r. Ɍ. Same legend: lion
seated r., forepaw on tympanon. *Cf. B.M.C.* 170 .. .. .. F 35/–

1700 Early 3rd Cent. A.D. Æ 25. ΙΕΡΑ CΥΝΚΛΗΤΟC. Bust of Senate r. Ɍ. ΣΜΥΡΝΑΙΩΝ Γ
ΝΕΩΚΟΡΩΝ. Two Nemeses standing facing each other. *B.M.C.* 228 .. F 50/–

1701 Æ 24. *Obv.* as preceding. Ɍ Legend as preceding: statue of Tyche in tetrastyle
temple *B.M.C.* 236 .. .. F/fair 45/–

1702 Mid 3rd Cent. A.D. Æ 24. *Obv.* as preceding. Ɍ. ΣΜΥΡΝΑΙΩΝ Γ ΝΕ ΕΠΙ ΚΤΗΤΟΥ.
Homonoia standing l. *B.M.C.* 247 .. .. *fair* 17/6

1703 *Augustus.* Æ 18. CΕΒΑCΤΟC. Bare head of Augustus r. Ɍ. ΙΜΥΡΝΑΙΩΝ. Aphrodite
standing facing. *B.M.C.* 248 .. .. *fair* 32/6

1704 *Augustus and Tiberius.* Æ 17. Heads of Augustus r. and Tiberius l. face to face. Ɍ.
ΛΙΒΙΑΝ ΖΜΥΡΝΑΙΩΝ ΚΟΡΩΝΟC. Type as previous. *B.M.C.* 259 .. R, *fair* 45/–

1705 *Livia.* Æ 21. Heads of the Senate r. and Livia l. face to face. Ɍ. Statue of Tiberius
in tetrastyle temple. *B.M.C.* 266 .. .. R, *fair* 52/6

1706 *Nero.* Æ 18. ΝΕΡΩΝΑ ΣΕΒΑCΤΟΝ. Laur. head of Nero r. Ɍ. ΣΜΥ ΡΑ ΓΕCCΙΟC
ΦΙΛΟΠΑΤΡΙC. Zeus seated l., with sceptre. *B.M.C.* 285 .. .. F/fair 35/–

1707 *Antinous.* Æ 35 *medallion.* ΑΝΤΙΝΟΟC ΗΡΩC. Bare head l. Ɍ. Legend uncertain:
ram standing r. *Cf. B.M.C.* 340 .. .. RR, *fair*/M £20

1708 *Faustina II.* Æ 19. Greek legend. Bust r. ℞. ΘΕΥΔΙΑΝΟC ΑΝΕΘΗΚΕ. Griffin r., forepaw on wheel. *B.M.C.* 349 .. .. F 42/6

1709 *Caracalla.* Æ 30. Greek legend. Bust r. ℞. ΕΠΙ CTPA . ΚΛ . POYΦINOY . COΦIΩN . CMYPNAIΩN. Zeus Akraios seated l., holding Nike and sceptre. *B.M.C.* 396 *fair* 40/–

1710 *Tranquillina.* Æ 22. Dr. bust r. ℞. CMYPNAIΩN Γ. NEΩKOPΩN. Herakles standing l. *B.M.C.* 448 .. .. *fair* 60/–
There are also a number of Greek Imperial pieces of Smyrna in alliance with other cities, such as Athens, Cyzicus, Nicomedia.

1711 **Teos.** 544-494 B.C. Æ *trihemiobol.* Griffin, with curled wing, seated r. ℞. Quadripartite incuse square, surface rough. *B.M.C.* 11-14 .. .. .. *good* F £10

1712 394-300 B.C. Æ *drachm.* Griffin seated r., with pointed wing. ℞. ΘΗΙΩΝ ΑΓ ΝΩΝ crosswise on incuse square with granulated surface. *B.M.C.* 24 .. R, VF £40

1712A Æ *triobol.* Griffin with pointed wing, seated r. ℞. ΘΗΙ above kantharos and magistrate's name. *B.M.C.* 27 .. .. VF £20

1713 3rd-1st Cent. B.C. Æ 11. Griffin running r. ℞. ΘΗΙΩΝ and magistrate's name. Lyre. *B.M.C.* 40-42 .. .. *fair*/F 21/–

1714 *Valerian II.* Æ 20. ΠΟ ΛΙΚ ΟΥΑΛΕΡΙΑΝΟC. His bust r. ℞. ΘΗΙΩΝ ΙΩΝΩΝ. Anacreon seated r., playing lyre. *B.M.C.* 87 .. .. R, F £5

ISLANDS OF IONIA.

1715 **CHIOS.** 7th Cent. B.C. Æ *half-stater* (wt. 61 grs.). Sphinx seated r. ℞. Rough incuse square. *Not in B.M.C., Baldwin-Brett or Mavrogordato* .. RR, *fair* £20

1716 6th Cent. B.C. Æ *didrachm.* Sphinx seated l.: in field, l., amphora. ℞. Quadripartite incuse square. *B.M.C.* 2-4 *and Mavrogordato,* pl. 2, 5 .. R, F £17

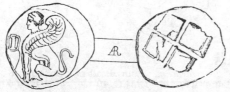

1717*   1718A

1717 478-412 B.C. Æ *didrachm.* Sphinx seated l.: in field, l., bunch of grapes and amphora; all on circular raised shield. ℞. as preceding. *B.M.C.* 8. (*The illustration above is of a larger coin, the tetradrachm of this issue, the bunch of grapes is missing*)
fair £8; *nearly* VF £35

1718 Æ *drachm.* Types similar to preceding. *B.M.C.* 17 .. .. .. F £15

1718A 412-350 B.C. Æ *tetradrachm.* As before. ℞. Shallow incuse square with magistrate's name on horizontal band. *B.M.C.* 28-33 .. .. .. R, *fair* £35

1718B Æ *drachm.* As last. *B.M.C.* 34-8 .. .. F £18

1719 *After* 84 B.C. Æ *drachm.* Sphinx seated l.: in field, l., bunch of grapes. ℞. ΔΕΡΚΥΛΟC ΧΙΟΣ. Amphora: beneath, cornucopia. *B.M.C.* 54 .. .. F £15

1720 Æ 17. Sphinx seated r.: in field, r., star. ℞. Magistrate's name and ΧΙΟΣ. Amphora: in field, l., prow. *Cf. B.M.C.* 74-8 .. .. F 30/–; VF/F 50/–

1721 Æ 10. Sphinx seated l. ℞. ΧΙΟΣ. Amphora. *B.M.C.* 101 *var.* .. F 25/–

1722 Imperial Times. Æ 29 *three assaria.* ΑCCΑΡΙΑ ΤΡΙΑ. Sphinx seated l.: to l., prow. ℞. ΕΠΙ ΑΡΧ ΕΙΡΗΝΑΙΟΥ ΧΙΩΝ. Apollo and Dionysos standing facing. *B.M.C.* 118 variety .. .. F £7

1723 Æ 25 *three assaria.* *Obv.* Similar, but type r. ℞. ΕΠ ΑΡΧ ΑΥΡ ΧΡΥCΟΓΟΝΟΥ ΧΙΩΝ. Amphora between corn-ears and stars. *B.M.C.* 129 .. .. F 60/–

1724 **ICARIA.** **Oenoe.** 3rd Cent. B.C. Æ 19. Head of Dionysos r. ℞. OINAIΩN.
Bunch of grapes. *B.M.C.* 2   ..   ..   *R,* F 75/-

1725 **SAMOS.** 494-439 B.C. Æ *drachm.* Forepart of winged boar r. ℞. Lion's scalp
within dotted square, all in incuse square. *B.M.C.* 45-53 ..   F £7; VF/F £12

1726 439-394 B.C. Æ *diobol.* Head of lioness l. ℞. Head of ram r. within deep incuse
square. *B.M.C.* 65   ..   ..   F £7

1727 390-365 B.C. Æ *tetradrachm.* Scalp of lion facing. ℞. Forepart of bull r.; to l.
olive branch; to r., ΣΑ; above, magistrate's name; below, mon. in circle. *B.M.C.* 134
VF £150

1728 Æ 14. Head of Hera l. ℞. ΣΑ below scalp of lion. *B.M.C.* 147   .. F 35/-

1729 322-205 B.C. Æ *didrachm.* Scalp of lion facing. ℞. Forepart of bull r.;
magistrate's name above; ΣΑ and olive-branch below. *B.M.C.* 161-5 *nearly* VF £13

1730 Æ 19. Similar. *B.M.C.*—   ..   ..   *good* F 50/-

1731 205-129 B.C. Æ *drachm.* Similar. ℞. ΣΑΜΙΩΝ above forepart of bull r., amphora and
olive-branch. below. *B.M.C.* 175-9 *var.*   ..   .. VF £15

1732 Æ 13. Head of Hera r. ℞. ΣΑΜΙΩΝ. Lion's scalp. *B.M.C.* 190   .. F 32/6

1733 Æ 12. Head of Hera facing. ℞. ΣΑΜΙΩΝ. Prow r. *B.M.C.* 193   .. F 30/-

1734 129-20 B.C. Æ 18. Head of Hera r. ℞. ΣΑΜΙΩΝ. Peacock standing r. on caduceus.
B.M.C. 201-8   ..   ..   F 50/-

1735 *Gordian III.* Æ 36. ΑΥΤ Κ Μ ΑΝΤ ΓΟΡΔΙΑΝΟC. Laur. and dr. bust r. ℞. CΑΜΙΩΝ.
Tetrastyle temple containing cultus-statue of Hera of Samos, etc. *B.M.C.* 294
F/fair £6

1736 *Etruscilla.* Æ 28. ΕΡΕΝ ΕΤΡΟΥCΚΙΛΛΑ CΕΒ. Bust r. ℞. CΑΜΙΩΝ. Nemesis standing
facing, veiled; at her feet, l., wheel. *B.M.C.* 359   ..   ..   .. VF £10

1737 *Gallienus.* Æ 28. ΑΥΤ Κ ΠΟ ΛΙΚΙΝ ΓΑΛΛΙΗΝΟC. Laur. and dr. bust r. ℞. CΑΜΙΩΝ.
Cultus statue of the Samian Hera and Nemesis facing. *B.M.C.* 375   F/VF £7

1727   1742

CARIA.

1738 **Alabanda** (Arab-hissar). *After* 168 B.C. Æ *tridrachm.* Laur. head of Apollo r. ℞.
ΑΛΑΒΑΝΔΕΩΝ. Pegasos galloping r.; all in laurel-wreath. *B.M.C.* 10   *R,* VF £60

1739 *Caracalla.* Æ 27. ΑV Κ Μ ΑVΡ ΑΝΤΩΝΙΝΟC. Laur. and dr. bust r. ℞. ΑΛΑΒΑΝΔΕΩΝ.
Lyre. *B.M.C.* 45 ..   ..   F 90/-

1740 **Alinda** (Demirjideresi). 2nd Cent. B.C. Æ 17. Laur. young male head r. ℞.
ΑΛΙΝΔΕΩΝ and winged thunderbolt within laurel-wreath. *B.M.C.* 8..   .. F 45/-

1740A **Amyzon.** Imperial Times. Æ 11. Bust of Artemis r. with quiver at shoulder. ℞.
ΑΜΥΣΟΝΕΩΝ. Flaming torch. *B.M.C.* 2   ..   ..   *RR,* F 65/-

1741 **Antiocheia ad Maeandrum.** Imperial Times. Æ 17. ΒΟΥΛΗ. Bust of the Boule
r. ℞. ΑΝΤΙΟΧΕΩΝ. Nike standing l., holding wreath and palm. *B.M.C.* 11 F 37/6

1742 **Aphrodisias.** Imperial Times. Æ 24. ΔΗΜΟC. Youthful bust of Demos r. ℞.
ΑΦΡΟΔΕΙCΙΕΩΝ. Aphrodite Eleutheria stg. l. *B.M.C.* 25   ..   .. VF 90/-

1743 Æ 25. ΙΕΡΑ CΥΝΚΛΗΤΟC. Youthful bust of the Senate r. ℞. Τ ΚΛΖΗΝΩΝ ΑΝΕΘ
ΑΦΡΟΔΙCΙΕΩΝ. Leafless tree with three branches; on either side of it a small figure
wearing Phrygian cap. *Cf. B.M.C.* 55 ..   ..   *R,* F 70/-

1744 *Augustus.* Æ 15. CΕΒΑCΤΟC. Laur. head r. ΑΦΡΟΔΙCΙΕΩΝ CΩΖΩΝ. Double-axe,
filleted. *B.M.C.* 90   ..   ..   F £42/-

1745 *Gallienus.* Æ 24. ΑΥ ΚΑΙ ΠΟ ΓΑΛΛΙΗΝΟC. Radiate and dr. bust l. ℞. ΑΦΡΟΔΕΙ-
CΙΕΩΝ. Tetrastyle temple containing cultus-statue of Aphrodite r. *B.M.C.* 133
F 70/-

1746 **Apollonia Salbace.** *Caracalla.* Æ 22. Greek legend. His laur. head r. ℞.
ΑΠΟΛΛΩΝΙΑΤΩΝ. Tyche standing l. *B.M.C.* 24   ..   .. *fair* 35/-

1746A **Astyra.** 4th Cent. B.C. Æ 10. Head of Aphrodite r. ℞. ΑΣΤΥ. Amphora; on r. oenochoë. *B.M.C.* 16 .. .. F 32/6

1747 **Attuda.** Imperial Times. Æ 21. ΙΕΡΑ ΒΟΥΛΗ. Bust of the Boule r. ˙℞. ΑΤΤΟΥ-ΔΕΩΝ. Tree: to r., altar. *B.M.C.* 24 .. .. F 45/-

1747A **Bargasa.** Imperial Times. Æ 20. As last. ℞. ΒΑΡΓΑ ΣΗΝΩΝ. Telesporus stg. front. *B.M.C.* 1 .. .. *fair* 40/-

1747B **Bargylia.** 1st Cent. B.C. Æ 19. Head of Artemis Kindyas r.; wreath border. ℞. ΒΑΡΓΥ ΛΙΗΤΩΝ. Pegasos flying r. *B.M.C.* 2 .. .. *R, fair* 32/6

1748 **Caunus.** *After* 166 B.C. Æ *hemidrachm.* Head of Athena r. ℞. ΚΑΥ. Sword in sheath, magistrate's name and symbol. *B.M.C.* 14-6 .. .. .. *R,* F £8˙

1748A Æ 10. Head of Apollo r. ℞. ΚΑΥ. Sword in sheath. *B.M.C.* 17 .. *fair* 30/-

1749 **Ceramus.** *After* 166 B.C. Æ *hemidrachm.* Laur. head of Zeus r. ℞. ΚΕΡΑΜΙΗ ΑΡΑ. Eagle l., head turned back. *Cf. B.M.C.* 1 .. .. .. *R, fair* 90/-

1749A **Cidramus.** *Elagabalus.* Æ 29. Laur. bust of Elagabalus dr. r. ℞. ΚΙΔΡΑΜΗΝΩΝ. Veiled goddess stg. facing. *B.M.C.* 8 .. .. *R, fair* 60/-

1750 **Cnidus.** 550-500 B.C. Æ *drachm.* Forepart of lion r. ℞. Head of Aphrodite r. within incuse square. *B.M.C.* 11 .. .. .. VF/*good* F £30

1750A 500-480 B.C. Æ *drachm.* As last but hair in lines instead of dots, finest style. *B.M.C.* 17 .. .. *good* VF/*nearly* EF £60

1750B 400-390 B.C. Æ *tetradrachm.* ΚΝΙ. Head of Aphrodite Euploia l., Σ on ampyx. ℞. ΕΟΒΩΛΟΣ beneath forepart of lion l. *B.M.C.* 24 .. .. .. *RR,* F £200

1751 390-300 B.C. Æ *drachm.* Head of Aphrodite Euploia, r. ℞. ΚΝΙ. Forepart of lion, r.: above, magistrate's name. *B.M.C.* 29/33 .. .. VF/F £7

1752 300-190 B.C. Æ *drachm.* As before but Aphrodite wears sphendone. *B.M.C.* 43 *good* F/VF £5

1753 Æ *tetrobol.* Head of Artemis r. ℞. ΚΝΙΔΙΩΝ and magistrate's name: tripod. *Cf. B.M.C.* 48/9 .. .. VF £6

1754 Æ 24. Type as last. *B.M.C.* 72 .. .. F 45/-

1755 Æ 13. *Obv.* as preceding. ℞. ΚΝΙ. Bull's head facing. *B.M.C.* 73 .. F 25/-

1756 1st Cent. B.C. Æ 27. Large head of young Dionysos l., wearing ivy-wreath. ℞. ΚΝΙΔΙΩΝ. Vine-branch with two bunches of grapes. *B.M.C.* 88 .. F/*fair* 45/-

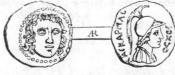

1750B   1759

1757 **Euromus** (Ayakly). 2nd Cent. B.C. Æ 15. Head of Zeus, laur., r. ℞. ΕΥΡΩΜΕΩΝ. Double-axe; all in wreath. *B.M.C.* 1 .. .. F 55/-

1758 **Halicarnassus.** 2nd-1st Cent. B.C. Æ 16. Head of Poseidon r. ℞. ΑΛΙΚΑΡ, and name. Trident-head with dolphins between the prongs. *B.M.C.* 20-37 F 32/6

1759 1st Cent. B.C. Æ *drachm.* Facing head of Helios. ℞. ΑΛΙΚΑΡΝΑΣ ΜΟΣΧΟΣ. Bust of Athena r. *B.M.C.* 46 .. .. *nearly* VF £20

1759A Æ 18. Head of Helios, radiate, r. ℞. ΑΛΙΚΑ ΔΙΟΝΥΣ. Lyre. *B.M.C.* 60 *fair*/F 25/-

1760 **Harpasa.** Imperial Times. Æ 16. ΑΘΗΝΑΓΟΡΟΥ. Bust of Athena r. ℞. ΑΡΠΑ-ΣΗΝΩΝ. Cultus statue of goddess. *B.M.C.* 2 .. .. .. *R,* F 65/-

1761 **Heraclea Salbace** (Makuf). Imperial Times. Æ 28. ΙΕΡΑ ΣΥΝΚΛΗΤΟΣ. Bust of the Senate l. ℞. ΗΡΑΚΛΕΩΤΩΝ. Sarapis seated l. *Not in B.M.C.* .. *fair* 50/-

1761A **Hydisus.** 1st Cent. B.C. Æ 19. Bust of Athena r. ℞. ΥΔΙΣΕΩΝ. Bearded figure stg. facing, looking r. *B.M.C.* 1 .. .. *R, fair* 50/-

1761B **Hyllarima.** Early Imperial Times. Æ 20. ΕΠΙΤΕΙΜΟΘΕΟΥ ΑΡΧΟΝΤΟΣ. Female head r., hair rolled. ℞. ΥΛΛΑΡΙΜΕΩΝ. Athena stg. front, head l. *B.M.C.* 1 *R, fair* 50/-

1762 **Iasus.** 280-190 B.C. *R drachm*. Head of Apollo, laur., r. ℞. IA. Youth (Hermias) and dolphin swimming r.: below, magistrate's name. *B.M.C.* 1-3

R, fair £8

1763 Æ 18. Types similar to preceding. *B.M.C.* 6-11 .. .. *fair* 25/–

1763A **Idyma.** 437-400 B.C. *R drachm*. Head of Pan full face. ℞. Incuse square in which ΙΔΥΜΙΟΝ around fig-leaf. *B.M.C.* 1 .. .. *R*, F £20

1763   1765A

1764 **Mylasa.** 2nd-1st Cent. B.C. Æ 16. Horse trotting r. ℞. ΜΥΛΑΣΕΩΝ. Ornamental trident. *B.M.C.* 9 .. .. F 37/6

1765 Æ 12. Double-axe. ℞. as preceding. *B.M.C.* 14 .. .. .. F 27/6

1765A Imperial Times. Æ 16. Free horse trotting l. ℞. ΜΥΛΑϹΕΩΝ. Double-axe, handle encircled by laurel-wreath. *B.M.C.* 17.. .. .. .. F 35/–

1766 *Septimius Severus.* Æ 25. ΑΥ Κ Λ Ϲ ϹΕΥΗΡΟϹ Π. Laur. and dr. bust r. ℞. ΜΥΛΑϹΕΩΝ. Ornamental trident and double-axe combined, handle standing on crab; all in wreath. *B.M.C.* 30 .. .. F 90/–

1767 *Geta.* Æ *medallion*, 38 *mm*. ΠΟ ϹΕΠΤΙΜΙΟϹ ΓΕΤΑϹ. Bare-headed bust dr. r. ℞. ΜΥΛΑϹΕΩΝ. Tetrastyle temple, within which cultus-statue of Zeus Labraundos facing, head l., holding double-axe and sceptre. *Cf. B.M.C.* 38   RRR, VF/F £50

1768 **Myndus.** 2nd-1st Cent. B.C. *R drachm*. Head of Zeus r. ℞. ΜΥΝΔΙΩΝ to l. of head-dress of Isis; to r., magistrate's name; below, symbol. *B.M.C.* 1-8 .. F £20

1768A Æ 16. Head of Zeus r. ℞. ΜΥΝΔΙΩΝ and magistrate's name. Winged thunderbolt. *B.M.C.* 18 .. .. F 32/6

1768B **Neapolis ad Harpasum** (Ineboli). *Gordian III.* Æ 21. Laur. bust dr. r. ℞. ΝΕΑΠΟΛΕΙΤΩΝ. Athena stg. front, head l. *B.M.C.* 1 .. .. .. *R, fair* 50/–

1768C **Orthosia** (Ortas). 1st Cent. B.C. Æ 18. ΟΡΘΩϹΙΕΩΝ. Head of Dionysos r. ℞. Magistrate's name and thyrsos filleted. *B.M.C.* 2 .. .. *R*, F 75/–

1769 **Plarasa and Aphrodisias.** 1st Cent. B.C. *R drachm*. Veiled bust of Aphrodite r. ℞. ΠΛΑΡΑΣΩΝ ΚΑΙ ΑΦΡΟΔΙΣΙΕΩΝ, magistrate's name. Eagle with closed wings l. on thunderbolt. *B.M.C.* 6-14 .. .. *R*, F £20

1768   1775A

1769A **Sebastopolis** (Kizilje). Imperial Times. Æ 19. Head of young Dionysos r. ℞. ϹΕΒΑϹΤΟΠΟΛΕΙΤΩΝ. Cista mystica. *B.M.C.* 2 .. .. .. *R, fair* 40/–

1770 **Stratoniceia** (Eski-Hissar). 166-88 B.C. *R hemidrachm*. Head of Zeus, laur., r. ℞. ΣΤ. Eagle r., wings open; all in shallow incuse square. *Cf. B.M.C.* 1-5   VF £8

1771 Æ 16. *Obv.* as preceding. ℞. ΣΤΡΑΤΟ. Eagle r., wings open, standing r. on torch. *B.M.C.* 9 .. .. F 30/–

1772 Imperial Times. Æ 24. ϹΤΡΑΤΟΝΙΚΕΩΝ. Zeus Panamaros radiate, on horseback r., holding sceptre and patera. ℞. ΨΗΦΙϹΑΜΕΝΟΥ ΦΛΑΥΒΙΟΥ ΔΙΟΜΗΔΟΥϹ. Hekate, with inflated veil, riding l. on lion. *B.M.C.* 42 .. .. VF £10

1773 **Tabae** (Davas). 1st Cent. B.C. Æ 15. Head of Zeus, laur., r. ℞. ΤΑΒΗΝΩΝ. Caps of the Dioskuri surmounted by stars. *Cf. B.M.C.* 4-12 .. .. .. *fair* 20/–

1774 Æ 14. Veiled female head r. ℞. ΤΑ. Forepart of humped bull r. *B.M.C.* 15

fair 20/–

1775 1st Cent. A.D. Æ *drachm.* Head of Athena r. ℞. ΤΑΒΗΝΩΝ and magistrate's name, Nike walking r. *B.M.C.* 21-25 .. .. VF £12

1775A — Another. ΤΑΒΗΝΩΝ. Head of young Dionysos r. ℞. Magistrate's name. Poseidon stg. r., dolphin behind. *B.M.C.* 29 .. .. F £6

1776 *Gallienus.* Æ 30. His bust r. ℞. ΕΠΙ ΑΡΧ ΔΟΜΕΣΤΙΧΟΥ ΤΑΒΗΝΩΝ. Poseidon l., foot on prow, holding Nike and trident. *B.M.C.* 102.. .. .. .. *fair* 37/6

1777 **Trapezopolis.** Imperial Times. Æ 23. ΙΕΡΑ CΥΝΚΛΗΤΟC. Dr. bust of Senate r. ℞. ΤΡΑΠΕΖΟΠΟΛΙΤΩΝ. Apollo standing r. *Grose* 8513 .. .. .. F 45/-

1777A **SATRAPS OF CARIA. Hecatomnus.** 395-377 B.C. Æ *drachm.* ΕΚΑ. Lion's head l. ℞. Ornamental star. *B.M.C.* (Miletus) 37. **Plate VI** .. .. EF £40

1778   1780

1778 **Mausolus.** 377-353 B.C. Æ *tetradrachm.* Head of Apollo, facing, with flowing hair. ℞. ΜΑΥΣΣΩΛΛΟ. Zeus Stratios standing r., holding double-axe over r. shoulder, and spear. *B.M.C.* 7 .. .. F/*fair* £40

1779 Æ *drachm.* Similar. *B.M.C.* 9 .. .. R, VF/*good* F £35

1779A **Hidrieus.** 351-344 B.C. Æ *drachm.* Similar but ΙΔΡΙΕΩΣ. *B.M.C.* 5 F £17/10/-

1780 **Pixodarus.** 340-334 B.C. Æ *didrachm.* Head of Apollo, facing, with flowing hair, chlamys fastened around neck. ℞. ΠΙΞΩΔΑΡΟ. Type as preceding. *B.M.C.* 5. **Plate VI** .. .. VF/EF £50

ISLANDS OFF CARIA.

1780A **ASTYPALAEA.** 2nd Cent. B.C. Æ 15. Head of Perseus r. wearing Phrygian helmet. ℞. ΑΣΤΥ. Head of Medusa facing. *B.M.C.* 5 .. .. .. F 42/-

1781 **CALYMNA.** 3rd Cent. B.C. Æ *didrachm.* Helmeted youthful male head r. ℞. ΚΑΛΥΜΝΙΟΝ below lyre. *B.M.C.* 3-9 .. .. .. VF/*good* F £32/10/-

1782 **CARPATHOS. Posidium.** 6th Cent. B.C. Æ *stater.* ΠΟΣ. Two dolphins, one above the other, swimming in opposite directions; underneath a third small dolphin. ℞. Deep incuse square, divided by broad band. *B.M.C.* 1 .. .. RR, *good* F£90

1783 **COS.** 366-300 B.C. Æ *didrachm.* Head of bearded Herakles r. ℞. ΚΩΙΟΝ. Veiled female head (Demeter ?) l. *Cf. B.M.C.* 20 *charming style, RR,* EF £350

1784 Æ 11. Veiled female head, r. ℞. ΚΩΙΟΝ. Crab: below, magistrate's name. *Cf. B.M.C.* 27-41 .. .. *fair* 25/-

1785 300-190 B.C. Æ *drachm.* Head of bearded Herakles, r. ℞. ΚΩΙΟΝ. Crab: below, club l. and ΠΟΛΥΑΡΧΟΣ. *B.M.C.* 63 .. .. *good* F £7

1786 Æ *hemidrachm.* Head of young Herakles r. ℞. ΚΩΙΟΝ above crab; ΔΗΜΤΗΡΙΟC below. *B.M.C.* 67 .. .. F 85/-

1787 190-166 B.C. Æ *drachm.* As No. 1785, but club r. and different magistrate's name. *B.M.C.* 76-83 .. .. F £5

1788 166-88 B.C. Æ *tetrobol.* Laur. head of Asklepios r. ℞. ΚΩ below coiled serpent; two magistrates' names; all in small incuse square. *B.M.C.* 132-155 .. VF £15

1789 88-50 B.C. Æ 24. Head of Apollo, r. ℞. ΚΩΙΩΝ. Lyre and ΕΥΚΡΑΤ: all in wreath. *B.M.C.* 174 .. .. F 40/-

1790 Æ 21. Head of Asklepios r. ℞. ΚΩΙΩΝ. Coiled serpent r., and magistrate's name. *B.M.C.* 194 .. .. *fair* 25/-

1791 *Trajan.* Æ 17. Greek legend. Laur. head r. ℞. ΚΩΙΩΝ. Club. *B.M.C.* 240 *fair* 25/-

1792 **MEGISTE.** 4th Cent. B.C. Æ *drachm.* Head of Helios with short hair, l., on rayed disk. ℞. ΜΕ. Open rose on stalk with bud either side. *B.M.C.* 1 *good* F £20

1793 **NISYROS.** 350-300 B.C. Æ 11. Head of Poseidon r. ℞. ΝΙ. Dolphin and trident. *B.M.C.* 2.. .. .. *fair* 25/-

1794 Æ 10. Female head, wearing stephane, r. Æ. ΝΙΣΥ. Dolphin and trident. *B.M.C.* 5 *fair* 25/-

1795 **RHODES : Camirus.** 600-500 B.C. Æ *stater*. Fig-leaf with sprouts between the lobes, and two tiny figs beside stalk. R. Incuse divided into two oblong compartments. *B.M.C.* 3 .. .. R, F £50

1796 Æ *tritemorion*. Fig leaf. R. Incuse square. *B.M.C.* 10.. .. R, F £7

1797 **Ialysus.** 500-408 B.C. Æ *hemidrachm*. Forepart of winged boar r. R. Eagle's head l., a floral volute above to l.; all in dotted square. *Bab.*, pl. xx, 13   R, F £40

1797A **Lindus.** 6th Cent. B.C. Æ *stater*. Lion's head r. R. ΛINDI reversed on central bar of divided incuse. *B.M.C.* 2 .. .. RR, VF £260

1797B 5th Cent. B.C. Æ *tetrobol*. Forepart of horse r. R. Lion's head l. in incuse square. *B.M.C.* 6 .. .. R, F £20

1798   1808A

1798 **Rhodus.** 400-333 B.C. Æ *tetradrachm*. Head of Helios three-quarter r., hair loose. R. POΔION. Rose, pendant bud on r.: symbol, sphinx on l. *B.M.C.* 11.. F £75

1798A Æ *didrachm*. As before: in field, l., symbol and EY. *B.M.C.* 27-36
F/fair £6; good F £12/10/-

1799 333-304 B.C. Æ *trihemiobol*. Head of Helios, radiate, r. R. P O. Two rose-buds; above, symbol. *B.M.C.* 63-69 .. .. F 65/-

1800 Æ 10. P O. Rose. R. Rose with bud. *B.M.C.* 70 .. .. .. F 21/-

1801 Æ 10. Head of Rhodos, wearing stephanos, r. R. P O. Rose with bud. *B.M.C.* 74 .. .. fair 15/-

1802 304-166 B.C. Æ *tetradrachm*. Head of Helios, radiate, slightly to r. R. POΔION. Rose with bud to r., and prow in field l.: below, AMEINIAΣ. *B.M.C.* 120
rev. slightly off-centre, otherwise VF/EF £45

1803 Æ *didrachm*. *Obv.* as preceding. R. PO. Type as preceding: in field, l., Athena advancing l.; above, MNAΣIMAXOΣ. *B.M.C.* 143 .. .. .. VF £22/10/-

1804 Æ *drachm*. Head of Helios, not radiate, slightly to r. R. P O. Rose with bud to r.: to l., bow in case: above, ΓOPΓOΣ. *B.M.C.* 164 .. .. .. VF £8

1805 Æ 18. Head of Zeus, laur., r. R. P O. Rose with bud on r.: in field, l., ΦI. *B.M.C.* 219 .. .. F 32/6

1806 166-88 B.C. Æ *drachm*. Head of Helios, radiate, r. R. P O. Rose with bud: to l., symbol: above, magistrate's name: all in incuse square. *B.M.C.* 235-290 VF £6

1807 Æ 14. Head of Rhodos, radiate, r. R. P O. Rose: all in incuse square. *B.M.C.* 327 .. .. fair 15/-; F 30/-

1808 88-43 B.C. Æ *drachm*. Head of Helios, radiate, three-quarter r. R. P O. Full-blown rose to front: magistrate's name and symbol. *B.M.C.* 335-341   good VF £12

1808A Æ 35. Facing head of Helios radiate. R. PO. Full-blown rose; magistrate's name, ZHNΩN; all in wreath. *B.M.C.* 342 .. .. R, fair £6

1809 Æ 18. Head of Helios, radiate, r. R. Similar to preceding. *B.M.C.* 348 F 27/6

1810 Æ 19. *Obv.* as preceding. R. POΔIΩN around four-petalled rose. *B.M.C.* 359
F 32/6

1811 43 B.C.-96 A.D. Æ 35. Head of Dionysos, radiate and wearing ivy-wreath, r. R. POΔIΩN. Nike standing l. on globe, holding wreath and palm: in field, EΠI and magistrate's name. *B.M.C.* 364-384 .. .. R, F £8

1812 Æ 34 *didrachm*. POΔIOI YΠEP TΩN CEBACTON. Bust of Tyche, turreted, r. R. ΔIAΡAXMON. Helios, radiate, standing l., crowning trophy. *Not in B.M.C.* R, F £12

1812A **TELOS.** 4th Cent. B.C. Æ 14. Head of Athena facing, in helmet with three crests. R. THΛI. Crab .. .. R, fair 40/-

LYDIA.

1812B 7th and 6th Cent. B.C. Electrum *third*. Lion's head r., globule on nose. ℞. Rectangle divided by central line into two incuse squares. *B.M.C.* 2. **Plate VI**
VF £62/10/–

1813 Time of Croesus, 561-546 B.C. *N stater*. Foreparts of lion r. and bull l., face to face ℞. Two small incuse squares, side by side. *B.M.C.* 2 .. .. .. VF £275

1814 — *R stater*. Type as preceding. *B.M.C.* 37 .. .. EF £100

1815 — *R half-stater* or *siglos*. Types as preceding. *B.M.C.* 41. **Plate VI** .. VF £30

1816 **Acrasus.** Time of Septimius Severus. Æ 13. Head of bearded Herakles r. ℞. ΑΚΡΑCΙΟΤΟΝ. Telesphoros facing. *B.M.C.* 5 .. .. *R*, F 37/6

1817 **Aninetus.** 2nd Cent. B.C. Æ 18. Laur. head of Apollo r. ℞. ΑΝΙΝΗΣΙΩΝ ΔΙΟΔΟ. Horse standing l. *B.M.C.* 1 .. .. *R, fair* 40/–

1817A **Apollonis.** Imperial Times. Æ 25. ΘΕΟΝCVΝ ΚΛΗΤΟΝ. Youthful male bust of the Roman Senate r. ℞. ΑΠΟΛΛΩΝΙΔΕΩΝ. Eagle stg. on bone. *B.M.C.* 5 .. F 75/–

1817B **Apollonos-hieron** or **Apollonieron.** Imperial Times. Æ 16. Bust of Athena or Roma r. ℞. ΑΠΟΛΛΩΝΙΕΡΙΤΩΝ. Zeus Lydios stg. l. *B.M.C.* 1 .. *fair* 30/–

1818 **Attalea.** Imperial Times. Æ 16. Head of Dionysos r. ℞. ΑΤΤΑΛΕΑΤΩΝ. Dancing Pan l., holding bunch of grapes and lagobolon. *B.M.C.* 3 .. ..˙ *R, fair* 35/–

1819 **Bagis.** *Geta.* Æ 24. Greek legend. His young dr. bust r. ℞. ΕΠΙ ΓΑΙΟV ΑΡΧ ΒΑΓΗΝΩΝ. Asklepios and Hygieia facing with Telesphoros between them. *B.M.C.* 47
F 75/–

1820 — in alliance with **Temenothyrae.** *Gallienus.* Æ 35. Greek legend. His bust r. ℞. ΚΑΙCΑΡΕΩΝΒΑΓΗΝΩΝ ΤΙΙΜΕΝΟΘΥΡΕΩΝ, in ex. ΟΜΟΝΟΙΑ. Mên and Tyche standing face to face. *B.M.C.* 54 .. .. *R, fair* £5

1821 **Blaundus** (Suleimanli). 2nd-1st Cent. B.C. Æ 20. Head of Zeus, laur., r. ℞. ΜΛΑΥΝ-ΔΕΩΝ ΘΕΟΤΙΜΙΔΟ. Eagle standing l., head r., between caduceus and corn-ear. *B.M.C.* 1
F 40/–

1821A **Briula.** *Antoninus Pius.* Æ 25. Greek legend. His laur. head r. ℞. ΒΡΙΟVΛΕΙΤΩΝ ΟΛΥΜΠΙΟC ΖΕVC. Zeus Olympios seated l. *B.M.C.* 4.. .. .. .. *R*, F £5

1821B **The Caÿstriani.** 2nd or 1st Cent. B.C. Æ 16. Hd. of Apollo r. ℞. ΚΑΥCΤΡΝΩΝΑΙ. Winged caduceus. *B.M.C.* 2 .. .. *fair* 32/6

1821C **The Cilbiani Superiores.** *Domitia.* Æ 21. ΔΟΜΙΤΙΑCΕ ΒΑCΤΗ. Her bust r. ℞. ΚΙΛΒΙΑΝΩΝΤΩΝΑΝΩ. Cultus-statue of Artemis Ephesia. *B.M.C.* 1 *R, fair* £5

1821D **The Cilbiani Inferiores** or **Nicaei.** Time of Caracalla. Æ 21. ΝΕΙΚΕΑ. Bust of city-goddess Nicaea r., turreted. ℞. ΚΙΛΒΙΑΝΩΝ. Dionysos stg. holding kantharos over panther and leaning on thyrsos. *B.M.C.* 4 .. .. *fair* 35/–

1821E **Clannudda.** 2nd or 1st Cent. B.C. Æ 20. Laur. head of Zeus r. ℞. ΚΛΑΝΝΟΥ-ΔΔΕΩΝ and eagle in wreath. *B.M.C.* 2 .. .. *R, fair* 42/–

1821F **Daldis.** Time of Severus. Æ 23. ΙΕΡΑCVΝΚΛΗΤΟC. Young male bust of Senate dr. r. ℞. ΔΑΛΔΙΑΝΩΝ. Zeus Lydios stg. l. *B.M.C.* 6 .. .. .. F 50/–

1821G **Dioshieron.** Time of the Antonines. Æ 16. ΔΗΜΟC. Bust of bearded Demos r. ℞. ΔΙΟCΙΕΡΕΙΤΩΝ. Asklepios stg. facing. *B.M.C.* 2 .. .. .. F 42/–

1822 **Germe ad Caïcum.** Imperial Times. Æ 16. ΙΕΡΑ CVΝΚΛΗΤΟC. Bust of the Senate r. ℞. ΓΕΡΜΗΝΩΝ. Bust of Apollo r. *B.M.C.* 1.. .. .. .. F 32/6

1823 *Trajan.* Æ 18. Greek legend. His laur. head r. ℞. As last. *B.M.C.* 16 F 47/6

1824 **Gordus-Julia** (Giordiz). Time of Commodus. Æ 15. ΙΟVΛΙΑ ΓΟΡΔΟC. Bust of Tyche r. ℞. ΙΟVΛ · ΓΟΡΔΗΝΩΝ. Cultus statue of Artemis Ephesia. *B.M.C.* 10 .. *fair* 25/–

1825 **Hermocapelia.** Time of Hadrian. Æ 15. ΘΕΟΝ CVΝΚΛΗΤΟΝ. Bust of the Senate r. ℞. ΕΡΜΟΚΑΠΗΛΙΤΩΝ. Dr. bust of Roma r. *B.M.C.* 11 .. .. *R*, F 45/–

1825A **Hieracome,** later **Hierocaesareia.** Time of Nero. Æ 16. ΕΠΙ ΚΑΠΙΤΩΝΟC. Bust of Artemis Persica r., with bow and quiver at her back. ℞. ΙΕΡΟΚΑΙCΑΡΕΩΝ. Artemis r. pulling down stag by the horns. *B.M.C.* 4 .. .. F 45/–

1826 **Hypaepa.** *Gordian III.* Æ 22. Greek legend. His laur. bust dr. r. ℞. ΥΠΑΙΠ-
ΗΝΩΝ CT · ΑΙ · ΑΝΤ ΤΑΕΤΑ. Two children seated on the ground below statue of Artemis-
Anaïtis. *B.M.C.* 59 .. .. F 65/-

1827 **Hyrcanis.** 2nd-3rd Cent. A.D. Æ 17. ΥΡΚΑΝΙC. Dr. and turreted bust of Hyrcanis
r. ℞. ΥΡΚΑΝΩΝ. Tyche standing l. *B.M.C.* 11 .. .. .. *R, fair* 32/6

1828 **Maeonia** (Menne). Time of Trajan Decius. Æ 25. ΙΕΡΑ CΥΝΚΛΗΤΟC. Bust of the
Senate l. ℞. ΕΠΙ ΑΥΡ ΑΠΦΙΑΝΟΥ Β ΑΡΧ ΜΑΙΟΝΩΝ. Cultus-statue of Kore facing.
B.M.C. 26 .. .. F 50/-

1829 *Nero.* Æ 18. ΝΕΡΩΝ ΚΑΙΣΑΡ. Laur. head r. ℞. ΕΠ ΤΙ ΚΛ ΜΕΝΕΚΡΑΤΟΥC ΜΑΙΟΝΩΝ.
Hestia standing r., veiled, holding sceptre. *B.M.C.* 32 .. .. .. F 60/-

1830 **Magnesia ad Sipylum** (Manisa). 2nd cent. B.C. Æ 22. Head of Herakles r. ℞. ΜΑΓ-
ΝΗΤΩΝ ΣΙΠΥΛΟΥ. Athena standing l., holding Nike. *B.M.C.* 8-10 .. *fair* 20/-

1830A *Proconsul M. Tullius Cicero Junior,* after B.C. 30. Æ 23. ΜΑΡΚΟΣ ΤΥΛΛΙΟΣ ΚΙΚΕΡΩΝ.
His bare head r. ℞. ΜΑΓΝΗΤΩΝΤΩΝ ΑΠΟ ΣΙΠΥΛΟΥ. Right hand holding wreath, two
ears of corn and vine-branch; in field, ΘΕΟΔΩΡΟC. *B.M.C.* 15 .. *RR, fair* £10

1830A   1839

1831 Imperial Times. Æ 18. CΙΠΥΛΟC. Bearded bust of Mt. Sipylos r. ℞. ΜΑΓΝ-
ΗΤΩΝ. Asklepios standing facing, head l., holding serpent-staff. *B.M.C.* 28 VF 85/-

1832 Æ 15. ΜΑΓΝΗCΙΑ. Bust of Tyche r. ℞. CΙΠΥΛΟΥ. Tripod. *B.M.C.* 34 F 35/-

1833 *Crispina.* Æ 19. ΚΡΙCΠΕΙΝΑ CΕΒΑCΤΗ. Bust r. ℞. ΜΑΓΝΗΤΩΝ CΙΠΥΛΟ. River-
god Hermos reclining l. *Not in B.M.C.* .. .. F 75/-

1834 **Mastaura.** *Maximinus.* Æ 21. Greek legend: bust r. ℞. ΜΑCΤΑΥΡΕΙΤΩΝ. Humped r. *B.M.C.* 14 .. .. *fair*/F 37/6

1835 *Philip II.* Æ 22. Greek legend; bust r. ℞. ΜΑCΤΑΥΡΕΙΤΩΝ. Leto running l.,
carrying her two children pursued by Python. *B.M.C.* 19 .. .. *fair* 32/6

1836 **Mostene.** *Claudius and Agrippina.* Æ 22. Greek legend. Their jugate heads r.
℞. Greek legend. Horseman r.; in ex. ΜΟCΤΗΝΩΝ. *B.M.C.* 7 .. *R, fair* 65/-

1837 **Nacrasa** (Bakir). Imperial Times. Æ 22. ΘΕΟΝ CΥΝΚΛΗΤΟΝ. Bust of the Senate r.
℞. ΝΑΚΡΑCΙΤΩΝ. Cultus-statue of Artemis Ephesia facing between two stags. *B.M.C.* 1
F 47/6

1838 *Trajan.* Æ 17. ΑΥ ΝΕΡ ΤΡΑΙΑΝΟΝ CΕ ΓΕΡ. Laur. head r. ℞. ΝΑΚΡΑCΙΤΩΝ. Statue
of Artemis r., in shrine. *B.M.C.* 16 .. .. VF/F 65/-

1839 **Nysa.** 2nd cent. B.C. Æ 20. Head of young Dionysos r. ℞. ΝΥCΑΕΩΝ. Hades
carrying off Persephone in quadriga r. *B.M.C.* 17 .. .. .. *fair* 32/6

1840 *Faustina II.* Æ 20. ΦΑΥCΤΕΙΝΑ CΕΒΑCΤΗ. Bust r. ℞. ΝΥCΑΕΩΝ. Infant Ploutos
seated l. on cornucopiae. *B.M.C.* 47 .. .. F 65/-

1841 **Philadelphia** (Alasehir). 2nd-1st Cent. B.C. Æ 15. Heads of the Dioskuri jugate and
laur., r. ℞. ΦΙΛΑΔΕΛΦΕΩΝ. Pilei of the Dioskuri, each surmounted by star. *B.M.C.* 19
fair 25/-

1841A 3rd Cent. A.D. Æ 23. ΔΗΜΟC. Head of young Demos r. ℞. ΦΛ ΦΙΛΑΔΕΛΦΕΩΝΝΕ.
Lion walking r.; in ex. ΩΚΟΡΩΝ. *B.M.C.* 41 .. .. F 50/-

1841B *Caligula.* Æ 14. ΓΑΙΟC ΚΑΙCΑΡ. His head r., star behind. ℞. ΦΙΛΑ / ΔΕΛΦΕΩΝ /
ΜΕΛΑΝΘΟΣ / Thunderbolt / ΙΕΡΕΥΣ ΓΕΡ / ΜΑΝΚΟ / Υ. *B.M.C.* 51 .. *fair*/F 37/6

1841C *Julia Domna.* Æ 27. ΙΟΥΛΙΑ CΕΒΑCΤΗ. Her bust r. ℞. ΕΠΙ ΚΙΛΚΑΠΙΤΩΝ ΟCΑΡΧΦΛ
and in ex. ΦΙΛΑΑΕΛΦΕΩΝ / ΝΕΩΚΟΡΩΝ. Agonistic table. *B.M.C.* 79.. .. F £5

1841D Alliance with **Smyrna.** Time of Caracalla. Æ 26. ΔΗΜΟC ΦΙΛΑΔΕΛΦΕΩΝ ΝΕΩΚ.
Youthful bust of Demos r. ℞. Κ CΜΥΡ . Γ . ΝΕΩΚ . ΟΜ. Kybele seated l. *B.M.C.* 113
fair 42/-

1842 **Saïtta** (Sidas Kale). Imperial Times. Æ 23. ΖΕΥC ΠΑΤΡΙΟC. Head of Zeus, wearing
taenia, r. ℞. ΕΠΙ ΑΡΤΕΜΙΔΩΡΟΥ ΑΡΧΑ CΑΙΤΤΗΝΩΝ. Apollo standing r., holding plectrum
and lyre. *B.M.C.* 6 .. .. *R, good* F 90/-

1843 Æ 22. ΔΗΜΟϹ ϹΑΙΤΤΗΝΩΝ. Youthful bust of Demos, laur., r. Ꞧ. ΕΠΙ ΑΤΤΙΚΟΥ ΑΡΧ Α ΤΟΒ. Kybele seated l. on throne, holding phiale. *B.M.C.* 9   *good* F   65/-
1844 Philip II. Æ 22. Μ ΙΟΥΛΙ ΦΙΛΙΠΠΟϹ Κ. Bust r. Ꞧ. ϹΑΙΤΤΗΝΩΝ. Athena standing l., holding phiale. *B.M.C.* 70 .. .. *fair* 32/6
1844A **Sala.** Time of Trajan. Æ 19. ϹΑΛΗΝΩΝ. Bust of Athena or Roma r. Ꞧ. ΕΠΙ ΑΛΕϹΙΕ ΡΕΩϹ. Kybele seated l.; at her feet, lion r. *B.M.C.* 8 .. .. *fair* 35/-
1845 **Sardes.** 2nd cent. B.C. Æ 15. Head of Apollo, laur., r. Ꞧ. ϹΑΡΔΙΑΝΩΝ. Club : all in oak-wreath. *B.M.C.* 10/21 .. .. F 35/-
1846 Æ 20. Bust of Tyche, turreted, r. Ꞧ. ϹΑΡΔΙΑΝΩΝ. Zeus Lydios standing l., holding eagle and sceptre: in field, l., monogram. *B.M.C.* 49/52 .. .. F 45/-
1847 *Hadrian.* Æ 23. Greek legend: laur. bust r. Ꞧ. ΠΑΦΙΗ ϹΑΡΔΙΑΝΩΝ. Temple of Aphrodite Paphia. *B.M.C.* 134 .. .. F £5

1847A 3rd Cent. A.D. Æ 42. As illustration. Head of city-goddess. Ꞧ. The rape of Persephone: Hades in quadriga carrying off struggling Persephone; Eros flying above horses heads carrying two torches. *B.M.C.* 89 .. .. .. R, F £32/10/-
1847B **Silandus.** *Domitian.* Æ 20. Greek legend. His laur. head r. Ꞧ. ϹΙΛΑΝΔΕΩΝ. Athena stg. l. *B.M.C.* 16 .. .. *fair* 45/-
1847C **Stratoniceia-Hadrianopolis** or **Indi-Stratoniceia.** *Hadrian.* Æ 19. As last. Ꞧ. ΑΔΡΙΑΝΟΠΟϹ and two mon. Zeus enthroned l. *B.M.C.* 10 .. .. *fair* 42/-
1848 **Tabala.** Imperial Times. Æ 20. ϹΥΝΚΛΗΤΟϹ. Dr. bust of Senate r. Ꞧ. ΤΑΒΑΛΕΩΝ. River-god Hermos recumbent l., ΕΡΜΟϹ in ex. *B.M.C.* 1 .. R, F 65/-
1849 **Thyatira** (Akhisar). Imperial Times. Æ 15. Head of bearded Herakles r. Ꞧ. ΘΥΑΤΕΙ ΡΗΝΩΝ. Eagle, wings open and head r. *B.M.C.* 43 .. .. F 30/-
1850 *Nero.* Æ 17. Greek legend: bust r. Ꞧ. Legend as preceding: double-axe. *B.M.C.* 58/64 .. .. *fair* 35/-

1850A Time of Sev. Alexander. Æ 19. ΘΥΑΤΕΙΡΑ. Turreted bust of city-goddess dr. r. Ꞧ. ΘΥΑΤΕΙΡΗΝΩΝ. Homonoia stg. l. *B.M.C.* 56 .. .. F 40/-
1850B Alliance of Thyatira and Smyrna. Æ 21. ΒΟΡΕΙΤΗΝΑ. Bust of Artemis Boreitene l. Ꞧ. ΘΥΑΤΚϹΜΥΡ ΟΜΟΝΟΙΑ. Poseidon r., foot on prow. *B.M.C.* 146 .. .. *fair* 35/-
1850C **Tmolus Aureliopolis.** *Commodus.* Æ 33. Greek legend. Laur. bust dr. and cuir. r. Ꞧ. ΑΠΟΛΛΩΝΙ ΔΗϹϹΤΡ . ΑΝΕΘ. Apollo in car drawn by two griffins galloping r.; ΑΥΡΗ below horses; ΛΙΟΠΟΛΕΙ in ex. *B.M.C.* 2 .. .. .. R, *fair* £5
1850D **Tomaris.** 3rd Cent. A.D. Æ 14. Head of bearded Herakles r. Ꞧ. ΤΟΜΑΡΗΝΩΝ. Lion walking r. *B.M.C.* 2 .. .. RR, *fair* 50/-
1851 **Tralles.** 2nd Cent. B.C. Ꞧ *cistophorus.* Cista mystica from which issues serpent. Ꞧ. ΤΡΑΛ. Two coiled serpents with bow-case between them; to r., thunderbolt. *B.M.C.* 7 .. .. R, VF £21
1852 **Tripolis.** Imperial Times. Æ 20. Bust of Athena, helmeted, l. Ꞧ. ΤΡΙΠΟΛΕΙΤΩΝ. Zeus Lydios standing l., holding eagle and sceptre. *B.M.C.* 10 .. *fair* 25/-
1853 Æ 25. ΔΗΜΟϹ ΤΡΙΠΟΛΕΙΤΩΝ. Bust of Demos r. Ꞧ. ΖΕΥϹ ϹΑΡΑΠΙϹ. Zeus Sarapis seated l., holding sceptre. *B.M.C.* 34 .. .. VF/F 75/-

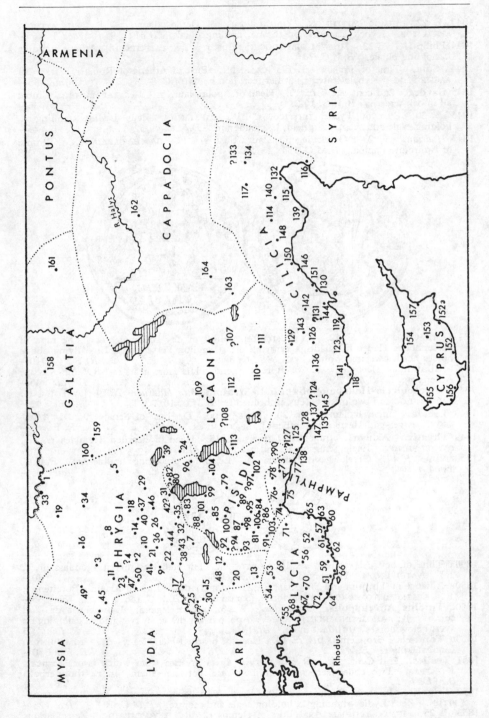

Phrygia
1 Accilaëum
2 Acmoneia
3 Aezanis
4 Alia ?
5 Amorium
6 Ancyra
7 Apameia
8 Appia
9 Bria
10 Bruzus
11 Cadi
12 Ceretapa
13 Cibyra
14 Cidyessus
15 Colossae
16 Cotiaeum
17 Dionysopolis
18 Docimeium
19 Dorylaëum
20 Eriza
21 Eucarpeia
22 Eumeneia
23 Grimenothyrae
24 Hadrianopolis-Sebaste
25 Hierapolis
26 Hieropolis
27 Hydrela ?
28 The Hyrgaleis
29 Julia (Ipsus)
30 Laodiceia ad Lycum
31 Lysias
32 Metropolis
33 Midaëum
34 Nacoleia
35 Ococleia
36 Otrus
37 Palaeobeudos or
       Beudos Vetos
38 Peltae
39 Philomelium
40 Prymnessus
41 Sebaste
42 Sibidunda ?
43 Siblia
44 Stectorium
45 Synaüs
46 Synnada
47 Temenothyrae
       Flaviopolis
48 Themisonium
49 Tiberiopolis ?
50 Trajanopolis

Lycia
51 Antiphellus
52 Arycanda
53 Balbura
54 Bubon
55 Calynda

56 Choma
57 Corydalla
59 Cyane
60 Gagae
61 Limyra
62 Myra
63 Olympus
64 Patara
65 Phaselis
66 Phellus
67 Pinara
68 Telmessus
69 Termessus Minor ?
70 Tlos
71 Trebenna
72 Xanthus

Pamphylia
73 Aspendus
74 Attalia
75 Magydus
76 Perga
77 Side
78 Sillyum

Pisidia
79 Adada
80 Amblada ?
81 Andeda
82 Antiocheia
83 Apollonia Mordiaeum
84 Ariassus
85 Baris
86 Codrula ?
87 Comama
88 Conana
89 Cremna
90 Etenna ?
91 Isinda
92 Lysinia
93 Olbasa
94 Palaeopolis ?
95 Panemoteichos
              (Cretopolis)
96 Pappa Tiberia
97 Pednelissus
98 Pogla
99 Prostanna
100 Sagalassus
101 Seleuceia
102 Selge
103 Termessus Major
104 Timbriada
106 Verbe

Lycaonia
107 Barata ?
108 Dalisandus
109 Iconium
110 Ilistra
111 Laranda

112 Lystra
113 Parlais

Cilicia
114 Adana
115 Aegeae
116 Alexandria ad Issum
117 Anazarbus
118 Anemurium
119 Aphrodisias
123 Celenderis
124 Cestrus
125 Cibyra Minor
126 Claudiopolis and/or
       Ninica Claudiopolis
127 Colybrassus ?
128 Coracesium
129 Coropissus
130 Corycus
131 Diocaesareia ?
132 Epiphaneia
133 Flaviopolis
134 Hieropolis-Castabala
135 Iotape
136 Irenopolis
137 Laerte
138 Lyrbe ?
139 Mallus
140 Mopsus or Mopsuestia
141 Nagidus
142 Olba
143 Philadelphia
144 Seleuceia ad
             Calycadnum
145 Selinus
146 Soli-Pompeiopolis
147 Syedra
148 Tarsus
149 Titiopolis
150 Zephyrium-
             Hadrianopolis
151 Elaeusa-Sebaste

Cyprus
152 Amathus
152a Citium
153 Idalium
154 Lapethus
155 Marium
156 Paphos (New and Old)
157 Salamis

Galatia
158 Ancyra
159 Germa
160 Pessinus
161 Tavium

Cappadocia
162 Caesareia
163 Cybistra
164 Tyana

PHRYGIA.

1854 **The Abbaëtae-Mysi.** 190-133 B.C. Æ 18. Head of Zeus, laur., r. ℞. ΜΥΣΩΝ ΑΒΒΑΙΤ-ΩΝ. Thunderbolt: all within wreath. *B.M.C.* 1 .. .. .. *good* F 40/-

1854A **Accilaëum.** *Gordian III.* Æ 27. Greek legend. His laur. bust dr. and cuir. r. ℞. ΑΚΚΙΛΑΕΩΝ. Mên stg. r. *B.M.C.* 1 .. .. .. *RR, fair* 60/-

1855 **Acmoneia.** 1st Cent. B.C. Æ 20. Bust of Athena r. ℞. ΑΚΜΟΝΕ[ΩΝ]. Eagle flying r. on thunderbolt between two stars; magistrate's name in ex. *B.M.C.* 1 *fair* 25/-

1855A *Nero.* Æ 19. ΑΥΤΟΚΡΑΤΩΡ ΝΕΡΩΝ ΚΛΑΥΔΙΟΣ ΚΑΙΣΑΡ ΣΕΒΑΣΤΟΣ ΓΕΡΜΑΝΙΚΟΣ. Bust r. ℞. ΕΠΙ ΛΕΥΚΙΟΥ ΣΕΡΟΥΗΝΙΟΥ ΚΑΠΙΤΩΝΟΣ ΑΚΜΟΝΕΩΝ. Zeus seated r. *B.M.C.* 37 .. .. *good* F 70/-

1856 *Gallienus.* Æ 28. ΑΥΤ Κ ΠΟΥ ΛΙΚ ΓΑΛΙΗΝΟΣ. Laur. bust r. ℞. ΑΚΜΟΝΕΩΝ. Cultus-statue of Artemis Ephesia facing. *B.M.C.* 111 .. .. .. *fair* 45/-

1855   1859A

1857 **Aezanis.** 1st cent. B.C. Æ 19. Head of Tyche l. ℞. ΕΖΕΑΝΙΤΩΝ. Dionysos standing l., with kantharos and thyrsos. *B.M.C.* 2 .. .. .. *fair* 21/-

1858 *Caligula.* Æ 20. ΓΑΙΟΣ ΚΑΙΣΑΡ. Laur. head r. ℞. ΑΙΖΑΝΙΤΩΝ ΕΠΙ ΜΗΔΗΟΥ. Zeus of Aezanis standing l., holding eagle and sceptre. *B.M.C.* 58 .. .. *fair* 32/6

1859 *Claudius.* Æ 18. Greek legend: laur. head r. ℞. ΕΠΙ ΚΛΑΥΔΙΟΥ ΙΕΡΑΚΟΣ. Type as preceding. *B.M.C.* 85. .. .. *fair*/F 32/6

1859A 3rd Cent. A.D. Æ 25. ΔΗΜΟΣ ΑΙΣΑΝΕΙΤΩΝ. Young male head of Demos r. ℞. ΑΙΖΑΝΕΙΤΩΝ. Tyche stg., looking r. *B.M.C.* 31 .. .. .. F 47/6

1860 **Alia.** *Gordian III.* Æ 25. Greek legend; his laur. bust dr. r. ℞. ΑΛΙΗΝΩΝ. Dionysos standing l. with panther. *B.M.C.* 12 .. .. F 75/-

1860A **Amorium.** *After* 133 B.C. Æ 18. Head of Zeus r. in oak-wreath. ℞. ΑΜΟΡΙΑΝΩΝ. Eagle on thunderbolt r.; in field, mon. *B.M.C.* 5 .. .. *fair* 25/-

1860B Time of M. Aurelius or later. Æ 23. ΘΕΑΡΩΜΗ. Bust of Roma r. ℞. ΑΜΟΡΙΑΝΩΝ. Two right hands clasped. *B.M.C.* 17 .. .. F 50/-

1861 **Ancyra.** Time of Septimius Severus. Æ 21. ΙΕΡΑ ΣΥΝΚΛΗΤΟΣ. Draped bust of the Senate r. ℞. ΑΝ / ΚΥΡΑ / ΝΩΝ in laurel-wreath. *B.M.C.* 11 .. .. F 45/-

1861   1863

1862 **Apameia.** 133-48 B.C. Æ 21. Head of Zeus r. ℞. ΑΠΑΜΕ and magistrate's name: cultus-statue of Artemis Anaïtis. *B.M.C.* 33-36 .. *fair* 17/6; F 35/-

1863 Æ 22. Helmeted bust of Athena r. ℞. ΑΠΑΜΕΩΝ. Eagle flying r. above maeander pattern between pilei of the Dioskuri: below, magistrate's name. *B.M.C.* 52-60 *fair* 17/6; F 35/-

1864 Æ 16. Turreted head of Artemis r. ℞. ΑΠΑΜΕ ΠΑΝΚΡ ΖΗΝΟ. Marsyas r., playing double flute. *B.M.C.* 91 .. .. F/*fair* 25/-

1865 **Appia** (Abia). Æ 19. Imperial Times. ΒΟΥΛΗ. Veiled bust of the Boule r. ℞. ΕΠ ΑΝΤΕΡ ΑΡΧ ΑΠΠΙΑΝΩΝ. Dionysos standing l., with kantharos and thyrsos. *B.M.C.* 4 *good* F 52/6

1866 **Bria.** Imperial Times. Æ 20. Bust of Sarapis r. ℞. ΒΡΙΑΝΩΝ. Isis standing l., holding sistrum and situla. *B.M.C.* 1 .. .. *R*, F 65/–

1866A **Bruzus** (Kara-Sandukli). *Gordian III.* Æ 24. Greek legend. His laur. bust dr. and cuir. r. ℞. ΒΡΟΥΖΗΝΩΝ. Hekate stg. r. *B.M.C.* 30 .. .. .. F 55/–

1867 **Cadi** (Gediz). *Claudius.* Æ 18. ΚΛΑΥΔΙΟΣ ΚΑΙΣΑΡ. Laur. head r. ℞. ΚΑΔΟΗΝΩΝ (in field); around, magistrate's name: Zeus Laodikeus standing l., holding eagle and sceptre. *B.M.C.* 16 .. .. *good* F 65/–

1867A **Ceretapa** (Kayadibi). Time of Caracalla. Æ 19. Head of young Herakles r. ℞. ΚΕΡΕΤΑΠΕΩΝ. Club and bow-case containing strung bow. *B.M.C.* 3 .. *fair* 35/–

1868 **Cibyra.** 166-84 B.C. Æ *tetradrachm.* Youthful male bust r. in crested helmet. ℞. ΚΙΒΥΡΑΤΩΝ in ex. Horseman galloping r.; behind, bee; ΑΚΕΔΟΔΙ below horses. *B.M.C.* 4 *R*, F £60

1868A Æ *drachm.* As before but eagle r. behind and nothing below horse. *B.M.C.* 9 F £10

1869 Imperial Times. Æ 19. Head of Helios, radiate, r. ℞. ΚΙΒΥΡΑΤΩΝ. Wicker basket. *B.M.C.* 26 .. .. *R*, VF £5

1870 *Diadumenian.* Æ 30. Μ ΟΠΕΛ . ΑΝΤΩΝΙΝΟC ΔΙΑ. Κ. Bare head, dr. bust r. ℞. ΚΙΒΥΡΑΤΩΝ. Zeus seated l. on throne, holding phiale and sceptre: at his feet, eagle. *Cf. B.M.C.* 56 .. .. *RRR*, VF £30

1871 *Trajan Decius.* Æ 24. ΑΥΤ ΚΑΙ ΤΡΑΙΑΝΟC ΔΕΚΙΟC. Rad. and dr. bust r. ℞. ΚΙΒΥΡΑΤΩΝ. Distyle shrine, containing wicker basket. *B.M.C.* 87.. .. F 75/–

1871A **Cidyessus.** *Geta.* Æ 19. ΛΣΕΠ . ΓΕΤΑC . Κ. His bare-headed bust cuir. r. ℞. ΚΙΔΥΗCCΕΩΝ. Asklepios standing front, head l. *B.M.C.* 9 .. .. *R, fair* 42/–

1872 **Colossae.** Time of Commodus. Æ 31. ΔΗΜΟC ΚΟΛΟCCHNΩΝ. Laur. head of the Demos r. ℞. ΚΟΛΟCCHNΩΝ. Helios in facing quadriga. *B.M.C.* 5 *R*, F £6

1873 **Cotiaeum** (Koutaya). Imperial Times. Æ 16. ΚΟΤΙΑΕΙC ΣΥΝΚΛΗΤΟΝ. Bust of the Senate r. ℞. ΕΠΙ Κ . ΣΕΚΟΥΝΔΟΥ. Kybele seated l., holding phiale. *B.M.C.* 2 *R*, F 50/–

1874 *Gallienus.* Æ 22. Greek legend; his laur. bust dr. r. ℞. Greek legend around. Herakles standing facing holding small figure of Telephos; in field, ΚΟΤ / Ι / ΑΕΩ / Ν. *Grose* 8802 .. .. *fair* 35/–

1875 **Dionysopolis.** 2nd Cent. B.C. Æ 16. Head of young Dionysos r. ℞. ΔΙΟΝΥΣ. Bunch of grapes. *B.M.C.* 1 .. .. *R*, F 55/–

1875A Time of Severus. As illustration below. Head of Zeus Poteos r. ℞. River-god Meander recumbent l. *B.M.C.* 6 .. .. *R*, VF £14

1875A   1876A

1876 **Docimeium** (Ichje Kara-hissar). *Lucilla.* Æ 26. ΛΟΥΚΙΛΛΑ CEBACTH. Bust r. ℞. ΔΟΚΙΜΕΩΝ ΜΑΚΕΟΝΩΝ. Zeus seated r. on throne, holding sceptre and thunderbolt. *Not in B.M.C.* .. .. *RR, almost* EF £30

1876A Time of Severus or later. Æ 20. As illustration above. Youthful head of Dokimos r· ℞. Asklepios stg. *B.M.C.* 8 .. .. F 45/–

1877 **Dorylaëum** (Eskisehir). *Trajan.* Æ 18. Greek legend; his laur. head r. ℞. ΔΟΡΥΛΑΕΩΝ
Apollo standing l. *Grose* 8807 .. .. *R, fair* 35/-

1877A **Eriza.** *Julia Domna.* Æ 22. ΙΟΥΛΙΑ CEΒΑCTH. Her bust r. ℞. ΕΡΙΖΗΝΩΝ.
Athena stg. r. *B.M.C.* 2 .. .. *RR, fair* 45/-

1878 **Eucarpeia** (Emir Hissar). Imperial Times. Æ 15. ΕΥΚΑΡΠΕΩΝ. Bust of Hermes r.:
behind, caduceus. ℞. ΕΠΙ Γ ΚΛ ΦΛΑΚΚΟΥ. Crescent and two stars: below, bucranium.
B.M.C. 9 .. .. *R, F* 65/-

1879 **Eumeneia** (Ishekli). *Nero.* Æ 20. ΝΕΡΩΝ ΣΕΒΑΣΤΟΣ. Youthful bust r. ℞. ΕΥΜΕΝΕΩΝ
and magistrate's name: Apollo standing l., holding raven and double-axe. *B.M.C.* 41
good F £5

1880 *Antoninus Pius.* Æ 25. ΑΥΤΟ . ΚΑΙC ΑΝΤΩΝΕΙΝΟC. Laur. bust r. ℞. ΕΥΜΕΝΕΩΝ
ΑΧΑΙΩΝ. Nike walking l., leading bull. *B.M.C.* 56 .. .. F 85/-

1881 **Grimenothyrae** (or Flavia Grimenothyrae). 2nd Cent. A.D. Æ 22. ΙΕΡΑ CVΝΚΛΗΤΟC.
Dr. bust of the Senate r. ℞. ΕΠΙ ΑCΚΛΗΠΙΑ ΔΟΥ ΑΠΓΡΙΜ. Herakles standing l.
B.M.C. 8 .. .. *R, fair* 35/-

1882 **Hadrianopolis-Sebaste.** *Philip I.* Æ 26. Greek legend; his laur. bust dr. r.
℞. ΕΠΙ ΧΡΟΝΦΟΥ. River god, Karmeios, recumbent l.; in ex., ΑΔΡΙΑΝΟC. *B.M.C.* 11
F 65/-

1883 **Hierapolis** (Pambuk Kalesi). Imperial Times. Æ 25. ΙΕΡΑΠΟΛΕΙΤΩΝ. Bust of Dionysos
r. ℞. ΕΥΠΟCΙΑ. Euposias, as Tyche, stg. l. *B.M.C.* 35 .. .. F/VF 80/-

1884 Æ 26. ΛΑΙΡΒΗΝΟC. Head of Apollo Lairbenos, radiate, r. ℞. ΙΕΡΑΠΟΛΕΙΤΩΝ.
Selene, holding two torches, in galloping biga, r. *B.M.C.* 55 .. .. F 75/-

1885 *Nero.* Æ 18. ΝΕΡΩΝ ΚΑΙCΑΡ. Young bust of Nero r. ℞. ΙΕΡΑΠΟΛΕΙΤΩΝ and
magistrate's name: Rider-god on horseback r. with double-axe over shoulder. *B.M.C.* 122
F 85/-

1886 **Hieropolis.** *Caracalla.* Æ 25. Greek legend. His laur. bust cuir. r. ℞. ΙΕΡΟΠΟ-
ΛΕΙΤΩΝ. Demeter stg. *B.M.C.* 18 .. .. *fair* 40/-

1886A **Hydrela.** *After* 133 B.C. Æ 13. Bust of Artemis r. ℞. ΥΔΡΗΛΙΤΩΝ. Mên stg. l.
B.M.C. 1 .. .. *R, fair* 40/-

1886B **The Hyrgaleis.** *Severus Alexander.* Æ 27. Greek legend. His laur. bust dr. and cuir. r.
℞. ΥΡΓΑΛΕΩΝ. Apollo and Artemis stg. face to face; in ex., ΤΤΓ (=year 306=222 A.D.).
B.M.C. 10 .. .. F £6

1887 **Julia (Ipsus).** *Nero.* Æ 19. ΝΕΡΩΝ ΚΑΙCΑΡ. His dr. bust r. ℞. CΕΡΓΙΩC
ΗΦΑΙCΤΙΩΝ ΙΟΥΛΙΕΩΝ. Mên on horseback r., shouldering double-axe. *B.M.C.* 3
R, fair 47/6

1888 **Laodiceia ad Lycum.** *After* 133 B.C. Æ 19. Female head r. ℞. ΛΑΟΔΙΚΕΩΝ.
Double cornucopiae. *B.M.C.* 32 .. .. F 32/6

1889 Imperial Times. Æ 15. ΛΑΟΔΙΚΕΩΝ. Bust of the god Mên, wearing Phrygian
cap, r. ℞. ΔΙΟΣΚΟΥΡΙΔΗΣ. Eagle facing, head l. *B.M.C.* 64 .. .. F 40/-

1890 Æ 20. ΔΗΜΟΣ ΛΑΟΔΙΚΕΩΝ. Bust of young Demos r. ℞. ΙΟΥΛΙΟΣ ΑΝΔΡΟΝΙΚΟΣ
ΕΥΕΡΓΕΤΗΣ. Zeus Laodikeus stg. l. *B.M.C.* 70 .. .. F 45/-

1891 Æ 21. ΔΗΜΟC. Type as preceding. ℞. ΛΑΟΔΙΚΕΩΝ. Zeus Aseis standing facing,
head r., holding infant Dionysos on l. arm; to l., goat. *B.M.C.* 124 .. .. F 45/-

There are also alliance coins with Smyrna, Ephesus, Pergamum, etc.

1892 **Lysias.** *Gordian III.* Æ 26. Greek legend; his laur. bust dr. r. ℞. ΛΥCΙΑΔΕΩΝ
Kybele enthroned l., lion at her feet. *B.M.C.* 6 .. .. F £5

1893 **Metropolis.** Æ 29. *Gallienus.* — — ΥΛΙΕΓΓΑΛΛΙΗΝΟCCEB. Radiate bust r. ℞.
ΜΗΤΡΟΠΟ Β Ν — — — — . Hekate Triformis, each head surmounted by kalathos,
holding in her six hands torches, dagger, spear, etc. *Not in B.M.C.* RR, F £10

1893A **Midaëum.** *Trajan.* Æ 20. Greek legend. Laur. head r. ℞. ΜΙΔΑΕΩΝ. Asklepios stg. towards l. *B.M.C.* 4 .. .. F 60/–

1893B **Nacoleia.** *Domitian.* Æ 17. As before. ℞. ΝΑΚΟΛΕΩΝ. Winged caduceus. *B.M.C.* 5 .. .. *fair* 32/6

1893C **Ococleia.** *Gordian III.* Æ 25. Greek legend. Laur. bust dr. and cuir. r. ℞. ΟΚΟΚΛΙΕΩΝ. Tyche stg. l. *B.M.C.* 9 .. .. *fair* 37/6

1893D **Otrus.** Time of Caracalla. Æ 13. Bust of bearded Demos r. ℞. ΟΤΡΟΗΝΩΝ. Telesphoros stg. front. *B.M.C.* 2 .. .. *R, fair* 35/–

1893E **Palaeobeudos** or **Beudos Vetos.** *Hadrian.* Æ 17. Greek legend. Laur. bust dr. and cuir. r. ℞. ΠΑΛΑΙΟΒΕΥΔΗΝΩΝ. Demeter stg. l. *B.M.C.* 3 .. .. *R, F* £5

1894 **Peltae.** 2nd Cent. B.C. Æ 18. Helmeted young male bust dr. r. ℞. ΠΕΛΤΗΝΩΝ. Lion seated l.; two mon. in ex. *B.M.C.* 1-2 .. .. *fair* 32/6

1895 **Philomelium** (Aksehir). *Trajan Decius.* Æ 24. Greek legend. His rad. bust dr. r. ℞. ΦΙΛΟΜΗΛΕΩΝ ΕΠ ΕΝΤΥΧΟΥϹ. River-god, Gallos, recumbent l., holding cornucopiae. *B.M.C.* 42 .. .. F 70/–

1896 **Prymnessus.** *Nero.* Æ 21. ΠΡΥΜΝΗϹϹΕΙϹ ΝΕΡΩΝ ΚΑΙϹΑΡ Α. His laur. head r. ℞. ΕΠΙΚΛΑΥΔΙΟΥΜΙ ΘΡΙΔΑΤΟΥ. Dikaiosyne standing l. *B.M.C.* 24 .. *fair* 40/–

1896A **Sebaste** (Sivasli). Imperial Times. Æ 19. Bust of god Mên dr. r., wearing Phrygian cap. ℞. ϹΕΒΑϹΤΗΝΩΝ. Hygieia stg., feeding serpent from phiale. *B.M.C.* 9 F 65/–

1896B *Nero.* Æ 20. ϹΕΒΑϹΤΟϹ. Bare-headed bust of young Nero dr. and cuir. r. ℞. ϹΕΒΑϹΤΗΝΩΝ ΙΟΥΛΙΟϹ ΔΙΟΝΥϹΙΟϹ. Zeus enthroned l. *B.M.C.* 24 .. .. *fair* 40/–

1896C **Sibidunda.** *Commodus.* Æ 20. Greek legend. His laur. bust dr. and cuir. r. ℞. ϹΙΒΙΔΟΥΝΔΕΩΝ. Artemis running r.; at her feet, stag. *B.M.C.* 3 .. *R, fair* 65/–

1896D **Siblia.** Time of Caracalla. Æ 20. ϹΕΙΒΛΙΑ. Bust of city-goddess r. ℞. ϹΕΙΒΛΙΑΝΩΝ. Tyche stg. l. *B.M.C.* 4 .. .. *R, fair* 50/–

1896E **Stectorium.** *Philip I.* Æ 24. As 1896C. ℞. ϹΤΕΚΤΟΡΗΝΩΝ. Athena stg. l. *B.M.C.* 15 .. .. *fair* 42/–

1896F **Synaus.** Time of the Antonines. Æ 23. ΙΕΡΑ ϹΥΝΚΛΗΤΟϹ. Youthful bust of the Senate r. ℞. ϹΥΝΑΕΙΤΩΝ. The two Nemeses stg. face to face. *B.M.C.* 8 F 55/–

1897 **Synnada.** *Gallienus.* Æ 32. ΑΥΤ ΚΑΙ Π ΛΙΚ ΓΑΛΛΙΗΝΟϹ ϹΕΒ. Laur. bust r. ℞. ϹΥΝΝΑΔΕΩΝ. Statue of Amaltheia, with infant Zeus and goat, standing r. in distyle shrine. *B.M.C.* 63 .. .. *R, F* £8

1897A **Temenothyrae Flaviopolis** (Ushak). Time of M. Aurelius. Æ 23. As 1896F. ℞. ϹΚΟΠΕΛΙΑΝΟϹ ΤΗΜΕΝΟΘΥΡΕΥϹΙ. The god Mên stg. l. *B.M.C.* 2 .. .. *fair* 35/–

1898 **Themisonium.** 3rd Cent. A.D. Æ 18. Bust of Sarapis r. ℞. ΘΕΜΙϹΩΝΕΩΝ. Isis standing three-quarter face to l. *B.M.C.* 7 .. .. *fair* 30/–

1899 **Tiberiopolis.** *Claudius.* Æ 15. ΤΙΒΕΡΙΩΠΟΛΕΙΤΩΝ. Laur. bust l. ℞. ΚΛΑΥΔΙΟϹ ΝΙΚΗ. Nike standing l. *Not in B.M.C.* .. .. *R, VF* 85/–

1900 **Trajanopolis.** 2nd Cent. A.D. Æ 20. ΔΗΜΟϹ. Dr. bust of Demos r. ℞. ΤΡΑΙΑΝΟΠΟΛΙΤΩΝ. As No. 1892. *B.M.C.* 1 .. .. F 50/–

LYCIA.

1901 520-480 B.C. Æ *stater.* Forepart of boar l., with monogram on shoulder. ℞. Incuse square decorated with crossing lines. *B.M.C.* 6 .. .. .. *R, F* £35

1902 Similar, without monogram. *B.M.C.* 5 .. .. *R, VF* £75

1903 500-460 B.C. Æ *stater.* Boar walking r. ℞. Tortoise in dotted incuse square. *B.M.C.* 17 .. .. *R, F/VF* £50

1904 Similar, but boar l. *B.M.C.* 18 .. .. *R, nearly* VF £60

1905 Æ *stater* (148 grs.). Boar walking l.: above, small triskeles: below, uncertain letter (? Θ). ℞. Triskeles, each arm of which ends in a cock's head: pellet in centre and three pellets around. *Not in B.M.C. Cf. Bab.* 823 .. .. *RRR, F* £100

1906 Sppntaza (dynast *c.* 470-450 B.C.). Æ *stater.* Head of Aphrodite l. ℞. Name in Lycian characters around tetraskeles: all in incuse square. *B.M.C.* 97 *RR, F* £80

1907 *c.* 380 B.C. Æ 9. Whelk-shell. ℞. Lion's head facing. *B.M.C.* 141 .. F 45/–

1908 Perikles. 380-362 B.C. Æ *tetrobol.* Lion's scalp facing. ℞. Π↑ΡΕΚΑ↑ around triskelis. *B.M.C.* 157 .. .. *good* F/VF £20

1909 Æ 13. Head of Pan, l., horned. ℞. Similar. *B.M.C.* 158 .. .. F 50/–

1909A **Lycian League.** 168 B.C.-43 A.D. Æ 10. Head of Apollo facing. ℞. ΛΥΚΙΩΝ. Bow and quiver. *B.M.C.* 1 .. .. *fair* 15/-
N.B. Most of the following Lycian coins are League coinage.

1909B **Antiphellus** (Andifilo). Æ 10. As last with AN added. *B.M.C.* 3 .. *R*, F 40/-

1909C **Arycanda** (Aruf). *Gordian III.* Æ 32. Greek legend. Laur. bust dr. and cuir. r. ℞. ΑΡΥΚΑΝΔΕΩΝ. Deity (Sozon ?) riding r. on horseback. *B.M.C.* 6 *R, fair* 75/-

1909D **Balbura** (Katara). *Caligula.* Æ 20. ΓΑΙΟC CЄΒΑCΤΟC. His head r. ℞. ΒΑΛΒΟΥ-ΡЄΩΝ. Herakles stg. facing. *B.M.C.* 4 .. .. *R, fair* 65/-

1909E **Bubon.** 81-43 B.C. Æ 10. Head of Artemis r. ℞. ΒΟΥ. Bow and quiver in saltire. *B.M.C.* 1 .. .. *R, fair* 32/6

1909F **Calynda.** 1st Cent. B.C. Æ 10. Head of Artemis r. ℞. ΚΑΛΥΝ. Stag stg. r. *B.M.C.* 4 .. .. *fair* 20/-

1909G **Choma.** *Gordian III.* Æ 28. As 1909C but ΧΩΜΑΤЄΙΤΩΝ .. *RR, fair* £5

1909H **Corydalla.** *Gordian III.* Æ 31. As last. ℞. ΚΟΡΥΔΑΛΛЄΩΝ. Pallas stg. front, looking r. *B.M.C.* 1 .. .. *R, fair* 85/-

1910 **Cragus.** 168-81 B.C. Æ *drachm.* ΛΥ. Laur. head of Apollo r. ℞. ΚΡ lyre; all in oblong incuse. *B.M.C.* 1-4. .. .. F £5

1910A — Laur. head of Apollo r. ℞. ΛΥΚΙΩΝ above lyre dividing Κ Ρ Λ Γ; all within incuse square. *B.M.C.* 12 .. .. VF/EF £20

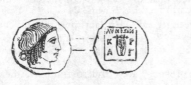 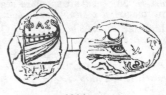

1910A   1914*

1911 *Augustus.* Æ *drachm.* His head r. ℞. ΛΥ ΚΡ. Lyre. *B.M.C.* 25 F/*fair* £7

1911A **Cyane** (Ya'u). Before A.D. 43. Æ 20. Bust of Artemis r., bow and quiver behind neck. ℞. ΚΥΑ above stag r. between ΛΥ. *B.M.C.* 3 .. .. .. *fair* 32/6

1911B **Gagae** (Ak-tash). 168-81 B.C. Æ *drachm.* As 1910A but Γ A beside lyre. *B.M.C.* 1 *R*, F £9

1911C **Limyra** (Duden-Su). 168 B.C.-43 A.D. Æ *drachm.* Similar but Λ Ι. *B.M.C.* 5 F £7

1912 **Masicytes.** 81-27 B.C. Æ *drachm.* ΛΥ. Head of Apollo, laur. r. ℞. ΜΑ. Lyre: in field l., laurel-branch. *B.M.C.* 8 .. .. *good* VF £15

1913 81 B.C. to Imperial Times. Æ 19. As 1911A but ΛΥ on *obv.* and ΜΑ on *rev. B.M.C.* 30 *good* F 50/-

1913A **Myra** (Dembre). 3rd Cent. B.C. Æ *hemidrachm.* Head of Athena r. ℞. ΜΥ. Bust of Artemis almost facing, slightly l., quiver on shoulder. *B.M.C.* 1 *R*, F £15

1913B 168-81 B.C. Æ 11. Laur. head of Apollo r. ℞. ΛΥΚΙ. Bow and quiver in saltire between ΜΥ *B.M.C.* 5 .. .. *fair* 27/6

1913C *Gordian III.* Æ 31. Laur. bust dr. and cuir. r. ℞. ΜΥΡЄWΝ. Simulacrum of Artemis Eleuthera in tetrastyle temple. *B.M.C.* 12 .. .. *fair* 65/-

1913D **Olympus.** 168-78 B.C. *Tranquillina.* Æ 30. Her bust r. ℞. ΟΛΥΜΠΗΝΩΝ. Apollo stg. l. against column. *B.M.C.* 2 .. .. *RR, fair* £10

1913E **Patara** (Gelemish). 168 B.C. to Imperial Times. Æ 11. Laur. head of Apollo r. ℞. ΠΑΤΑΡЄΩΝ. Head of Artemis l. wearing stephane. *B.M.C.* 5 .. .. *fair* 25/-

1914 **Phaselis** (Tekirova). 400-330 B.C. Æ 15. Prow of galley r. ℞. ΦΑΣΗ above stern of galley r. *B.M.C.* 5. [*The illustration is a silver stater, very similar] .. F 35/-

1915 81-30 B.C. Æ 14. Head of Athena r. ℞. Φ Α Athena fighting r. *B.M.C.*— *nearly* F 25/-

1915A **Phellus.** 168 B.C.-43 A.D. Æ 11. As 1913B but ΛΥΚΙΩΝ and ΦЄ. *B.M.C.* 1 *fair* 27/6

1915B **Pinara** (Minara). Early 2nd Cent. B.C. Æ 10. Head of Apollo r. ℞. ΠΙΝΑΡЄΩΝ Bucranium. *B.M.C.* 1 .. .. F 35/-

1916 **Telmessus** (Makri). 196-189 B.C. Æ 16. Facing head of Helios . ℞. ΤΕΛΜΗ. Apollo l. seated on omphalos. *B.M.C.* 1 .. .. *fair*/F 30/-

1917 **Termessus Minor.** 1st Cent. B.C. Æ 21. Head of Zeus r., with sceptre. ℞. ΤΕΡΜΗΣΣΕΩΝ. Winged thunderbolt. *B.M.C.* Pisidia 9 .. .. *R*, F 47/6

1917A **Tlos** (Duver). B.C. 168-81. Æ *drachm.* As 1910A but lyre divides ΤΛ; in field, helmet. *B.M.C.* 2 .. .. *good* VF £20

1917B **Trebenna.** *Gordian III.* Æ 35. His laur. bust dr. and cuir. r. ℞. ΤΡΕΒΕΝΝΑΤΩΝ. Zeus seated l. *B.M.C.* 2.. .. .. *R*, *fair* 80/-

1917C **Xanthus.** B.C. 169-81. Æ *drachm.* As 1910A but lyre divides ΞΑ. *B.M.C.* — *good* F £12

PAMPHYLIA.

1918 **Aspendus** (Balkyzi). 400-300 B.C. Æ *stater.* Two wrestlers facing each other. ℞. ΕΣΤFΕΔΙΙΥΣ. Slinger discharging sling r.: in field, r., triskeles of human legs and F. *B.M.C.* 39 .. .. *nearly* VF £20

1919 — Similar, of coarser style, uncertain monogram between wrestlers. *Cf. B.M.C.* 65 VF £15

1920 3rd Cent. B.C. Æ 16. Forepart of bridled horse r. ℞. FA. Sling. *B.M.C.* 70 F 32/6

1921 *Gallienus.* Æ 31. Greek legend; his laur. bust dr. r. ℞. ΑΣΠΕΝΔΙΩΝ. River-god Eurymedon reclining l. *B.M.C.* 102 .. .. F £8

1922 **Attalia** (Adalya). Imperial Times. Æ 18. Two helmeted heads of Athena, side by side, r. ℞. ΑΤΤΑΛΕΩΝ. Nike l., holding wreath. *B.M.C.* 5 .. .. *fair* 40/-

1923 Æ 16. Bust of Poseidon r. ℞. As preceding. *B.M.C.* 10 .. .. *fair* 21/-

1924 **Magydus** (Laara). *Trajan.* Æ 20. Greek legend; his laur. head r. ℞. ΜΑΓΥΔΕ ΩΝ. Athena standing l.: in field l., ΙΑ. *B.M.C.* 2 .. .. F 45/-

1925 **Perga** (Murtana). 2nd Cent. B.C. Æ *hemidrachm.* Laur. head of Artemis r. ℞. ΑΡΤΕΜΙΔΟΣ ΠΕΡΓΑΙΑΣ. Artemis as huntress standing l.; to l., stag l. *B.M.C.* 3 .. VF £12

1926 Æ 16. Simulacrum of Pergaean Artemis in distyle temple. ℞. ΑΡΤΕΜΙΔΟΣ ΠΕΡΓΑΙΑΣ. Bow and quiver. *B.M.C.* 10 .. .. F 35/-

1927 2nd-1st Cent. B.C. Æ 17. Sphinx seated r. ℞. Legend in Pamphylian characters: Artemis standing l., with wreath and sceptre. *B.M.C.* 17 .. .. .. F 32/6

1928 *Domitian.* Æ 19. ΔΟΜΙΤΙΑΝΟΣ ΚΑΙΣΑΡ. Laur. head r. ℞ ΑΡΤΕΜΙΔΟΣ ΠΕΡΓΑΙΑΣ. Artemis advancing r., holding torch and bow. *B.M.C.* 23 .. .. *good* F £5

1928A *Hadrian.* Æ 30. Greek legend. Laur. bust dr. and cuir. r. ℞. ΑΡΤΕΜΙ ΔΟΣ ΠΕΡΓΑΙΑΣ. Simulacrum of Pergaean Artemis between two sphinx in distyle temple. *B.M.C.* 26 .. .. *fair*/F £5

1929 *Philip II.* Æ 21. ΑΥ Κ Μ ΙΟΥ ΣΕΟΥ ΦΙΛΙΠΠΟΣ ΣΕ. Bust r. ℞. ΠΕΡΓΑΙΩΝ. Chest, on which three purses. *B.M.C.* 60 .. .. *fair* 32/6

1930 **Side** (Eski-Adalia). 4th Cent. B.C. Æ *stater*. Athena standing l., holding Nike, lance and shield; to l., pomegranate. ℞. Pamphylian legend. Apollo l., pouring libation over lighted altar; raven l. behind. *Cf. B.M.C.* 15 .. .. .. *good* F £45

1931 3rd Cent. B.C. Æ 17. Head of Athena r. ℞. Pomegranate. *B.M.C.* 59
nearly F 30/-

1932 190-36 B.C. Æ *tetradrachm*. Helmeted head of Athena r. ℞. Nike advancing l., holding wreath: in field, pomegranate and ΔΕΙ. *B.M.C.* 25 .. VF/F £13

1933 200-36 B.C. Æ 15. Similar. ℞. ΣΙΔΗΤΩΝ. Similar. *B.M.C.* 65 .. F 25/-

1934 *Gordian III.* Æ 26. Greek legend; his laur. bust dr. r. ℞. ΣΙΔΗΤΩΝ. Athena standing l., holding palm and dropping pebble into vase. *B.M.C.* 93 .. *fair* 35/-

1935 **Sillyum.** *Saloninus.* Æ 32. Greek legend; his laur. bust dr. r. ℞. ΣΙΛΛΥΕΩΝ. Head of Mên r. *Grose* 8932 .. .. F £6

PISIDIA

1935A **Adada** (Karabaulo) 1st Cent. B.C. Æ 12. Bucranium. ℞. Triskelis. *B.M.C.* 3
R, fair 35/-

1935B **Amblada** (Asar-Dagh). *Philip II.* Æ 25. Greek legend. Bust r. ℞. ΑΜΒΛΑΔΕΩΝ ΛΑΚΕΔΑΙ. Nemesis advancing r. *B.M.C.* 3 .. .. *R, fair* 45/-

1935C **Andeda** (Andiya). *Sev. Alexander.* Æ 25. Similiar. ℞. ΑΝΔΗΔΩΝ. Artemis stg. r., stag at her side. *B.M.C.* 4 .. .. *R, fair* 45/-

1936 **Antiocheia** (Yalovadj). *Septimius Severus.* Æ 31. IMP CAES L SEP SEVERVS PER AVG. Laur. head r. ℞. COL CAES ANTIOCH. Mên standing facing, head r., holding sceptre and Nike on globe: in field S R. *B.M.C.* 20 .. .. F £6

1936A *Geta.* Æ 35. Latin legend. Similar. ℞. as illustration below .. F £10

1936A   1938

1937 *Gordian III.* Æ 35. IMP CAES M ANT GORDIANOVS AVG. Laur. bust r. ℞. VICTORIA DOMINI ANTI COLONI. Nike adv. l., with wreath and palm. *B.M.C.* 96 .. *fair* 50/-

1938 *Volusian.* Æ 23. IMP C VIR AP CALVSIANO AVG. Radiate bust r. ℞. ANTIOCHI COL S R. River-god reclining l. *B.M.C.* — .. .. F 60/-

1939 **Apollonia Mordiaeum** (Oluburlu). *Gallienus.* Æ **medallion,** 40 *mm.* ΑΥΤ Κ Π Λ ΓΑΛΛΙΗΝ. Laur. bust r. ℞. ΑΠΟΛΛΩΝΙΑΤΩΝ ΛΥΘΡΚΟ. Octastyle temple, within which, standing male figure looking l. and holding sceptre. *B.M.C.* 5 .. .. RR, F £25

1939A **Ariassus.** *Caracalla.* Æ 19. Greek legend. Bust r. ℞. ΑΡΙΑCCЄΩΝ. Dionysos standing facing, looking·l.; at his feet, panther. *B.M.C.* 5 .. .. *R, fair* 45/-

1940 **Baris** (Isbarta). *Julia Mamaea.* Æ 26. ΙΟVΛΙΑ ΜΑΜΕΑ CЄ. Her dr. bust r. ℞. ΒΑΡΗΝΩΝ. Tyche seated l. *Grose* 8974 .. .. *R, F* £5

1940A **The Ceraïtae.** 1st Cent. B.C. Æ 11. Head of Artemis r. ℞. Club; н above, κ ε below. *B.M.C.* 2 .. .. *R, fair* 27/6

1940B **Codrula.** Æ 25. *Julia Domna.* ΙΟΥΛΙΑ ΔΟΜΝΑ ϹΕΒ. Her bust r. ℞. ΚΟΔΡΟΥΛΕΩΝ. Dionysos stg. l.; at feet, panther. *B.M.C.* 1.. .. .. .. *RR, fair* 52/6

1940C **Comama** (Sheher Eyuk). *Septimius Severus.* Æ 23. Bust r. ℞. COL. AVG COMAMENORVM. Three military standards. *B.M.C.* 2 .. .. .. *R,* F £5

1941 **Conana** (Gönen). Imperial Times. Æ 15. Cuirass. ℞. ΚΟΝΑΝΕΩΝ. Humped bull r. *B.M.C.* 1 .. .. *R,* F 40/-

1942 **Cremna** (Girme). 36-25 B.C. Æ 18. Head of Zeus r. ℞. ΚΡΗ. Winged thunderbolt: above, ε. *B.M.C.* 3 *var.* .. .. F 32/6

1943 **Etenna.** 1st Cent. B.C. Æ 13. Two men in combat. ℞. ΕΤΕΝ. Female figure adv. r., holding snake. *B.M.C.* 3 .. .. *R,* F 45/-

1944 **Isinda.** Imperial Times. Æ 19. Head of Zeus r. ℞. ΙϹΙΝΔΕΩΝ. Helmeted horseman galloping r. *B.M.C.* 10 .. .. *RR,* VF £6

1944A **Lysinia.** *Caracalla.* Æ 26. Greek legend. Bust r. ℞. ΛΥϹΙΝΙΕΩΝ. Kybele stg. front between two lions. *B.M.C.* 1 .. .. .. *RR, fair* 52/6

1944B **Olbasa** (Belengly). *M. Aurelius.* Æ 21. Bare head. r. ℞. COL/AVG/OLB in laurel-wreath. *B.M.C.* 1 .. .. *R, fair* 40/-

1945 **Palaeopolis.** *Caracalla.* Æ 20. Greek legend; his laur. head r. ℞. ΠΑΛΕΟΠΟΛΕΙΤΩΝ. Mên standing l. *B.M.C.* 2 .. .. F 45/-

1945A **Panemoteichos, Cretopolis.** *Julia Domna.* Æ 24. Greek legend. Bust r. ℞. ΠΑΝΕΜΟΤΕΙΧΕΙΤΩΝ. Horseman riding r. *B.M.C.* 1.. .. .. *RR, fair* 60/-

1945B **Pappa Tiberia.** *Antoninus.* Æ 20. Greek legend. Laur. head r. ℞. ΤΙΒΕΡΙΕΥΝΠΑΠΠΗΝΥΝ. Mên stg. r. *B.M.C.* 2 .. .. .. *RR, fair* 50/-

1945C **Pednelissus.** *M. Aurelius.* Æ 11. As last. ℞. ΠΕΔΝΗΛΙϹϹΕΩΝ. Baity-lion in distyle temple. *B.M.C.* 3 .. .. *R, fair* 32/6

1945D **Pogla** (Fughla). *Maximinus.* Æ 24. Greek legend. Bust r. ℞. ΠΩΓΛΕΩΝ. As 1940B. *B.M.C.* 7 .. .. *R, fair* 40/-

1945E **Prostanna.** (Egherdir). Imperial Times. Æ 21. ΠΟΛΙϹ. Bust of the City r. ℞. ΠΡΟϹΤΑΝΝΕΩΝ. Aphrodite stg. l. *B.M.C.* 3 .. .. F 55/-

1946 **Sagalassus** (Aghlasan). Imperial Times. Æ 14. Head of Zeus r. ℞. ϹΑΓΑΛΑ. Two goats confronted, standing on their hind legs. *B.M.C.* 7 .. .. *fair* 2!/-

1947 *Claudius Gothicus.* Æ 35. Greek legend; his laur. bust dr. r. ℞. ϹΑΓΑΛΑϹϹΕΩΝ. Herakles standing l., slaying the Hydra. *B.M.C.* 49 .. .. .. F £8

1947A **Seleuceia** (Self). *Claudius Gothicus.* Æ 31. Greek legend. Bust r. ℞. ΚΛΑΥΔΙΟ ϹΕΛΕΥΚΕΩΝ. Tyche stg. front, looking l. *B.M.C.* 16 .. .. F £6

1948 **Selge** (Seruk). 400-333 B.C. Æ *obol.* Gorgoneion. ℞. Head of Athena r.; behind, astragalos. *B.M.C.* 9 .. .. VF £7

1949 300-190 B.C. Æ *stater.* Two wrestlers, κ between legs. ℞. ϹΕΛΓΕΩΝ. Slinger slinging to r.; in field r., triskellis, club and cornucopiae. *B.M.C.* 20 *scarce,* F £15

1949   1955

1950 2nd-1st Cent. B.C. Æ 11. Head of Herakles three-quarter r. ℞. ϹΕΛ. Forepart of stag r., head l. *B.M.C.* 42 .. .. F 25/-

1951 Æ 12. Head of Herakles r. ℞. ϹΕ. Winged thunderbolt and bow. *B.M.C.* 50 F 25/-

1952 *Lucius Verus.* Æ 20. ΒΗΡΟϹ ΚΑΙ. His bare head r. ℞. ϹΕΛΓΕΩΝ. Strung bow and thunderbolt. *B.M.C.* 75 .. .. *fair* 32/6

1953 **Termessus Major.** 71-36 B.C. Æ 18. Head of Zeus r. ℞. ΤΕΡ. Forepart of horse, l.; κε (=25=46 B.C.) above. *B.M.C.* 18 .. .. F/*fair* 27/6

1954 Imperial Times. Æ 29. ΤΕΡΜΗϹϹΕΩΝ. Bust of Hermes r.: behind, caduceus. ℞. ΤΩΝ ΜΕΙΖΟΝΩΝ. Athena standing l., holding Nike and spear. *B.M.C.* 29 *fair* 35/-

1955 Æ 27. As illustration. Head of Zeus. ℞. Nike. *B.M.C.* 49 .. .. VF £6

1955A **Timbriada.** *Geta.* Æ 15. Greek legend. Laur. bust r. ℞. ΤΙΜΒΡΙΑΔΕΩΝ. Hermes stg. l. *B.M.C.* 2 .. .. *RR, fair* 52/6
1955B **Tityassus.** *Plautilla.* Æ 22. Greek legend. Bust r. ℞. ΤΙΤΥΑCCEΩΝ. Tetrastyle Ionic temple. *B.M.C.* 6 .. .. *RR, fair* 75/-
1955C **Verbe.** *Commodus.* Æ 24. Greek legend. Laur. head r. ℞. ΟΥΕΡΒΙΑΝΩΝ. Athena stg. l. *B.M.C.* 1 .. .. *RR,* F £7

LYCAONIA.

1955D **Barata** (Bin-Bir-Kilisse). *Faustina II.* Æ 21. Greek legend. Bust l. wearing stephane. ℞. ΒΑΡΑΤΕΩΝ ΚΟΙ ΛΥΚΑΟΝΙΑC. Demeter stg. l. *B.M.C.* 1 *R, fair* 55/-
1955E **Dalisandus.** *Philip I.* Æ 27. Greek legend. Laur. bust dr. and cuir r. ℞. ΔΑΛΙCΑΝΔΕΩΝ ΚΟΙΝΟΝ ΛΥΚΑΟ. Herakles stg. facing. *B.M.C.* 2 .. *RR, fair* 75/-
1956 **Iconium** (Konia). 1st Cent. B.C. Æ 16. Head of Zeus r. ℞. ΕΙΚΟΝΙΕΩΝ. Perseus standing l., holding harpa and Gorgon's head. *B.M.C.* 1 .. .. .. F 40/-
1956A **Ilistra** (Ilisra). *Philip II.* Æ 27. Greek legend. Bare-headed bust l. ℞. ΙΛΙCΤΡΕΩΝ ΚΟΙΝΟΝ ΛΥΚΑΟΝΙΑC. Herakles stg. facing. *B.M.C.* 4 .. *R, fair* 65/-
1956B **Laranda.** *Otacilia.* Æ 24. Greek legend. Bust r. ℞. CΕΒ ΛΑΡΑΝΔΕΩΝ ΜΗΤΡΟ. Tyche seated l. on rock; at her feet, upper part of river-god swimming l. *B.M.C.* 2
RR, F £6
1956C **Lystra.** *Augustus.* Æ 26. ΙΜΡΕ ΑVGVSTI. Laur. head l.; behind, cornucopiae. ℞. COL IVL/FEL GEM above priest ploughing l., LVSTRA in ex. *B.M.C.* 1 *RR, fair* £5
1957 **Parlais.** *Julia Domna.* Æ 23. ΙVLIA DOMNA AVG. Her dr. bust l. ℞. IVL . AVG . COL . PARLAIS. Mên standing l., foot on bucranium. *B.M.C.* 1 .. .. F 85/-

CILICIA.

1958 **Adana.** 1st Cent. B.C. Æ 20. Head of Demeter r. ℞. ΑΔΑΝΕΩΝ. Zeus seated l., holding sceptre and Nike. *B.M.C.* 1 .. .. F 40/-
1959 **Aegeae** (Ayas). 2nd-1st Cent. B.C. Æ 22. Turreted and veiled head of Tyche of the City r. ℞. ΑΙΓΕΑΙΩΝ ΤΗC ΙΕΡΑC ΚΑΙ ΑΥΤΟΝΟΜΟΥ. Bridled horse's head l. *B.M.C.* 2 F 37/6
1960 *Alexander Severus.* Æ 24. Greek legend; his laur. bust dr. r. ℞. ΑΔΡΙΑΛΕΞΑΝΔΡΟΥΠΟ ΑΙΓΕΑΙΩΝ ΕΟC (=275=228/9 A.D.). Bust of Athena l. *B.M.C.* 36 *fair* 40/-
1960A **Alexandria ad Issum** (near Alexandretta, Iskanderun) 1st Cent. B.C. Æ 21. Head of Alexander the Great as youthful Herakles r. ℞. ΑΛΕΞΑΝΔΡΕΩΝ. Zeus stg. l.; in field, mon.; the whole in wreath. *B.M.C.* 4 .. .. .. *R, fair* 50/-
1961 **Anazarbus.** *Valerian.* Æ 30. ΑΥΤ Κ Π ΛΙΚ ΟΥΑΛΕΡΙΑΝΟC CΕ. Laur. bust r. ℞. ΑΥΤΚ ΟΥΑΛΕΡΙΑΝΟC ΑΝΑΖΑΡΒ ΑΥΤ ΓΑΛΛΙΗΝΟC. Valerian and Gallienus seated l. *B.M.C.* 39 .. .. F £7/10/-
1961A **Anemurium.** *Valerian.* Æ 27. Very similar. ℞. ΑΝΕ/ΜΟΥΡΙ/ΕΩΝ/ΕΤΓ in laurel-wreath with amphora at top. *B.M.C.* 13 .. .. *fair* 60/-
Aphrodisias. The coins given here to Mallus are attributed by Head, following Imhoof, to this town.
1961B **Augusta.** *Livia.* Æ 17. Her bust r. ℞. ΑΥΓΟΥCΤΑΝΩΝ. Capricorn r., holding globe: above, Julian star. *B.M.C.* 2 .. .. *R, fair* 75/-
1961C **Carallia.** *Maximinus.* Æ 19. Greek legend. Laur. bust r. ℞. ΚΑΡΑΛΛΙΩΤΩΝ. Demeter stg. l. *B.M.C.* 5 .. .. *fair* 47/6
1961D **Casae.** *Gordian III.* Æ 32. As last. ℞. ΚΑCΑΤΩΝ. Athena seated l. *B.M.C.* 1
R, fair 65/-

1962A

1962 **Celenderis** (Gelindere). 450-400 B.C. Æ *stater.* Nude horseman l., riding sideways, whip in hand. ℞. ΚΕΛΕΝ. Goat kneeling l., looking back. *B.M.C.* 10
R, good F £25
1962A 4th Cent. B.C. Æ *stater.* Similar but types r. *B.M.C.* 20 .. .. VF £50
1963 4th-3rd Cent. B.C. Æ *obol.* Forepart of Pegasos r. ℞. ΚΕ above goat kneeling r., head turned back. *B.M.C.* 31 .. .. F 90/-

1963A **Cestrus.** *Faustina II.* Æ 20. Greek legend. Bust r. ℞. ΚΕΣΤΡΗΝΩΝ. Tyche stg. l. *B.M.C.* 1 .. .. *RR, fair* 75/-

1963B **Cibyra Minor.** 2nd or 1st Cent. B.C. Æ 24. Head of Zeus r. ℞. ΚΙΒΥΡΑΤΩΝ with numerals ΔΚΝΕΚ. Hermes stg. l. .. .. *RR, fair* 65/-

1963C **Claudiopolis** (Mut). *Hadrian.* Æ 24. Greek legend. Laur. head r. ℞. ΚΛΑΥΔΙΟΠΟΛΙΤΩ. Tyche stg. l. *B.M.C.* 1 .. .. *RR, F* £7

1963D **Colybrassus.** *Valerian II.* Æ 30. ΠΟ ΛΙΚ ΚΟΡΟ ΟΥΑΛΕΡΙΑΝΟΝ ΚΑΙΣΕΒ. Bareheaded bust r.; in front, ΙΑ; below, eagle. ℞. ΚΟΛΥΒΡΑΣΣΕΩΝ. Zeus stg. l. in temple with four columns. *B.M.C.* 14 .. .. *R, F* £7

1963E **Coracesium** (Aláya). *Caracalla.* Æ 27. Greek legend. Bust r. ℞. ΚΟΡΑΚΗΣΙΩΤΩΝ Goddess r. on horseback; in front, altar. *B.M.C.* 1 .. .. .. *RR, fair* 75/-

1963F **Coropissus.** *Maximus.* Æ 20. As last. ℞. ΚΟΡΟΠΙΣΣΕΩΝ. Bust of Athene l. *B.M.C.* 3 .. .. *R, fair* 50/-

1964 **Corycus** (Korgos). 1st Cent. B.C. Æ 21. Turreted female head (the City) r., ΑΝ behind. ℞. ΚΩΡΥΚΙΩΤΩΝ. Hermes stg. l.; on l., ΔΙ/ΝΙ/ΑΝ. *B.M.C.* 1 .. F 35/-

1964A *Valerian I.* Æ 27. Greek legend; his rad. bust dr. r. ℞. ΚΩΡΥΚΙΩΤΩΝ ΑΥΤΟΝΟΜΟΥ. Artemis hunting r.; at her feet, stag. *Grose* 9061 .. .. *fair* 52/6

1965 **Diocaesareia.** *Philip I.* Æ 31. ΑΥΤ Κ Μ ΙΟΥΛΙΟΣ ΦΙΛΙΠΠΟΣ ΣΕΒ. Radiate bust r. ℞. ΑΔΡΙ ΔΙΟΚΕΣΑΡΕΩΝ ΜΗΤΡ ΚΕΝΝΑΤΩ. Veiled and turreted female figure seated r. facing Tyche standing l. *B.M.C.* 16 .. .. F £6

1965A **Epiphaneia.** *Julia Mamaea.* Æ 33. ΙΟΥΛ ΜΑΜΑΙΑΝ ΣΕΒΑΣΤΗΝ. Bust r. ℞. ΕΠΙΦΑΝΕΩΝ. Athena stg. l.; in field, Η ϘϹ (=398=231 A.D.). *B.M.C.* 3 *R, fair* £6

1965A 1967

1966 **Flaviopolis.** *Trajan.* Æ 27. Greek legend; his laur. head r. ℞. ΕΤΟΥΣ Μ (=40=114 A.D.). ΦΛΑΥΙΟΠΟΛΕΙΤΩΝ. Tyche standing l. *Grose* 9063 .. F 75/-

1967 **Hieropolis-Castabala** (Bedrum). 1st Cent. B.C. Æ 22. Head of Tyche r., mon. behind. ℞. ΙΕΡΟΠΟΛΙΤΩΝ ΤΩΝ ΠΡΟΣ ΤΩΙ ΠΥΡΑΜΩΙ. Goddess of Hieropolis enthroned. *B.M.C.* 1 .. .. F 32/6

1967A **Iotape.** *Hadrian.* Æ 19. Greek legend; his laur. head r. ℞. ΙΩΤΑΠΕΙΤΩΝ. Tyche stg. l. *B.M.C.* 1 .. .. *R, fair* 50/-

1967B **Irenopolis.** *Domitian.* Æ 23. As last. ℞. ΙΡΗΝΟΠΟΛΕΙΤΩΝ ΕΤΒΜ (=42 =94 A.D. ?). Hygieia stg. *B.M.C.* 3 .. .. *fair* 45/-

1968 **Laerte.** *Valerian.* Æ 28. Radiate bust r. ℞. ΛΑΕΡΤΕΙΤΩΝ. Athena r., with spear and shield, fighting with serpent-footed giant. *Not in B.M.C.* *RR, fair* 60/-

1969 **Lyrbe.** *Tranquillina.* Æ 26. Greek legend; her dr. bust r. ℞. ΛΥΡΒΕΙΤΩΝ. Tyche standing l. *B.M.C.* 8 .. .. *R, F* £10

1970 **Mallus.** 520-485 B.C. Æ *stater*. Figure with curved wings running l. in kneeling attitude, hands extended. ℞. Conical baetyl in rude incuse square. *B.M.C.* 4
fair £14; F £40

1971 485-425 B.C. Æ *stater*. *Obv.* Similar, but figure wears long sleeved chiton. ℞. Conical baetyl with two handles, between two objects resembling birds with closed wings. *B.M.C.* 6 .. .. *good* F/VF £80

1972 **Mopsus or Mopsuestia** (Missis). 2nd Cent. B.C. Æ 20. Head of Zeus r. ℞. ΜΟΨΕΑΤΩΝ. Lighted circular altar between monograms. *B.M.C.* 2 .. .. F 35/–; VF 80/–

1973 Æ 21. As preceding, with additional *rev.* legend ΤΗΣ ΙΕΡΑΣ ΚΑΙ ΑΥΤΟΝΟΜΟΥ. *Cf.* *B.M.C.* 4-7 .. .. *fair* 22/6

1974 **Nagidus** (Boz Yazi). 420-400 B.C. Æ *stater*. Aphrodite seated l. on throne, holding phiale: in field, l., Eros flying r. with wreath. ℞. ΝΑΓΙΔΙΚΟΝ. Dionysos standing l., holding grapes and thyrsos: in field, l., ΑΘΗ. *B.M.C.* 2 .. .. R, VF £120

1974A **Ninica Claudiopolis.** *Trajan.* Æ 26. Roman legend. Laur. head r. ℞. COL IVL AVG FELI NINIC CLAVD. Eagle stg. between two vexilla. *B.M.C.* 2
F 85/–

1975 **Olba** (Oura). Ajax, high-priest of Olba and governor of Lalassis and Cennatis. Æ 20. ΑΙΑΝΤΟΣ ΤΕΥΚΡΟΥ. Head of Ajax as Hermes r. ℞. ΑΡΧΙΕΡΕΩΣ / ΤΟΠΑΡΧΟΥ / ΕΤΑ (= year 1 = 10/11 A.D.) / ΚΕΝΝΑΤ / ΛΑΛΑΣΣ. Triskeles l. in centre. *B.M.C.* 2 VF £12

1976 *Augustus.* Æ 23. ΚΑΙΣΑΡΟΣ ΣΕΒΑΣΤΟΥ. His laur. head r. ℞. ΚΕΝΝΑΤΩΝ ΚΑΙ ΛΑΛ-ΑΣΣΕΩΝ etc. Winged thunderbolt. *B.M.C.* 10 .. .. F £6

1976A **Philadelphia.** *Maximinus.* Æ 27. Greek legend. Bust r. ℞. ΦΙΛΑΔΕΛΦΕΩΝ ΚΗΤΙΔΟC. Zeus stg. *B.M.C.* 3 .. .. *R, fair* 50/–

1977 **Seleuceia ad Calycadnum** (Selefké). 2nd-1st Cent. B.C. Æ 24. Head of Athena r., ΣΑ behind. ℞. ΣΕΛΕΥΚΕΩΝ ΤΩΝ ΠΡΟΣ ΤΩΙ ΚΑΛΥΚΑΔΝΩΙ. Nike advancing l.; in field, ΔΙΟΦ/ΗΡΑ. *B.M.C.* 7 .. .. F/*fair* 35/–

1978 *Gordian III.* Æ 30. Radiate bust r. ℞. CEΛΕΥΚΕΩΝ ΤΩ ΠΡΟC ΚΑΛΥ. Type as No. 1968. *B.M.C.* 38 .. .. *R, fair*/F 70/–

1979 *Philip I.* Æ 35. Radiate bust r. ℞. Legend similar to preceding: busts of Apollo, laur., l., and Tyche, r., facing each other. *B.M.C.* 50 .. .. F £7/10/–

1977   1981A

1979A **Selinus** (Selinti). *Sev. Alexander.* Æ 31. Greek legend. Bust r. ℞. ΤΡΑΙΑΝ CΕΛΙΝΟ. Trajan and Zeus in temple of four columns: in pediment ΘΕ/ΤΡΑ: in ex., ΤΗCΙΕ. *B.M.C.* 2. [*Trajan died here*] .. .. *R, fair* 60/–

1980 **Soli-Pompeiopolis.** 450-386 B.C. Æ *stater*. Archer kneeling l., examining bow. ℞. ΣΟΛΕΩΝ. Bunch of grapes; to r., fly. *B.M.C.* 3. **Plate VI** *R, fair/good* F £20

1981 Æ *stater*. Head of Athena r. in Athenian helmet. ℞. ΣΟΛΙΟ. Bunch of grapes in diamond-shaped incuse. *B.M.C.* 15 .. .. F/VF £30

1981A 386-333 B.C. Æ *stater*. Head of Athena r. in Corinthian helmet. ℞. Bunch of grapes between ΑΠΟ and owl; below, ΣΟΛΕΩΝ. *B.M.C.* 28 .. *nearly* VF £40

1982 2nd-1st Cent. B.C. Æ 20. Veiled and turreted head of Tyche r. ℞. ΣΟΛΕΩΝ ΑΡΤ. Pilei of the Dioskuri. *B.M.C.* 42 .. .. *fair* 27/6

1983 *Cn. Pompeius Magnus. c.* 66 B.C. Æ 21. Bare head of Pompey r. ℞. ΠΟΜΠΗΙΟ ΠΟΛΙΤΩΝ. Athena seated l., holding Nike and spear. *B.M.C.* 52 *RR*, F £12

1984 **Syedra.** *Gallienus.* Æ 30. Greek legend; his laur. bust dr. r.; ΙΑ to r. ℞. CΥΕΔ-ΡΕΩΝ. Bearded male figure seated r. on rock. *B.M.C.* 13 .. .. *fair*/F 75/–

1985 **Tarsus.** Satraps of Tarsus: Pharnabazus. 379-374 B.C. Æ *stater*. Baaltars seated l. on diphros, holding sceptre, Phoenician inscr. behind. ℞. Bearded and helmeted male head l., Phoenician inscr. around. *B.M.C.* 21. **Plate VI** VF/EF £35

1986 Satraps: Datames. 378-372 B.C. Æ *stater*. Baaltars seated three-quarter r. on diphros, holding sceptre, ear of corn and bunch of grapes; all within ornamental border. ℞. Datames and Ana standing facing each other, thymiaterion between them; all in linear square. *B.M.C.* 35 .. .. F/VF £13

1987 — — Female head facing. ℞. Similar inscription. Type as No. 1985. *B.M.C.* 28 VF £21

1988 — Mazaeus. 361-333 B.C. Æ *stater*. *Obv.* type as No. 1985, with ear of corn and grapes in field l. ℞. Lion l. killing bull: above, Phoenician inscr. *B.M.C.* 45. **Plate VI** .. .. VF £30

1989 — — Æ *stater*. *Obv.* Similar, but eagle in field l. ℞. Lion r. killing bull: above, Phoenician inscr. *B.M.C.* 51 .. .. .. *chisel-cut on rev., otherwise* F £20

1990 — — Æ *stater*. *Obv.* As 1988. ℞. Bust of Athena facing in triple-crested helmet. *B.M.C.* 70 .. .. F £9

1991 4th Cent. B.C. Æ *obol*. Baal seated l. ℞. Forepart of wolf r.: above, crescent with horns downwards; all in dotted square. *B.M.C.* 84 .. .. R, VF £6

1992 2nd-1st Cent. B.C. Æ 20. Bust of Tyche, turreted, r. ℞. ΤΑΡΣΕΩΝ. Sandan standing r. on horned animal: in field, l., ΔΙΟΘΕΟ. *B.M.C.* 100 .. .. F 45/–

1993 Æ 20. *Obv.* as preceding. ℞. ΤΑΡΣΕΩΝ. Pyramidal structure containing figure of Sandan as on preceding, mounted on garlanded base: in field, l., A and two monograms. *Cf. B.M.C.* 106 .. .. VF/F 85/–

1994 Æ 24. Tyche seated r. on throne, holding corn-ears: before her, river-god Kydnos swimming r. ℞. ΤΑΡΣΕΩΝ. Zeus seated l. on throne, holding Nike and sceptre: in field, l., ΣΑΝ and ΙΛΗ. *Cf. B.M.C.* 118 .. .. .. *fair* 21/–; VF 80/–

1995 Imperial Times. Æ 16. ΤΑΡϹΟΥ. Veiled female bust with star above forehead, l. ℞. ΜΗΤΡΟΠΟΛΕΩϹ. Sandan r. on horned animal. *B.M.C.* 132 VF/F 45/–

1996 *Elagabalus.* Æ 29. ΑΥΤ ΚΑΙ Μ ΑΥΡ ΑΝΤΩΝΕΙΝΟϹ. Laur. bust r. ℞. ΤΑΡϹΟΥ ΤΗϹ ΜΗΤΡΟΠΟΛΕΩϹ; Altar surmounted by wreath: to r., archieratic crown decorated with seven heads and letters Γ and Β. *B.M.C.* 207. **Plate VII** .. .. RR, F £7/10/–

1997 *Maximinus I.* Æ 36. Greek legend: laur. bust r. ℞. ΤΑΡϹΟΥ. Athena, Tyche and Nemesis standing: in ex., ΜΗΤΡΟ. *B.M.C.* 221 .. .. *fair* 57/6

1997A **Titiopolis.** *L. Verus.* Æ 30. As last ℞. ΕΤΟϹΓ. ΤΙΤΙΟΠΟΛΕΙΤΩΝ. Tyche stg. l. in distyle arched temple. *B.M.C.* 1 .. .. RR, *fair* £5

1997B **Zephyrium-Hadrianopolis.** (Mersina) 1st Cent. B.C. Æ 18. Turreted head of the City r. ℞. ΖΕΦΥΡΙΩΤΩΝ. Athena seated l.; in field, two mon. *B.M.C.* 4 *fair* 30/–

1998 **Elaeusa-Sebaste.** (Island now joined to mainland) 1st Cent B.C. Æ 20. Laur. head of Zeus r. ℞. ΕΛΑΙΟΥΣΙΩΝ. Nike advancing l.; to l., mon. and ΕΡ. *B.M.C.* 9 *fair* 22/6

1998A **Kings of Cilicia.** Tarcondimotus, 39-31 B.C. Æ 21. His diad. head r. ℞. ΒΑΣΙΛΕΩΣ ΤΑΡΚΟΝΔΙΜΟΤΟΥ. Zeus seated l., in ex. ΦΙΛΑΝΤ. *B.M.C.* 1 .. R, *fair* 50/–

1998B Philopator, *c.* 30 or 20 B.C. Æ 23. Veiled and turreted female head r. ℞. ΒΑΣΙΛΕΩϹ ΦΙΛΟΠΑΤΟΡΟϹ. Athena stg. l. *B.M.C.* 1 .. .. RR, *fair* 80/–

CYPRUS.
For map, see page 144.

1998C **Amathus.** 450-400 B.C. Æ *hemiobol*. Lion lying r. ℞. Forepart of lion r. within incuse square. *B.M.C.* 5 .. .. RR, F £8

1998D Zotimus, *circa* 385 B.C. Æ *didrachm*. Lion lying r.; above, eagle flying r. ℞. Forepart of lion r., ΖΟ ΤΙ ΜΟ in Cypriote script. *B.M.C.* 10 .. R, F/*good* F £60

1999 **Citium** (Larnaca). Baalmelek I, 479-449 B.C. Æ *stater*. Herakles advancing r.; in field, ΒΚ in Phoenician script. ℞. Lion seated r.; Phoenician inscription for Baalmelek. *B.M.C.* 2-6 .. .. RR, F/VF £100

1999A Baalmelek II, *c.* 450-420 B.C. Æ *diobol*. Herakles, wearing lion-skin, r. ℞. Lion r., killing stag: inscription as last. *B.M.C.* 43 .. .. F/*fair* £5

2000 Æ *obol*. Head of Herakles r. ℞. as preceding. *B.M.C.* 49 .. .. *fair* 57/6

2001 Pumiathon, 361-312 B.C. *N tenth*. Head of Herakles r. ℞. Lion r., killing stag. *B.M.C.* 82 .. .. F/VF £25

2001A **Idalium.** Gras, *circa* 460 B.C. Æ *stater*. Sphinx seated l.; Cypriot ΒΑ, etc., in field. ℞. Lotus flower between ivy-leaf and astragalos. *B.M.C.* 10-19 .. RR, F £90

2001B Stasikypros, *circa* 460-450 B.C. Æ *third*. Similar but ΣΑ. *B.M.C.* 20-28. R, VF £45

2002 **Lapethus.** *c.* 480 B.C. Æ *stater.* Head of Aphrodite r. ℞. Helmeted head of Athena l., in incuse square. *B.M.C.* 2 .. .. .. RR, M/F £17

2002A **Marium.** Stasioecus II, *circa* 315 B.C. Æ 15. Head of Aphrodite r. ℞. *Ankh* with pellet in ring: the whole in wreath. *B.M.C.* 6 .. .. .. R, F 60/–

2003 **Paphos.** 480–400 B.C. Æ *stater.* Bull standing l. ℞. Eagle's head l.: to l., palmette: all within dotted square in incuse square. *B.M.C.* 8 R, F/VF £75

2004 Stasandros, *ca.* 450 B.C. Æ *obol.* Similar. ℞. Eagle stg. l. ; at its feet, vase; above, ivy-leaf. *B.M.C.* 24 .. .. F £8

2005 350–332 B.C. Æ 15. Head of Aphrodite l. ℞. Dove r. *B.M.C.* 48 .. *fair* 35/–

2006 **Salamis.** Euelthon, 560–525 B.C. Æ *stater.* Ram lying l. ℞. *Ankh* symbol (cross surmounted by ring) in incuse square. *B.M.C.* 12 .. .. .. R, F £35

2006A Euagoras I, 411–374 B.C. Æ *tenth.* Head of Herakles r. ℞. Forepart of kneeling goat r. *B.M.C.* 52 .. .. R, VF/good VF £50

2006B Pnytagorus, 351–332 B.C. Æ *tetrobol.* Head of Aphrodite l., PN behind. ℞. Bust of Artemis r., BA behind. *B.M.C.* 80 .. .. VF £50

2007 4th Cent. B.C. Æ 14. Head of Athena l. ℞. Prow l. *B.M.C.*, pl. xxiv, 17 *fair* 30/–

2008 **Cyprus under the Romans.** *Augustus.* Æ 17. Bare head r. ℞. A PLAVTIVS PRO COS. Temple of Aphrodite at Paphos, containing cone: on either side, candelabrum: in front, paved semi-circular court. *B.M.C.* 2 .. .. .. *fair*/F 40/–

2009 *Drusus Caesar.* Æ 18. DRVSVS CAESAR. Bare head r. ℞. Zeus Salaminios standing l.: to r., temple of Aphrodite as in preceding. *B.M.C.* 7 F 75/–; VF £8

2010 *Vespasian.* Æ 27. ΑΥΤΟΚΡΑΤΩΡΟΥ ΟΥΕCΠΑCΙΑΝΟC CΕΒΑCΤΟC. Laur. head r. ℞. ΚΟΙΝΟΝ ΚΥΠΡΙΩΝ ΕΤΟΥC Η (=year 8=76/77 A.D.). Zeus Salaminios standing facing, with phiale and sceptre. *B.M.C.* 22 .. .. F 80/–

2011 *Antoninus Pius and M. Aurelius.* Æ 32. ΑΥΤ Κ Τ ΑΙΛ ΑΔΡΙ ΑΝΤΩΝΙΝΟC CΕΒ ΕΥ. Laur. head r. ℞. Μ ΑΥΡΗΛΙΟC ΚΑΙCΑΡ VΙΟC CΕΒΑC. Bare head, dr. bust r. *B.M.C.* 42. **Plate VII** .. .. *fair* 65/–

GALATIA.

2012 **Kings of Galatia.** Amyntas, 36–25 B.C. Æ *tetradrachm.* Head of Athena r. ℞. ΒΑCΙΛΕΩC ΑΜΥΝΤΟΥ. Nike advancing l., holding sceptre. *B.M.C.* 5 *nearly* VF £30

2013 Æ 24. Head of Herakles r.; at neck, club; behind, mon. ℞. Similar legend. Lion advancing r. *B.M.C.* 8 .. .. F/fair 35/–

2014 Æ 16. Bust of Artemis r. ℞. Similar legend. Hind r. *B.M.C.* 15 F/fair 27/6

2013   2015

2015 **Koinon of Galatia.** Trajan. Æ 26. ΑΥ Ν ΤΡΑΙΑΝΟC ΚΑΙCΑΡ CΕΒ. Laur. head r. ℞. ΕΠΙ ΒΑC ΚΟΙΝΟΝ ΓΑΛΑΤΙΑC. Mên stg. l. *B.M.C.* 7 .. .. *fair* 40/–

2016 **Ancyra** (Ankara). *Caracalla.* Æ 17. ΑΝΤΩΝΙΝΟC ΑΥ. His laur. head r. ℞. ΜΗΤΡΟΠ ΑΝΚΥΡΑC. Palm in prize urn. *B.M.C.* 27 .. .. F 80/–

2016A **Germa.** *Commodus.* Æ 26. Latin legend. Bust r. ℞. CO GERME NORVM. Eagle l. between two standards. *B.M.C.* 1 .. .. RR, F £7

2017 **Pessinus.** *Julia Domna.* Æ 30. ΙΟΥΛΙΑ ΑΥΓΟΥCΤΑ. Her dr. bust r. ℞. ΠΕCΙΝΟVΝΤΙΩΝ. Goddess standing facing, head l., holding patera and sceptre. *Grose* 9201 *fair* 50/–

2017A **Tavium** (Böyuk Nefez Keui). 1st Cent. B.C. Æ 22. Humped bull running r. ℞. ΤΑΥΙΩΝ. Amphora between the pilei of the Dioskuri. *B.M.C.* 1 .. R, *fair* 45/–

CAPPADOCIA.

2017B Kings of Cappadocia: Ariarathes I, 330-322 B.C. Æ *drachm* (87 grs.). Baal of Gaziura on throne l.; B'L GZUR in Aramaic script in r. ℞. Griffin attacking stag l.; ARIORAT in Aramaic below. *B.M.C.* 1 .. .. *RR*, VF £50

2018 Ariarathes IV, 220-163 B.C. Æ *drachm*. Young head of king r. ℞. ΒΑΣΙΛΕΩΣ ΑΡΙΑΡΑΘΟΥ ΕΥΣΕΒΟΥΣ. Athena standing l., with Nike, spear and shield. *B.M.C.* 1 F 65/-

2019 — — Older head of king, r. ℞. Similar. *Cf. B.M.C.* 2-18 .. *good* F/F 75/-

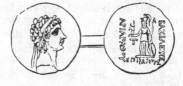

2019   2020

2019A Ariarathes V, 163-130 B.C. Æ *drachm*. As last but young head with curly hair. *B.M.C.* 2 .. . . *R, good* F £6

2020 Ariarathes VI, 125-111 B.C. Æ *drachm*. Head of king, r. ℞. ΒΑΣΙΛΕΩΣ ΑΡΙΑΡΑΘΟΥ ΕΠΙΦΑΝΟΥΕ. Type as preceding. *Cf. B.M.C.* 1-8 .. .. .. F 50/-; VF £5

2021   2022

2021 Ariarathes VII, 111-99 B.C. Æ *drachm*. Head of king, r. ℞. ΒΑΣΙΛΕΩΣ ΑΡΙΑΡΑΘΟΥ ΦΙΛΟΜΗΤΟΡΟΣ. Type as preceding. *B.M.C.* 1 .. .. F 45/-

2022 Ariarathes IX, 99-87 B.C. Æ *drachm*. Head of king, r. ℞. ΒΑΣΙΛΕΩΣ ΑΡΙΑΡΑΘΟΥ ΕΥΣΕΒΟΥΣ. Type as preceding. *B.M.C.* 4 .. .. VF £5

2023 Ariobarzanes I, 95-62 B.C. Æ *drachm*. Head of king, r. ℞. ΒΑΣΙΛΕΩΣ ΑΡΙΟΒΑΡ-ΖΑΝΟΥ ΦΙΛΟΡΩΜΑΙΟΥ. Type as preceding. *Cf. B.M.C.* 1-23 *good* F 60/-; VF £5

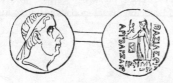

2023   2024

2024 Ariobarzanes III, 52-42 B.C. Æ *drachm*. Head of king, r. ℞. ΒΑΣΙΛΕΩΣ ΑΡΙΟΒΑΡ-ΖΑΝΟΥ ΕΥΣΕΒΟΥΣ ΚΑΙ ΦΙΛΟΡΩΜΑΙΟΥ. Type as preceding. *B.M.C.* 1 .. F 50/-

2024A Archelaus, 36 B.C.-17 A.D. Æ *drachm*. His diad. head r.; bead and real border. ℞. ΒΑΣΙΛΕΩΣ ΑΡΧΕΛΑΟΥ ΦΙΛΟΠΑΤΡΙΔΟΧ ΤΟΥ ΚΤΙΣΤΟΥ. Club; in field, Μ (=year 40) *B.M.C.* 3 .. .. *nearly* VF £12

2024A   2039

2025 **Caesareia** (Kayseri). 36 B.C.-17 A.D. Æ 16. Bust of Artemis, turreted and crested, r. Ŗ.
ΕΥΣΕΒΕΙΑΣ. Palm-branch. *B.M.C.* 9 ..   .. VF 45/-

2026 *Germanicus. Æ drachm.* GERMANICVS CAES TI AVGV COS II P M. Bare head r. Ŗ.
DIVVS AVGVSTVS. Radiate head of Augustus l. *Not in B.M.C.*; *M. & S.* 10   F £12

2027 *Vespasian. Æ didrachm.* ΑΥΤΟΚΡΑ ΚΑΙϹΑΡ ΟΥΕϹΠΑϹΙΑΝΟϹ ϹΕΒΑϹΤΟϹ. Laur. head r.
Ŗ. ΝΙΚΗ ϹΕΒΑϹΤΗ. Nike standing r., with wreath and palm. *B.M.C.* 16   F £6

2028 *Nerva. Æ didrachm.* ΑΥΤΟΚΡΑΤ ΝΕΡΟΥΑϹ ΚΑΙϹΑΡ ϹΕΒΑϹΤΟϹ ΥΠΑΤ Γ. Laur. head r.
Ŗ. ΟΜΟΝ ϹΤΡΑΤ. Clasped hands holding standard on prow. *B.M.C.* 44   F £5

2029 *Trajan. Æ drachm.* ΑΥΤ ΚΑΙΣ ΝΕΡ ΤΡΑΙΑΝ ΣΕΒ ΓΕΡΜ. Laur. head r. Ŗ. ΔΗΜΑΡΧ
ΕΞ ΥΠΑΤ Γ. Head of Zeus Ammon r. *B.M.C.* 54 ..   .. F 65/-

2030 — *Æ hemidrachm.* Similar. *B.M.C.* 56   ..   .. F 50/-

2031 — *Æ didrachm. Obv.* Similar to preceding. Ŗ. ΔΗΜΑΡΧ ΕΞ ΥΠΑΤΟϹ. Representation of Mount Argaeus. *B.M.C.* 80   ..   .. VF £10

2032 — *Æ* 20. *Obv.* Similar to preceding. Ŗ. ΔΗΜΑΡΧ ΕΞ ΥΠΑΤ Β within wreath.
B.M.C. 106   ..   .. F 32/6

2033 *Hadrian. Æ hemidrachm.* ΑΥΤΟ ΚΑΙϹ ΤΡΑΙ ΑΔΡΙΑΝΟϹ ϹΕΒΑϹΤ. Laur. bust r. Ŗ.
ΕΤ Δ (year 4). Nike r., with wreath and palm. *B.M.C.* 140   ..   *good* F 75/-

2034 *Antoninus Pius. Æ didrachm.* ΑΝΤΩΝΙΝΟϹ ϹΕΒΑϹΤΟϹ. Laur. head r. Ŗ. ΥΠΑ Β
ΠΑ ΠΑΤΡ. Mount Argaeus, surmounted by small figure holding globe and sceptre.
Not in B.M.C.   ..   .. R, VF £7/10/-

2035 *M. Aurelius. Æ didrachm.* ΑΥΤΟΚΡ ΑΝΤΩΝΕΙΝΟϹ ϹΕΒ. Laur. bust r. Ŗ. ΥΠΑΤ
ΟϹ Γ. Type as No. 2034. *B.M.C.* 169 ..   .. F 65/-

2036 *Æ* 24. *Obv.* Similar to preceding, but head radiate. Ŗ. ΔΗΜΑΡΧ ΙΚ ΕΞΟΥϹ ΚΔ.
Head of Zeus Ammon r. *B.M.C.* 185 ..   .. F 35/-

2037 *Sept. Severus. Æ drachm.* ΑΥ Λ ϹΕΠ ϹΕΟΥΗΡΟϹ. Laur. head r. Ŗ. ΜΗΤΡΟ ΚΑΙϹΑΡ.
Mount Argaeus, star on summit. *B.M.C.* 219   ..   ..   .. F 65/-

2038 *Æ* 27. Types similar to preceding. *B.M.C.* 262 ..   ..   .. *fair*/F 25/-

2039 *Caracalla. Æ drachm.* ΑΥΚ Μ ΑΥΡ ΑΝΤΩΝΙΝ. Young laur. head r. Ŗ. ΜΗΤΡ ΚΑΙϹΑ·
As last; in ex. ΕΤΙΕ (=year 15). *B.M.C.* 269. *Illustrated at bottom of page* 159 VF £5

2040 *Elagabalus. Æ* 26. Somewhat similar, but with radiate bust. *B.M.C.* 289 *fair* 45/-

2041 *Gordian III. Æ* 22. ΑΥ ΚΑΙ Μ ΑΝΤ ΓΟΡΔΙΑΝΟϹ. Laur. bust r. Ŗ. ΜΗΤΡ ΚΑΙ Β
ΝΕ ΕΤ Ζ. Six ears of corn bound together. *B.M.C.* 346   ..   .. F 35/-

2041A **Cybistra** (Eregli). Time of *Trajan. Æ* 17. ΕΠΙ ΡΟΥϹΩΝΟϹ. Bust of Tyche r.
Ŗ. ΚΥΒΙϹΤΡΕΩΝ. Harpa. *B.M.C.* 1 ..   .. RRR, *fair* £7

2041B **Tyana** (Kiz Hissar). *Antoninus Pius. Æ* 23. Greek legend. Laur. hd. r. Ŗ
ΤΥΑΝΕΩΝΤ . Π . Τ. ΙΕΡ. ΑϹΥ. ΑΥΤ. Tyche seated l.; below, river-god swimming; in field,
ΕΤ ΘΙ (=19=157 A.D.)   ..   .. R, *fair* 55/-

SYRIA.

For maps, see pages 167 *and* 174.

KINGS OF SYRIA.

2042 **Seleucus I.** 312-280 B.C. Æ *tetradrachm.* Type of Alexander the Great. Head of Herakles r. ℞. ΣΕΛΕΥΚΟΥ ΒΑΣΙΛΕΩΣ. Zeus seated l.; in field to l., bust of Athena r. *B.M.C.* 12. **Plate VII** .. .. *good* VF/VF £30

2043 Æ *tetradrachm.* Head of Zeus, laur., r. ℞. ΒΑΣΙΛΕΩΣ ΣΕΛΕΥΚΟΥ. Four horned elephants harnessed to a chariot, in which stands Athena, with spear and shield, r.: in field, anchor and two monograms. *B.M.C.* 25. **Plate VII** .. *R, good* F/F £50

2044 Æ *tetradrachm.* Helmeted head of king r. ℞. ΣΕΛΕΥΚΟΥ ΒΑΣΙΛΕΩΣ. Nike standing r., placing wreath on trophy: in field, H ΔΧ. *B.M.C.* 37 .. .. *RR,* VF £350

2044A Æ *hemidrachm.* As last. *B.M.C.* 40 .. .. *R,* VF £45

2045 Æ 21. Helmeted head of Athena r. ℞. Legend as preceding: Nike standing l., with wreath and palm; before her, large anchor inverted. *B.M.C.* 44 .. F 45/–

2046 Æ 22. Elephant r. ℞. Similar legend: head of bridled horse, with bull's horns, l. *B.M.C.* 49 .. .. F 52/6

2047 Æ 14. Heads of the Dioskuri l. ℞. Legend as preceding: elephant's head r. *B.M.C.* 55 .. .. *fair* 25/–

2048 Æ 20. Head of Medusa, winged, r. ℞. Similar legend: humped bull butting r. *B.M.C.* 62/8 .. .. F 40/–

2044

2050

2049 **Antiochus I.** 280-261 B.C. Æ *tetradrachm.* Middle-aged head of king, diademed, r. ℞. ΒΑΣΙΛΕΩΣ ΑΝΤΙΟΧΟΥ. Apollo seated l. on omphalos, holding arrow and bow: in field, r. and l., monograms. *B.M.C.* 7. **Plate VII** .. .. VF £35

2050 — Similar but elderly portrait; two mon. in ex. *B.M.C.* 19 *R,* VF/*good* F £40

2051 Æ 18. Young head of king, diad., r. ℞. Legend similar: Apollo l., r. foot on omphalos, holding arrow and bow. *B.M.C.* 24 .. .. F 40/–

2052 Æ 19. Head of Zeus r. ℞. Legend similar: thunderbolt, monogram and jaw-bone of boar. *B.M.C.* 41 .. .. VF 65/–

2053 **Antiochus II.** 261-246 B.C. Æ *drachm.* As No. 2049, but different portrait and mon. *B.M.C.* 4 .. .. VF £20

2053A Æ *tetradrachm.* His diad. head r. ℞. ΒΑΣΙΛΕΩΣ ΑΝΤΙΟΧΟΥ. Herakles seated l. on rock; to l., T and mon.; to r., mon. *B.M.C.* 8 .. .. .. *RR,* VF £165

2054 Æ 18. Head of Apollo r. ℞. Same legend. Tripod-lebes. *B.M.C.* 14 F 35/–

2055 Seleucus II. 246-226 B.C. Æ *tetradrachm.* Head of king, diademed, r. ℞. ΒΑΣΙΛΕΩΣ ΣΕΛΕΥΚΟΥ. Apollo laur. standing l., holding arrow and leaning on tripod-lebes: in field, monogram ΔΗ and ΜΡ. *B.M.C.* 1 .. .. .. VF/*good* F £45

2056 Æ 14. Similar types, different monograms and horse's head in *rev.* field. *B.M.C.* 14 .. .. F 35/-

2057 Æ 14. Head of Apollo r. ℞. The Dioskuri galloping r. *B.M.C.* 28 .. *fair* 17/6

2058 Æ 16. *Obv.* as preceding. ℞. Humped bull l. *B.M.C.* 33 .. .. *fair* 25/-

2059 Æ 21. Head of king, bearded, r. ℞. Bow-case and quiver. *B.M.C.* 36 *fair* 21/-

2061 Seleucus III. 226-222 B.C. Æ *tetradrachm.* Head of king, diad., r. ℞. ΒΑΣ-ΙΛΕΩΣ ΣΕΛΕΥΚΟΥ. Apollo seated l. on omphalos, holding arrow and bow: in field, mono-grams ΞΥ and ΣΩ. *B.M.C.* 2 .. .. R, VF £37/10/-

2062 Æ 15. Head of Artemis r. ℞. Apollo seated l. on omphalos. *B.M.C.* 8 *fair* 17/6

2055   2063

2063 Antiochus III, the Great. 222-187 B.C. Æ *tetradrachm.* Head of king, diad., r. ℞. ΒΑΣΙΛΕΩΣ ΑΝΤΙΟΧΟΥ. Type as preceding: in field, two monograms. *B.M.C.* 4-17 .. .. *good* F £18; *good* VF/VF £37/10/-

2064 Æ *drachm.* Type as preceding. *B.M.C.* 14 .. .. .. *nearly* F £6

2065 Æ 22. As before but *rev.* type, elephant r. and anchor. *B.M.C.* 36 *fair* 21/-

2066 Achaeus, rebel satrap, *c.* 214 B.C. Æ 19. Head of Apollo, laur., r. ℞. ΒΑΣΙΛΕΩΣ ΑΧΑΙΟΥ. Eagle r., palm over l. shoulder: countermarked with horse's head r. *B.M.C.* 3 RR, F £5

2067 Seleucus IV. 187-175 B.C. Æ *tetradrachm.* Head of king, diademed, r.: good portrait in high relief. ℞. ΒΑΣΙΛΕΩΣ ΣΕΛΕΥΚΟΥ. Apollo seated l. on omphalos, with arrow and bow: in field l., wreath and palm-branch: in ex., monogram ΔΙ. *B.M.C.* 12 R, F £40

2068 Æ *drachm.* Somewhat similar type. *B.M.C.* 3 .. .. .. *scarce,* F £12

2069 Æ 15. Head of Apollo r. ℞. Tripod-lebes. *B.M.C.* 15 .. *fair* 17/6

2070 Æ 22 serrate. *Obv.* Similar. ℞. Apollo l., holding arrow and leaning on tripod. *B.M.C.* 19-24 .. .. F/*fair* 30/-

2071 Antiochus IV. 175-164 B.C. Æ *tetradrachm.* Head of king, diad., r. ℞. ΒΑΣ-ΙΛΕΩΣ ΑΝΤΙΟΧΟΥ ΘΕΟΥ ΕΠΙΦΑΝΟΥΣ ΝΙΚΗΦΟΡΟΥ. Zeus seated l. on throne, holding Nike and sceptre: in field l., monogram ΔΙ. *B.M.C.* 17 .. .. VF £35

2072 Æ *drachm.* Somewhat similar type. *Naville* x, 1033 .. *nearly* VF/F £6

2071   2080

2073 Æ 20 *dichalkon.* Head of king, radiate, r.: behind, BX. ℞. ΒΑΣΙΛΕΩΣ ΑΝΤΙΟΧΟΥ. Kybele (or Tyche) seated l., holding Nike. *B.M.C.* 24 .. .. .. *fair* 30/-

2074 Æ 21 *of Sidon.* *Obv.* Similar. ℞. Legend similar; galley l., ΣΙΔΩΝΙΟΝ and Phoenician legend below. *B.M.C.* 51 .. .. F/*fair* 37/6

2075 Æ 20 *of Laodiceia.* *Obv.* Similar. ℞. Legend similar, followed by Phoenician inscr.: Poseidon standing l., holding patera and trident. *B.M.C.* 57 .. R, *fair* 45/-

2076 Æ 19 *of Seleuceia Pieria.* *Obv.* Similar. ℞. ΣΕΛΕΥΚΕΩΝ ΤΩΝ ΕΜ ΠΙΕΡΙΑΙ. Winged thunderbolt. *Cf. B.M.C.* 83/4 .. .. F 45/-

2077 Æ 16. Head of Demeter, veiled, r. ℞. ΒΑΣΙΛΕΩΣ ΑΝΤΙΟΧΟΥ. Elephant's head l. *B.M.C.* p. 43, 1-4 .. .. F 35/-

2078 **Antiochus V.** 164-162 B.C. Æ *tetradrachm.* His young head diad. r. ℞. ΒΑΣΙΛΕΩΣ ΑΝΤΙΟΧΟΥ ΕΥΠΑΤΟΡΟΣ. Zeus seated l., holding Nike and sceptre: in field l., monogram ΔΙ. *B.M.C.* 3 .. .. R, *almost* VF £50

2079 **Demetrius I.** 162-150 B.C. Æ *drachm.* Head of king, diad., r. ℞. ΒΑΣΙΛΕΩΣ ΔΗΜΗΤΡΙΟΥ ΣΩΤΗΡΟΣ. Apollo l., as on No. 2067. *B.M.C.* 5 .. .. F 75/-

2080 Æ *tetradrachm.* Head of king, diad., r. ℞. ΒΑΣΙΛΕΩΣ ΔΗΜΗΤΡΙΟΥ ΣΩΤΗΡΟΣ. Tyche seated l., holding sceptre and cornucopiae: in field l., monogram and ΜΙ; in ex., ΑΞΡ (=161=152/1 B.C.). *B.M.C.* 19. *Illustrated on page* 162 .. .. .. VF £30

2081 Æ *drachm.* As No. 2079, but *rev.* type, cornucopiae. *B.M.C.* 37 .. VF £8

2082 Æ 15. *Obv.* Similar. ℞. Legend similar: pilei of the Dioskuri. *B.M.C.* 55 F 32/6

2083 Æ 15 serrate. Head of horse l. ℞. Shortened legend: elephant's head r. *B.M.C.* 60 F 27/6

2084 **Alexander I.** 152-144 B.C. Æ *tetradrachm.* Diad. and dr. bust r. ℞. ΑΛΕΞΑΝΔΡΟΥ ΒΑΣΙΛΕΩΣ. Eagle l. on palm-branch: in field, ΓΞΡ (=163=150/49 B.C.), and ΗΡ. monogram. *B.M.C.* 1 .. .. VF £20

2085 Æ *tetradrachm.* *Obv.* Similar. ℞. ΒΑΣΙΛΕΩΣ ΑΛΕΞΑΝΔΡΟΥ ΘΕΟΠΑΤΟΡΟΣ ΕΥΕΡΓΕΤΟΥ. Zeus seated l. on throne, holding Nike and sceptre: in field, monogram: in ex., ΙΞΡ. (=167). *B.M.C.* 12 .. .. VF £27/10/-

2086 Æ *drachm.* *Obv.* as preceding. ℞. Legend as preceding, type as No. 2067. *B.M.C.* 24/6 .. .. *nearly* VF £7

2087 Æ 20 serrate. *Obv.* Similar. ℞. ΒΑΣΙΛΕΩΣ ΑΛΕΞΑΝΔΡΟΥ. Athena l., holding Nike and spear. *B.M.C.* 37 .. .. *fair* 17/6

2088 Æ 19. Head of king, wearing lion-skin, r. ℞. Legend as preceding: Apollo stdg. l., with arrow and bow. *B.M.C.* 44 .. .. VF/F 45/-

2089 Æ 21 *of Antioch.* *Obv.* as No. 2087. ℞. ΑΝΤΙΟΧΕΩΝ. Zeus standing facing, head l., holding wreath. *B.M.C.* 63 .. .. F/*fair* 30/-

2084   2091

2090 **Demetrius II.** First reign, 146-138 B.C. Æ *tetradrachm.* Head of king, diad., r. ℞. ΔΗΜΗΤΡΙΟΥ ΒΑΣΙΛΕΩΣ. Eagle l., palm over shoulder; in field, ΒΟΡ (=172 =141/0 B.C.), monogram ΠΑ, ΣΙΔΩ (Sidon) and aplustre. *B.M.C.* 3 .. .. .. VF £20

2091 — ℞. ΒΑΣΙΛΕΩΣ ΔΗΜΗΤΡΙΟΥ ΘΕΟΥ ΦΙΛΑΔΕΛΦΟΥ ΝΙΚΑΤΟΡΟΣ. Apollo l., as on No. 2067; in ex. ΙΞΡ (=167=146/5 B.C.) and Θ. *B.M.C.* 10 .. .. *nearly* VF £30

2091A Æ 24. Head of Zeus laur. r. ℞. As last but two mon. in ex. *B.M.C.* 30 F 40/-

2092 **Antiochus VI.** 145-142 B.C. Æ *drachm.* Head of king, radiate, r. ℞. ΒΑΣΙΛΕΩΣ ΑΝΤΙΟΧΟΥ ΕΠΙΦΑΝΟΥΣ ΔΙΟΝΥΣΟΥ. Apollo l., as on No. 2067: in field, monogram ΧΑΡ: in ex., ΟΡ (=170) and ΣΤΑ. *B.M.C.* 11 .. .. F £5; VF £12

2092A Æ *tetradrachm.* As illustration below; same date as last. *B.M.C.* 5 R, VF £75

2093 Æ 20. Somewhat similar. ℞. Legend similar: amphora. *Cf. B.M.C.* 25 *et seq.* .. .. *fair* 21/-

2094 Æ 20 serrate. *Obv.* Similar. ℞. Legend as preceding: elephant l., holding torch: to r., cornucopiae. *B.M.C.* 45 .. .. F 30/-

2095 **Tryphon.** 142-139 B.C. Æ 18. Head of Tryphon, diad., r. ℞. ΒΑΣΙΛΕΩΣ ΤΡΥΦΩΝΟΣ ΑΥΤΟΚΡΑΤΟΡΟΣ. Spiked Macedonian helmet. *B.M.C.* 5-15. **Plate VI** *scarce*, F 40/-; VF 90/-

2092A   2097

2096 **Antiochus VII.** 138-129 B.C. Æ *tetradrachm.* Diad. and dr. bust r. ℞. ΑΝΤΙΟΧΟΥ ΒΑΣΙΛΕΩΣ. Eagle standing l., palm over shoulder: in field, l., Α ΡΕ and monogram ΤΥΡ on club: in field, r., Α, monogram ΣΚ, and ΙΟΡ (=177=136/5 B.C.); below, monogram ΤΗΡ. *Mint of Tyre. B.M.C.* 7 .. .. *nearly* VF £15

2097 — Diad. hd. r. ℞. ΒΑΣΙΛΕΩΣ ΑΝΤΙΟΧΟΥ ΕΥΕΡΓΕΤΟΥ. Athena standing l., holding Nike and spear: in field, l., monogram ΔΙ and Α: all within laurel-wreath. *B.M.C.* 19 *good* F £13

2097A Æ *didrachm* of Tyre. As 2096. *B.M.C.* —. **Plate VII** .. R, *good* F £15

2098 Æ 22. Prow of galley r. ℞. Legend as last: trident. *Ḃ.M.C.* 46 .. F 35/-

2099 Æ 18. Bust of Eros, wearing myrtle-wreath, r. ℞. Legend as preceding: head-dress of Isis. *B.M.C.* 52 .. .. F 30/-

2100 Æ 14. Lion's head r. ℞. Legend as preceding: club. *B.M.C.* 64 .. F 25/-

2101 Æ 15, *struck at Jerusalem.* Lily. ℞. Legend as preceding: anchor. *B.M.C.* 69 R, *fair* 27/6; F 65/-

2102 **Demetrius II.** Second reign, 130-125 B.C. Æ *tetradrachm.* Bust of king, beardless, diad. and dr. r. ℞. ΔΗΜΗΤΡΙΟΥ ΒΑΣΙΛΕΩΣ. Eagle l. on beak of galley, palm over shoulder: in field, l., Α ΡΕ and monogram ΤΥΡ on club: in field, l., Α, monogram ΣΚ and ΓΠΡ (=183): between eagle's legs, monogram ΓΗΡ. *B.M.C.* 1. *Struck at Tyre* VF £16

2103 Æ *tetradrachm.* Diademed and bearded head of king r. ℞. ΒΑΣΙΛΕΩΣ ΔΗΜΗΤΡΙΟΥ ΘΕΟΥ ΝΙΚΑΤΟΡΟΣ. Zeus seated l., holding Nike and sceptre: in field, l., monogram ΔΗ: below throne, ΑΠ: in ex., ΙΠΡ (=187=126/5 B.C.) *Cf. B.M.C.* 16 R, VF £45

2104 **Alexander II.** 128-123 B.C. Æ *tetradrachm.* Head of king, diademed, r. ℞. ΒΑΣΙΛΕΩΣ ΑΛΕΞΑΝΔΡΟΥ. Zeus seated l. on throne, holding Nike and sceptre: in field, l., monogram ΔΗΡ and Ι below throne. *B.M.C.* 4 *var.* *good* F/F £10; *good* VF £25

2105 Æ 21. Similar but *rev.* type, double cornucopiae. *B.M.C.* 20 .. .. F 32/6

2106 Æ 20. His rad. head r. ℞. Athena l., holding Nike and spear. *B.M.C.* 17 F 32/6

2107 Æ 17 serrate. Head of young Dionysos r. ℞. Legend similar: Tyche stdg. l. with rudder and cornucopiae. *B.M.C.* 32 .. .. VF/F 45/-

2108 **Cleopatra and Antiochus VIII.** 125-121 B.C. Æ *tetradrachm.* Jugate heads of Cleopatra, diademed and veiled, and Antiochus, diad., r. ℞. ΒΑΣΙΛΙΣΣΗΣ ΚΛΕΟΠΑΤΡΑΣ ΘΕΑΣ ΚΑΙ ΒΑΣΙΛΕΩΣ ΑΝΤΙΟΧΟΥ. Zeus seated l., holding Nike and sceptre: monograms in l. of field and below throne. *B.M.C.* 3. **Plate VII** RR, *good* VF/VF £85

2109 Æ 14. Female head, wearing modius, r. ℞. Legend as preceding, omitting ΘΕΑΣ: lamp suspended from candelabrum. *B.M.C.* 16 .. .. .. R, *fair* 30/-

2111   2117

2110 **Antiochus VIII.** 121-96 B.C. Æ *tetradrachm.* Head of king, diad., r. ℞. ΒΑΣ-
ΙΛΕΩΣ ΑΝΤΙΟΧΟΥ ΕΠΙΦΑΝΟΥΣ. Zeus standing l., naked, holding star and sceptre: above
head, crescent: in field, l., AP and ΕΣ: in ex., ΓϞΡ (=193=120 B.C.). *B.M.C.* 2
                                                     EF/VF   £27

2111 Similar, but Zeus wears mantle, and in l. of *rev.* field, monogram: no letters
in ex. *B.M.C.* 13 ..   ..   VF   £17/10/-

2112 *Obv.* Similar. ℞. Legend similar: Zeus seated l., holding Nike and sceptre: in
field, l., monogram PE and A: below throne, monogram ΔΙ. *Cf. B.M.C. (Antiochus XI)*
2 ..   ..   VF   £15

2113 Æ *drachm. Obv.* Similar. ℞. Legend similar: tripod-lebes. *Cf. B.M.C. (Antiochus
XI)* 6 *var.* ..   ..   R, F   £7

2114 Æ *hemidrachm. Obv.* Similar. ℞. Legend similar: Nike advancing l. *B.M.C.* 24
                                                    RR, F   £10

2115 Æ 18. Head of king, radiate, r. ℞. Legend as preceding: eagle l., with sceptre.
B.M.C. 25 ..   ..   F   30/-

2116 Æ 14. Bust of Artemis r. ℞. Legend as preceding: Apollo l., with arrow and bow.
B.M.C. 30 ..   ..   *fair*   17/6

2117 **Antiochus IX.** 116-95 B.C. Æ *tetradrachm.* Head of king, diademed, r. ℞.
ΒΑΣΙΛΕΩΣ ΑΝΤΙΟΧΟΥ ΦΙΛΟΠΑΤΟΡΟΣ. Athena standing l., holding Nike and spear, and
leaning on shield: in field l., monogram ΗΑ and cornucopiae; all within wreath. *B.M.C.* 10
                                                     VF   £15

2118 Æ 19. *Obv.* Similar. ℞. Legend similar: winged thunderbolt. *B.M.C.* 16
                                                     fair   21/-

2119 Æ 17. Bust of Eros r. ℞. Legend similar: Nike adv. l., holding wreath. *B.M.C.* 27
                                                     F   30/-

2120 **Seleucus VI.** 96-95 B.C. Æ *tetradrachm.* Head of king, diad., r. ℞. ΒΑΣΙΛΕΩΣ
ΣΕΛΕΥΚΟΥ ΕΠΙΦΑΝΟΥΣ ΝΙΚΑΤΟΡΟΣ. Zeus seated l., holding Nike and sceptre: below
throne, Π: all within wreath. *B.M.C.* 1 *var.* ..   ..   ..   *nearly* VF   £35

2121 Similar but *rev.* type, Athena standing l., holding Nike and spear: in field, l., monogram
ΔΙΚΡ (or similar) and ΖΗ: to l., outside legend, palm branch. *B.M.C.* 4
                                                     R, *almost* EF/EF   £55

2121   2122

2122 **Antiochus X.** 94-83 B.C. Æ *tetradrachm.* Head of king diad. r. ℞. ΒΑΣΙΛΕΩΣ
ΑΝΤΙΟΧΟΥ ΕΥΣΕΒΟΥΣ ΦΙΛΟΠΑΤΟΡΟΣ. Type as No. 2120: Σ/Α on l.: all within wreath.
B.M.C. 2 ..   ..   R, VF   £50

2123 Æ 20. *Obv.* Similar. ℞. Legend similar: pilei of the Dioskuri surmounted by
stars: in field l., monogram ΣΩ. *B.M.C.* 3 ..   ..   ..   R, F 40/-; VF   90/-

2123A **Antiochus XI.**   92 B.C.   Æ *tetradrachm.*   As 2122 but ΒΑΣΙΛΕΩΣ ΑΝΤΙΟΧΟΥ ΕΠΙΦΑΝΟΥΣ
and ΕΑ on l.   *B.M.C.* 1-5   ..   ..   R, F   £36

2123A   2125A

21 24 **Philippus.**   92-83 B.C.   Æ *tetradrachm.*   Head of king, diad., r.   ℞.   ΒΑΣΙΛΕΩΣ
ΦΙΛΙΠΠΟΥ ΕΠΙΦΑΝΟΥΣ ΦΙΛΑΔΕΛΦΟΥ.   Zeus seated l., holding Nike and sceptre: below
throne, monogram ΔΙ: to l., ΦΑ: all within wreath.   *B.M.C.* 1   *good* F £8; VF   £12
2125 **Demetrius III.**   95-88 B.C.   Æ *tetradrachm.*   Head of king, diad., r.   ℞.   ΒΑΣ-
ΙΛΕΩΣ ΔΗΜΗΤΡΙΟΥ ΘΕΟΥ ΦΙΛΟΠΑΤΟΡΟΣ ΣΩΤΗΡΟΣ.   Archaic cultus-statue of Demeter,
decorated with ears of barley.   *Cf. B.M.C.* 1-4   ..   ..   *RR, almost* VF   £75
2125A **Æ 20.**   Similar.   ℞.   ΒΑΣΙΛΕΩΣ/ΔΗΜΗΤΡΙΟΥ/ΦΙΛΟΜΗΤΟΡΟΣ/ΕΥΕΡΓΕΤΟΥ/ΚΑΛΛΙΝΙΚΟΥ
above and below thunderbolt.   *B.M.C.* 7   ..   ..   R, F   75/-
2126 **Antiochus XII.**   89-84 B.C.   Æ 20.   Head of king, bearded and diad., r.   ℞.
ΒΑΣΙΛΕΩΣ ΑΝΤΙΟΧΟΥ ΔΙΟΝΥΣΟΥ ΕΠΙΦΑΝΟΥΣ ΦΙΛΟΠΑΤΟΡΟΣ ΚΑΛΛΙΝΙΚΟΥ.   Zeus standing l.,
holding Nike and sceptre.   *B.M.C.* 5   ..   ..   R, VF   £10/10/-

2126   2127

2127 **Tigranes** *of Armenia.*   83-69 B.C.   Æ *tetradrachm.*   Head of king r., wearing Armenian
tiara decorated with star and two eagles.   ℞.   ΒΑΣΙΛΕΩΣ ΤΙΓΡΑΝΟΥ.   The Tyche of
Antioch seated l. on rock, holding palm: before her, river-god Orontes swimming:
all within wreath.   *B.M.C.* 2-5   R, VF   £75

COMMAGENE.

2128 **REGAL COINAGE.   Antiochus IV.**   38-72 A.D.   Æ 28.   ΒΑΣΙΛΕΥΣ ΜΕΓΑΣ
ΑΝΤΙΟΧΟΣ.   Head of king, diad., r.   ℞.   ΚΟΜΜΑΓΗΝΩΝ.   Scorpion: all in laurel-wreath.
B.M.C. 7   ..   ..   *light green patina,* VF   £12/10/-
2129 **Iotape,** *wife of Antiochus IV.*   Æ 25.   ΒΑΣΙΛΙΣΣΑ ΙΟΤΑΠΗ ΦΙΛΑΔΕΛΦΟΣ.   Head of queen
r.   ℞.   Similar to preceding.   *B.M.C.* 4   ..   ..   ..   *R, almost* VF   £15
2130 **STATE COINAGE.**   *c.* 72 A.D.   Æ 16.   Capricorn r.; above, star.   ℞.   Scorpion.
B.M.C. 4   ..   ..   VF   £6
2131 **CITIES.   Antiocheia ad Euphratem.**   *M. Aurelius.*   Æ 21.   Greek legend.   His
laur. bust cuir. r.   ℞.   ΑΝΤΙΟΧΕΩΝ ΠΡΟΣ ΕΥΦΡΑΤΗΝ.   Bust of Athena r.   *B.M.C.* 1
F   65/-
2132 **Doliche** (Duluk).   *Commodus.*   Æ 21.   Greek legend; his young bare-headed bust dr.
r.   ℞.   ΔΟΛΙ / ΧΑΙΩΝ / Α in wreath.   *B.M.C.* 4   ..   ..   *fair*   32/6

2133 **Germanicia Caesareia** (Marash). *Commodus.* Æ 24. Similar but bearded and laur. ℞.
ΚΑΙϹ / ΓΕΡΜΑ / ΚΟΜ / Β in laurel-wreath. *B.M.C.* 3 .. .. .. F 80/-
2134 **Samosata** (Samsat). 31 B.C —38 A.D. Æ 20. Head of Zeus, laur., r. ℞. ϹΑΜΟϹΑΤΩΝ.
Lion r. *B.M.C.* 2 .. .. F/fair 30/-
2135 *Hadrian.* Æ 17. ΑΔΡΙΑΝΟϹ ϹΕΒΑϹΤΟϹ. Laur. bust r. ℞. ΦΛΑ / ϹΑΜΟ / ΜΗΤΡΟ /
ΚΟΜ in wreath. *B.M.C.* 20 .. .. F 40/-
2136 *Antoninus Pius.* Æ 24. Greek legend: laur. bust r. ℞. Φ ϹΑΜΟϹ ΙΕΡ ΑϹΥ ΑΥΤΟΝΟ
ΜΗΤΡ ΚΟΜ. Tyche of Samosata seated l., holding corn-ears. *B.M.C.* 26 .. F 50/-
2137 *Philip I.* Æ 30. ΑΥΤΟΚ Κ Μ ΙΟΥΛΙ ΦΙΛΙΠΠΟϹ ϹΕΒ. Laur. bust dr. r. ℞. ΦΑ ϹΑΜΟ-
ϹΑΤΕΩΝ ΜΗΤΡΟΠ ΚΟΜ. Tyche seated l.: at her feet, Pegasos l. *B.M.C.* 48 F 75/-
2138 *Philip II.* Æ 28. *Obv.* Similar to preceding. ℞. ϹΑΜΟϹΑΤΕΩΝ. Type as preceding. *B.M.C.* 56 .. .. F 75/-

2138   2140

2139 **Zeugma** (opposite Birejik). *Philip I.* Æ 28. *Obv.* Similar to preceding. ℞. ΖΕΥΓΜΑΤΕΩΝ.
Tetrastyle temple, with peribolos containing grove and having portico in front: within
temple, statue: in ex., capricorn l. *B.M.C.* 29 .. .. .. F 65/-
2140 *Philip II.* Æ 27. Similar but capricorn r. *B.M.C.* 35 .. .. F 70/-

SYRIA	Cyrrhestica	Seleucis and Pieria	20 Raphanea	29 Singara
Commagene	6 Beroea	12 Apameia	21 Rhosus	Seleuceia ad
1 Antiochia ad	7 Cyrrhus	13 Emisa	22 Seleuceia Pieria	Tigrim is off the
Euphratem	8 Hieropolis	14 Epiphaneia	MESOPOTAMIA	map to the
2 Doliche	*Chalcidice*	15 Gabala	23 Anthemusia	South-East; it
3 Germanicia	9 Chalcis ad	16 Laodiceia ad	24 Carrhae	is north of
Caesareia	Belum	Mare	25 Edessa	Babylon
4 Samosata	*Palmyrene*	17 Larissa	26 Nisibis	(see map in
5 Zeugma	10 Palmyra	19 Paltos	27 Rhesaena	front of book)

CYRRHESTICA

2141 **Beroea** (Aleppo). *Trajan.* Æ 25. Laur. head r. ℞. BEPOIAIⲰN and Γ in wreath.
B.M.C. 7 .. .. F 65/-

2142 **Cyrrhus.** *Antoninus Pius.* Æ 22. Greek legend: laur. head r. ℞. ΔΙΟC
ΚΑΤΑΙΒΑΤΟΥ ΚΥΡΡΗCΤⲰΝ. Zeus Kataibates seated l., with thunderbolt and sceptre:
before him, eagle. *Cf. B.M.C.* 9 .. .. *nearly* F 45/-

2143 *Philip I.* Æ 27. ΑΥΤΟΚ Κ Μ ΙΟΥΛΙ ΦΙΛΙΠΠΟC CEB. Laur. bust dr. r. ℞. ΔΙΟC
ΚΤΕΒΑΤΟΥ ΚΥΡΗCΤⲰΝ. Hexastyle temple, containing statue of Zeus Kataibates: above
temple, ram running l. *B.M.C.* 32 .. .. F/VF 85/-

2144 **Hieropolis** (Membij). *Philip II.* Æ 28. *Obv.* Similar to preceding. ℞. ΘΕΑC CΥΡΙΑC
ΙΕΡΟΠΟΛΙΤⲰΝ. Atergatis, holding sceptre, riding on lion r. *B.M.C.* 57 *fair*/F 65/-

CHALCIDICE.

2145 **Chalcis ad Belum.** *Trajan.* Æ 24. Greek legend: laur. bust r. ℞. ΦΛ
ΧΑΛΚΙΔΕⲰΝ Α in wreath. *B.M.C.* 1 .. .. *fair*/F 37/6

PALMYRENE

2145A **Palmyra.** 2nd Cent. A.D. Æ 15. ΠΑΛΜΥΡΑ. Head of city-goddess r. ℞. Lion
running r.; above, crescent. *B.M.C.* 7 .. .. *R, fair* 50/-

SELEUCIS AND PIERIA.

2146 **Antiocheia ad Orontem** (Antakya). 1st Cent. B.C. Æ 22. Head of Zeus, laur., r. ℞.
ΑΝΤΙΟΧΕⲰΝ ΤΗC ΜΗΤΡΟΠΟΛΕⲰC. Zeus seated l., holding Nike and sceptre: in field, head-
dress of Isis: in ex. ΣΛΣ (=236=76 B.C.). *B.M.C.* 24. .. .. .. F 22/6

2147 1st Cent. A.D. Q. Caecilius Metellus Creticus Silanus, legate 11-17 A.D. Æ 22. Head
of Zeus r. ℞. ΕΠΙ CΙΛΑΝΟΥ ΑΝΤΙΟΧΕⲰΝ. Ram leaping r., looking back at star: below,
ΔΜ (=44=13 A.D.) *B.M.C.* 65 .. .. F 40/-

2148 C. Ummidius Durmius Quadratus, legate 51-60 A.D. Æ 19. ΑΝΤΙΟΧΕⲰΝ. Bust of
Tyche, turreted, r. ℞. ΕΠΙ ΚΟΥΑΔΡΑΤΟΥ. Type as preceding: below, ET EP (=105=
56 A.D.). *B.M.C.* 74 .. .. F 37/6

2149 Æ 16. Bust of Artemis r. ℞. ΑΝΤΙΟΧΕ ΗΡ (=108). Lyre. *B.M.C.* 80 *good* F 37/6

2150 Æ 20. ΑΝΤΙΟΧΕⲰΝ. Head of Zeus r. ℞. ETO EIP (=115). Female figure seated l., dropping
pebble into voting urn. *B.M.C.* 87 .. .. .. F 32/6; VF/F 50/-

2151 *Augustus.* Æ 27. IMP AVGVST TR POT. Laur. head r. ℞. S C in wreath. *B.M.C.*
126 .. .. F 62/6

2152 *Tiberius.* Æ 26. Greek legend: laur. head r. ℞. Α ΕΠΙ CΙΛΑΝΟΥ ΑΝΤΙΟΧΕⲰΝ ЄΜ
(=45=14 A.D.) in wreath. *B.M.C.* 150 .. .. *fair*/F 40/-

2153 *Nero.* Æ 21. IM NER CLAV CAESAR. Bare head r.: in front, lituus. ℞. S C in wreath.
B.M.C. 182 .. .. F 50/-

2154 Æ *tetradrachm.* ΝΕΡⲰΝΟΣ ΚΑΙΣΑΡΟΣ ΣΕΒΑΣΤΟΥ. Laur. head r. ℞. Eagle, wings
open, standing l. on thunderbolt: in field, l., palm; in field r., ΖΘΡ (=109). *B.M.C.* 190
F 70/-

2155 — *Obv.* as preceding. ℞. ΕΤΟΥΣ ΑΙΡ (=111=62 A.D.) Θ. Eagle standing r. on thunderbolt, wings open: to r., palm. *B.M.C.* 195 .. .. F 60/-

2156 *Otho.* Æ *tetradr.* ΑΥΤΟΚΡΑΤΩΡ ΜΑΡΚΟC ΟΘΩΝ ΚΑΙCΑΡ CΕΒΑΣΤΟC. His laur. head r. ℞. ΕΤΟΥCΑ below eagle standing l. on laurel branch. *B.M.C.* 214 .. F £20

2157 Æ 26. IMP.M.OTHO.CAE.AVG. ℞. S C in wreath. *B.M.C.* 207 .. .. F £10

2158 *Vespasian.* Æ 27. IMP CAESAR VESPASIAN AVG. Laur. head l. ℞. S C in wreath. *B.M.C.* 216 .. .. *fair* 22/6

2159. Æ *tetradr.* ΑΥΤΟΚΡΑΤ ΚΑΙΣΑ ΟΥΕΣΠΑΣΙΑΝΟΥ. Laur. head r. ℞. ΕΤΟΥΣ Β ΙΕΡΟΥ. Eagle, wings open, standing l. on club. *B.M.C.* 230 .. .. .. F £5

2160 *Domitian.* Æ 24. Latin legend: laur. head r.: countermark, small figure of Athena r., with spear and shield. ℞. S C in wreath. *B.M.C.* 242 .. .. R, *fair* 40/-

2161 *Trajan.* Æ 26. ΑΥΤΟΚΡΑ ΚΑΙC ΝΕΡ ΤΡΑΙΑΝΟC CΕΒ ΓΕΡΜ ΔΑΚ. Laur. head r. ℞. S C/Є in wreath. *B.M.C.* 274 .. .. F 40/-

2162 Æ *tetradr.* *Obv.* nearly as preceding. ℞. ΔΗΜΑΡΧ ΕΞ ΥΠΑΤ Β. Eagle, wings open and head l., standing facing on thunderbolt. *B.M.C.* 288 .. .. .. F 75/-

2163 *Antoninus Pius.* Æ 22. Greek legend: laur. head l. ℞. S C: above, Δ: below, eagle: all in wreath. *B.M.C.* 323 var. .. .. *fair* 21/-

2164 *Macrinus.* Æ 19. Greek legend: laur. head r. ℞. S C ΔΕ in wreath. *B.M.C.* 385 *fair/F* 42/6

2165 *Elagabalus.* Billon *tetradrachm.* Greek legend: laur. head r. ℞. ΔΗΜΑΡΧ ΕΞ ΥΠΑΤΟC Β. Eagle facing, wings open and head l., wreath in beak: between legs, star. *B.M.C.* 416 .. .. *fair/F* 50/-

2166 Æ 21. Latin legend: laur. head r. ℞. ΔΕ and star in wreath. *B.M.C.* 447 *fair* 17/6

2167 *Philip I.* Billon *tetradrachm.* ΑΥΤΟΚ Κ Μ ΙΟΥΛ ΦΙΛΙΠΠΟC CΕΒ. Radiate bust r. ℞. ΔΗΜΑΡΧ ΕΞΟΥCΙΑC. Eagle standing facing on palm branch, wings open and head l., wreath in beak: in cx., S C. *B.M.C.* 505 .. .. EF/*almost* FDC £12/10/-

2168 — *Obv.* as preceding. ℞. ΔΗΜΑΡΧ ΕΞΟΥCΙΑC ΥΠΑΤΟ Γ. Type as preceding, but eagle's head r.: in ex., ΑΝΤΙΟΧΙΑ/SC. *B.M.C.* 512 .. .. .. F 50/-

2169 Æ 30. *Obv.* as preceding, but bust r. ℞. ΑΝΤΙΟΧΕΩΝ ΜΗΤΡΟ ΚΟΛΩΝ. Bust of Tyche r.: above, ram leaping r., head l.: in field, ΔΕ and S C. *B.M.C.* 526 .. F 50/-

2170 *Trajan Decius.* Billon *tetradrachm.* ΑΥΤ ΚΓ ΜΕ ΚΥ ΤΡΑΙΑΝΟC ΔΕΚΙΟC CΕΒ. Laur. bust r. ℞. ΔΗΜΑΡΧ ΕΞΟΥCΙΑC. Eagle, standing on palm branch, wings open and head l., wreath in beak: in ex., S C. *B.M.C.* 578 .. .. *good* VF/VF £6

2171 *Trebonianus Gallus.* Æ 29. ΑΥΤΟΚ Κ Γ ΟΥΙΒ ΤΡΕΒ ΓΑΛΛΟC CΕΒ. Laur. head r. ℞. ΑΝΤΙΟΧΕΩΝ ΜΗΤΡΟ ΚΟΛΩΝ. Tetrastyle shrine containing statue of the Tyche of Antioch, facing: above, ΔΕ: in ex., S C. *B.M.C.* 654. **Plate VII** .. VF, *patinated* £10

2172 **Apameia** (Kul'at el Mudik). 30/29 B.C. Æ 21. Bust of Athena r. ℞. ΑΠΑΜΕΩΝ ΤΗΣ ΙΕΡΑΣ ΚΑΙ ΑΥΤΟΝΟΜΟΥ. Nike walking l.: to l., ΓΠΣ (=283 of the Seleucid era= 29 B.C.) *B.M.C.* 8 .. .. F 42/6

2173 **Emisa** (Homs) *Julia Domna.* Æ 25. ΙΟΥΛΙΑ ΔΟΜΝΑ ΑΥΓ. ℞. ΕΜΙCΩΝ ΚΟΛΩΝΙΑC. The great altar of Elagabal at Emisa: in ex. ΖΚΦ (=527=215 A.D.). *B.M.C.* 9 R, EF £20

2173A *Caracalla.* Æ 30. As illustration. ℞. ΕΜΙCΩΝ ΚΟΛΩΝ. Hexastyle temple of Elagabal at Emisa; eagle is seen in front of the conical stone of Elagabal; in ex. ΖΚΦ (=527=215 A.D.). *B.M.C.* 15 .. .. R, F £7/10/-

2174 **Epiphaneia** (the Hamath of the Old Testament). 2nd Cent. B.C. Æ 19. Veiled and turreted head of Tyche of the City. ℞. ΕΠΙΦΑΝΕΩΝ ΤΗΣ ΙΕΡΑΣ ΚΑΙ ΑΣΥΛΟΥ. Zeus seated l.; in ex., ΖΡ (=107=151 B.C.). *Hunter* 2 .. .. .. *R, fair* 40/-

2175 **Gabala** (Jebeleh). *Caracalla.* Æ 26. Greek legend: laur. head r. ℞. ΓΑΒΑΛΕΩΝ. Tyche seated l., holding rudder and cornucopiae. *B.M.C.* 13 .. F/fair 80/-

2176 **Laodiceia ad Mare** (Latakia). 1st cent. B.C. Æ *tetradrachm.* Bust of Tyche of Laodiceia r. ℞. ΛΑΟΔΙΚΕΩΝ ΤΗΣΙΕΡΑΣΚΑΙ ΑΥΤΟΝΟΜΟΥ. Zeus seated l.; in field, ΙΒ; under seat, mon.; in ex., ΚΑ. *B.M.C.* 4.. .. .. VF £25

2176A Æ 23. Head of Helios, radiate, r. ℞. ΛΑΟΔΙΚΕΩΝ ΤΗΣ ΙΕΡΑΣ ΚΑΙ ΑΥΤΟΝΟΜΟΥ. Artemis standing l., holding spear and bow. *B.M.C.* 12 .. .. .. F 40/-

2177 *Trajan.* Æ 25. Greek legend: his laur. head r. ℞. ΙΟΥΛΙΕΩΝ ΤΩΝ ΚΑΙ ΛΑΟΔΙΚΕΩΝ ΒΕΡ (=162 of the Pharsalian era=114 A.D.). Veiled and turreted bust of the Tyche of Laodiceia. *B.M.C.* 41 .. .. F 50/-

2178 *Antoninus Pius.* Æ 24. Greek legend: laur. head r. ℞. ΙΟΥΛΙΕΩΝ ΤΩΝ ΚΑΙ ΛΑΟΔΙΚΕΩΝ. Bust of Tyche r.: in field, ΗΠΡ (=188) and ΜΟ. *B.M.C.* 60 F/fair 37/6

2178A **Larissa** (Kul'at es-Seijâr). 1st cent. B.C. Æ 19. Head of Zeus r. ℞. ΛΑΡΙΣΑΙΩΝ ΤΗΣ ΙΕΡΑΣ. Throne of Zeus; beneath, ΔΙ mon./Μ/ΙΚΣ(=227). *B.M.C.* 1 RR, fair 57/6

2178B **Nicopolis Seleucidis.** *Sept. Severus.* Æ 30. Greek legend. Bust r. ℞. ΝΕΙΚΟ/ΠΟΛΕΙ/ΤΩΝ in wreath, ΤΗΣ ΣΕΛΕΛΚΙΔΟΣ ΤΙΕΡΑΣ around. *B.M.C.* 1 R, fair 55/-

2179 **Paltos** (Baldeh) *Geta.* Æ 26. Greek legend: his laur. headed bust dr. r. ℞. ΠΑΛΤΗΝΩΝ ΗΓΛΑΔ. Bust of Julia Domna r., resting on base: in field, ΗΝΥ (=458= 200 A.D.). *Hunter* 5 .. .. R, fair 47/6

2180 **Raphanea.** *Elagabalus.* Æ 24. Greek legend: his laur. bust dr. r. ℞. ΡΕΦΑΝΕΩΤΩΝ Male figure standing l.: in field to l. and to r., eagle: in front, a bull l. *B.M.C.* 3 F £5

2181 **Rhosus.** Time of Trajan. Æ 12. Head of Tyche l.: in front, ΕΤΟΗΜΡ (=109 A.D.). ℞. ΡΩΣΕΩΝ. Harpa. *Hunter* 2 .. ..R, F 32/6

2182 **Seleuceia Pieria** (Süveydiye). 2nd cent. B.C. Æ 20. Head of Zeus, laur., r. ℞. ΣΕΛΕΥΚΕΩΝ ΤΩΝ ΕΜΠΙΠΕΡΙΑΙ. Thunderbolt: in ex., monogram and SΕΡ (=166=146 B.C.): all in laurel wreath. *B.M.C.* 11 .. .. F 37/-

2183 1st cent. B.C. Æ *tetradrachm.* Bust of Tyche, turreted, r. ℞. ΣΕΛΕΥΚΕΩΝ ΤΗΣ ΙΕΡΑΣ ΚΑΙ ΑΥΤΟΝΟΜΟΥ. Thunderbolt on cushion placed on stool: below stool, ΓΙ (=13 =96/5 B.C.); in field, r., Γ; all in laurel wreath. *Cf. B.M.C.* 18 .. .. EF £50

2184 Æ 20. Similar to preceding but ΘΚ (=29) and Ν. *B.M.C.* 25 .. .. F 32/6

2185 *Trajan.* Æ 22. Greek legend: laur. head r. ℞. ΣΕΛΕΥΚΕΩΝ ΠΙΕΡΙΑΣ. Type as preceding. *B.M.C.* 35 .. .. fair/F 32/6

2186 Æ 24. ΑΥΤΟΚΡΑ ΚΑΙ ΝΕΡ ΤΡΑΙΑΝΟC ΑΡΙCΤ CEB ΓΕΡΜ ΔΑΚ. Laur. bust r. ℞. CEΛEYKEωΝ
ΠΕΙΕΡΙΑC. Sacred stone of Zeus Kasios within shrine of four pillars and pyramidal roof
surmounted by eagle: in ex., ΖΕΥC ΚΑCΙΟC. *B.M.C.* 37–41 .. .. F 70/-

2187 *Severus Alexander.* Æ 30. ΑΥΤ ΚΑΙ ΜΑΡ ΑΥΡ CE ΑΛΕΞΑΝΔΡΟC. Laur. bust r. ℞.
Legend as preceding: sacred stone of Zeus Kasios within tetrastyle temple surmounted
by eagle: in ex., ΟΒΟ. *B.M.C.* 58 .. .. VF/F £12

COELE-SYRIA, TRACHONITIS AND DECAPOLIS.

Map, on page 174

2188 **COELE-SYRIA: Chalcis sub Libano** (Mejdel 'Anjar). Ptolemy, son of Mennaeus,
85–40 B.C. Æ 20. Laur. head of Zeus r. ℞. ΠΤΟΛΕΜΑΙΟΥ ΤΕΤΡΑΡΧΟΥ ΚΑΙ ΑΡΧΙΕΡ. Two
warriors standing facing. *B.M.C.* 3 .. .. .. F/fair 50/-

2189 **Damascus.** 1st cent. B.C. Æ 24. Bust of city-goddess r. ℞. ΔΑΜΑCΚΗΝΩΝ.
Tyche stg. l.; in field, ΣΤ (=307=5 B.C.). *B.M.C.* 2 .. .. scarce, fair 35/-

2189   2190A

2190 *Philip I.* Æ 30. Latin legend: his laur. bust dr. r. ℞. COL . DAMA METP . XPVCOPA.
The river-god Chrysoroas seated l. *Cohen* 323 .. .. .. F £6

2190A *Trebonianus Gallus.* Æ 25. Similar. ℞. COL ΔAMAS METR. Doe (*dama*) stg. r., suckling
child; in ex., ram running r., looking back. *B.M.C.* 29 .. .. F £5

2190B **Demetrias.** 95–85 B.C. Æ 21. Laur. male head r. ℞. ΔΗΜΗΤΡΙΕΩΝ ΤΗΣ ΙΕΡΑΣ.
Zeus (?) stg. l. *B.M.C.* 3 .. .. fair 25/-

2191 **Heliopolis** (Baalbek). *Geta.* Æ 22. Latin legend: his bust r., laur. ℞. COL . HEL.
Turreted and veiled bust of Tyche l. *B.M.C.* 13 .. .. .. F 75/-

2192 *Valerian.* Æ 24. Latin legend: his laur. bust dr. r. ℞. COL . IVL . AVG. FEL . HEL.
Palm-branch in agonistic urn on table. *Grose* 9440 .. .. .. F 95/-

2192A **Leucas on the Chrysoroas.** *Claudius.* Æ 18. ΛΕΥΚΑΔΙΩΝ. Rad. head of
Claudius r. ℞. ΤΩΝ ΚΑΙ ΚΛΑΝΔΙΑΙΩΝ. Head of Agrippina II r.; on head, crescent.
B.M.C. 1 .. .. R, fair 65/-

2193 **TRACHONITIS: Caesareia Panias** (Baniyas). *M. Aurelius.* Æ 25. Greek legend: his
laur. bust dr. r. ℞. ΚΑΙ . CEB . ΙΕΡ . ΚΑΙ . ΑCY ΥΠ ΠΑΝΕΙΩ. Pan, with legs crossed, leaning
against tree-stump, playing flute; ΡΟΒ (=172=169 A.D.). *Grose* 9441 .. fair 50/-

2193A **Gaba.** *Domitian.* Æ 19. ΔΟΜΙΤΙΑ ΚΑΙCΑ. His laur. head r. ℞. ΓΑΒΗΝΩΝ.
Mên stg. facing; in field, ΡΛΣ (=136=76 A.D.). *B.M.C.* 1 .. .. R, fair 47/6

2194 **DECAPOLIS: Antiocheia ad Hippum.** *M. Aurelius.* Æ 25. Greek legend: his laur.
bust dr. r. ℞. ANTIOX . ΠΡ . ΙΠ . ΙΕΡ . ΑCVΛΟ. Tyche of the City l., leading horse by bridle:
in ex., ΘΚC (=166 A.D.). *B.M.C.* 1 .. .. F £6

2194A **Canata or Canatha** (Kunawât). *Domitian.* Æ 12. ΔΟΜΙΤΙ ΚΑΙCΑΡ. Laur. head l.
℞. ΚΑΝΑΤ ΖΝΡ (=157=93 A.D.). Turreted head of city-goddess l. *B.M.C.* 2
R, fair 32/6

2194B **Capitolias.** *L. Verus.* Æ 25. Greek legend. Laur. head r. ℞. ΚΑΠΙΤωΛΙΕωΝ.
Astarte or city-goddess stg. l. in hexastyle temple; to l., Ι.Α.Α.Ο (=70=168 A.D.). *B.M.C.* 2
R, fair 65/-

2194C **Dium.** *Geta.* Æ 24. ΠΟΥΠC ΓΕΤΑC Κ. Bust r. ℞. ΔΕΙΗΝΩΝ. Hadad (?),
horned, stg. between two bulls; in field, ΗΞC(=268=204 A.D.). *B.M.C.* 1 R, fair 65/-

2195 **Gadara** (Umm Keis). *Titus.* Æ 19. ΤΙΤΟΣ ΚΑΙΣΑΡ. His laur. head r. ℞. ΓΑΔΑΡΕΩΝ.
Two cornucopiae crossed: in field, L ΖΑΡ (=137=77 A.D.). *B.M.C.* 3 .. F £5

2195A **Gerasa** (Jerash, Jordan). *Hadrian.* Æ 15. Greek legend; laur. hd. r. ℞. ΑΡΤΕΤΥ
ΓΕΡΑCωΝ. Bust of Artemis-Tyche r. *B.M.C.* 5 .. .. .. fair 40/-

2196 **Philadelphia** (Amman; the Rabbath-Ammon of the Old Testament). *M. Aurelius.*
Æ 26. Greek legend: his laur. head r. ℞. ΦΙΛ . ΚΟΙ . CYPI . ΘΕΑ . ΑCΤΕΡΙΑ. Bust of
goddess Asteria veiled r. *B.M.C.* 2 .. .. R. fair 85/-

PHOENICIA
Map, on page 174

2197 Aradus. Early 4th Cent. B.C. Æ *tetrobol*. Figure of marine deity, half human and half fish, holding two dolphins. ℞. Galley to r.; below, winged hippocamp. *B.M.C.* 8
R, *fair* £9

2198 — Head of male deity, laureate and bearded, r. ℞. As preceding. *B.M.C.* 17
RR, F £16

2199 Æ *stater*. As last but without hippocamp. *B.M.C.* 21 .. F £15

2200 400-350 B.C. Æ *stater*. *Obv.* Similar. ℞. Galley r. over waves, eye at prow; on the prow, figure-head; above, Phoenician inscr.; all in incuse square. *B.M.C.* 36A VF £21

2201 Æ *tetrobol*. Similar types. *B.M.C.* 37 .. .. .. F/*nearly* VF £7/10/–

2202 Æ *obol*. Similar types. *B.M.C.* 45 .. .. VF £6

2203 185-139 B.C. Æ *drachm*. Bee with straight wings, between monograms. ℞. ΑΡΑΔΙΩΝ. Stag standing r. in front of palm-tree. *B.M.C.* 157 .. .. .. F £5

2204 Æ 21. Bust of Tyche r. ℞. Poseidon seated l. on ship's prow. *B.M.C.* 143
F 32/6

2205 Æ 16. Head of Zeus r. ℞. Triple-pointed ram of galley and Phoenician inscr. *B.M.C.* 104 .. .. F 25/–

2206 Æ 12. As 2204. ℞. Aphlaston. *B.M.C.* 173 .. .. .. F 21/–

2207 137-46 B.C. Æ *tetradrachm*. Bust of Tyche, turreted, r. ℞. ΑΡΑΔΙΩΝ. Nike standing l., holding aphlaston and palm: in field, l., ΣΑΡ (=125/4 B.C.) ΛΕΝ: all within olive-wreath. *B.M.C.* 191 .. .. VF £12

2208 Æ 21. *Obv.* as preceding. ℞. Poseidon seated l. on prow of galley, holding trident. *B.M.C.* 300 .. .. F 32/6

2209 Time of Trajan. Æ 20. Rad. bust of Helios dr. r. ℞. ΑΡΑΔΙWΝ. Basket containing ears of barley and grapes; above, ΕΟΤ (=117 A.D.). *Hunter* 106 .. .. F 45/–

2207   2210A

2210 Berytus (Beirut). 2nd Cent. B.C. Æ 20. Bust of Tyche r. ℞. Baal-Berit standing l. in car drawn by four hippocamps. *B.M.C.* 1 .. .. *fair*/F 35/–

2210A 1st Cent. B.C. Æ 21. Head of Poseidon (Baal-Berit) r., trident behind neck. ℞. ΛΓΝ (=28/7 B.C.) ΒΗΡΥΤΙ. As last. *B.M.C.* 18 .. .. *fair* 32/6

2211 Imperial Times. Æ 10. COL. Statue of Marsyas standing l., with wine-skin. ℞. BER. Prow of galley. *B.M.C.* 27 .. .. F 30/–

2212 Æ 10. Nike advancing l. ℞. Lituus between c and B. *B.M.C.* 40 .. F 22/6

2213 *Julia Domna*. Æ 25. IVLI AVG PIA FELIC. Bust r. ℞. COL IVL ANT AVG FEL BER. Tetrastyle temple containing figure of Astarte, etc. *B.M.C.* 132 *fair* 37/6; VF/F £8

2214 *Caracalla*. Æ 22. IMP M AVRELI ANTON AVG. Laur. bust r. ℞. COL ANT BER. Poseidon stdg. l., holding dolphin and trident. *B.M.C.* 141 .. .. F 50/–

2215   2216A   2216B

2215 **Berytus.** *Elagabalus.* Æ 29. IMP CAES M AVR ANTONINVS AVG. Laur. bust r. ℞. COL IVL AVG FEL BER. Type similar to 2213. *B.M.C.* 175 .. .. *good* F £8

2216 Æ 25. *Obv.* as preceding. ℞. Legend as preceding: Arched gateway surmounted by figure riding r. on lion: under arch, figure of Marsyas r., with wine-skin. *B.M.C.* 192 .. .. VF/*good* F £10

2216A Æ 25. As 2215 but *rev.* type, the eight Kabeiroi seated l. in a circle; in ex., galley r. *B.M.C.* 207 .. .. *fair* 80/–

2216B *Gallienus.* Æ 30. Roman legend. Bust r. ℞. Legend as before. Astarte standing, crowned by Nike. *B.M.C.* 266 .. .. F 95/–

2216C **Botrys.** *Elagabalus.* Æ 28. Greek legend. Bust r. ℞. Astarte in temple of eight columns; in ex., ΒΟΤΡΟ; on l., Ɔ; on r., Ν (=250=219/20 A.D.). *B.M.C.* 1
RR, fair £6

2217 **Byblus** (Jebail). *Caracalla.* Æ 25. Greek legend. Laur. bust dr. r. ℞. ΙΕΡΑC ΒVΒΛΟV. Tetrastyle temple surmounted by arch of shell-pattern, containing figure of Astarte r., crowned by Nike standing on column. *B.M.C.* 29 .. .. .. *fair*/F 75/–

2218 *Macrinus.* Æ 30. Similar. ℞. ΙΕΡΑC ΒVΒΛΟV. Temple precinct with court attached in which cone-shaped object surrounded by lattice-work. *B.M.C.* 37 F £10

2219 **Caesareia ad Libanum.** *Antoninus Pius.* Æ 22. Greek legend. His laur. bust dr. r. ℞. ΚΑΙCΑΡΕΙΑC ΛΙΒΑΝΟΥ. Male figure standing l., holding ensign and bow; in field, ΒΞΥ (=462=150 A.D.). *B.M.C.* 2 .. .. *fair* 37/6

2220 **Carne.** 3rd-2nd Cent. B.C. Æ 19. Turreted head of Tyche r. ℞. Asklepios standing r. before column, on which Nike l. who crowns him. *B.M.C.* 3 .. F 50/–

2221 **Dora** (Tantura). Imperial Times. Æ 18. Turreted bust of Tyche dr. r. ℞. Δ ΩΡΙΤ ΩΝ. Astarte standing r.; to l., ΛΡΚΗ (=64/5 A.D.). *B.M.C.* 16 .. F 57/6

2222 **Marathus.** 180-168 B.C. Æ 20. Laur. head of Egyptian king as Hermes r., caduceus over shoulder. ℞. Marathus standing l.; Phœnician legend. *B.M.C.* 19 F 60/–

2222A **Orthosia.** Æ 18. Bust of Tyche r.; across field, ΗΞΤ (=56/7 A.D.). ℞. ΟΡΘ on r., ΩCΙΕΩΝ in ex. Zeus seated l. *B.M.C.* 3 .. .. *R, fair* 35/–

2223 **Ptolemaïs-Ace** (Akka, St. Jean d'Acre). *Elagabalus.* Æ 26. Latin legend: laur. bust r. ℞. COL . PTO. Tetrastyle temple containing statue of Tyche, etc. *B.M.C.* 37
R, fair 75/–

2224 **Sidon** (Saida). 384-370 B.C. Æ *double shekel.* War-galley l., with oars; above, Phœnician letter; below, double line of waves. ℞. King of Persia in chariot l., with charioteer: behind, on foot, figure of Egyptian king l. *B.M.C.* 17 .. .. *R*, F £32/10/–

2225 370-358 B.C. Æ *one-sixteenth shekel.* *Obv.* as preceding. ℞. King of Persia r., fighting rampant lion. *B.M.C.* 36 .. .. F £7/10/–

2226 1st Cent. B.C. Æ 19. Tetrastyle temple on podium. ℞. ΣΙΛΩΝΙΩΝ ΛΓΡ (= 9/8 B.C.). Europa on bull l. *B.M.C.* 164 .. .. *fair* 30/–

2227 1st Cent. A.D. Æ 16. Head of Tyche r. ℞. ΘΞΡ (=58/9 A.D.) ΣΙΛΩΝΟΣ ΘΕΑΣ. Galley l. *B.M.C.* 173 .. .. F/VF 40/–

2228 2nd Cent. A.D. Æ 22. Head of Tyche r.: in front, star. ℞. ΣΙΛΩΝΟΣ ΘΕΑΣ. Car of Astarte, containing baetyl under canopy: in ex., ΗΚΣ (=117/8 A.D.). *B.M.C.* 202
F 45/–

2229 *Elagabalus.* Æ 23. IMP M A ANTONINVS AVG. Laur. bust r. ℞. A P SID CO METR. Europa on bull r. *B.M.C.* 233 .. .. *good* VF £10

2230 Æ 29. As last. ℞. COL AVR PIA METR SIDON around, ΙΕΡΕΟΕ CIS in ex. Agonistic table. *B.M.C.* 281 .. .. F £6

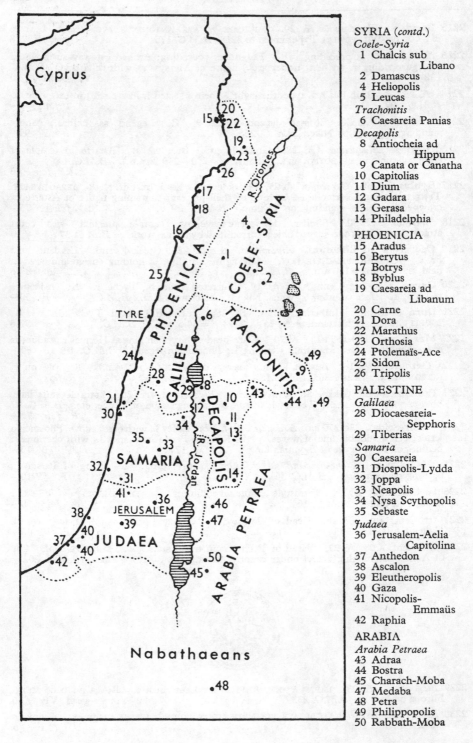

SYRIA (contd.)
Coele-Syria
1 Chalcis sub
             Libano
2 Damascus
4 Heliopolis
5 Leucas
Trachonitis
6 Caesareia Panias
Decapolis
8 Antiocheia ad
             Hippum
9 Canata or Canatha
10 Capitolias
11 Dium
12 Gadara
13 Gerasa
14 Philadelphia

PHOENICIA
15 Aradus
16 Berytus
17 Botrys
18 Byblus
19 Caesareia ad
             Libanum
20 Carne
21 Dora
22 Marathus
23 Orthosia
24 Ptolemaïs-Ace
25 Sidon
26 Tripolis

PALESTINE
Galilaea
28 Diocaesareia-
             Sepphoris
29 Tiberias
Samaria
30 Caesareia
31 Diospolis-Lydda
32 Joppa
33 Neapolis
34 Nysa Scythopolis
35 Sebaste
Judaea
36 Jerusalem-Aelia
             Capitolina
37 Anthedon
38 Ascalon
39 Eleutheropolis
40 Gaza
41 Nicopolis-
             Emmaüs
42 Raphia

ARABIA
Arabia Petraea
43 Adraa
44 Bostra
45 Charach-Moba
47 Medaba
48 Petra
49 Philippopolis
50 Rabbath-Moba

2231 **Tripolis.** 112 B.C. Æ *tetradrachm.* Jugate busts of the Dioskuri, laur. and dr., r. Ɓ. ΤΡΙΠΟΛΙΤΩΝ ΤΗΣ ΙΕΡΑΣ ΚΑΙ ΑΥΤΟΝΟΜΟΥ. Tyche standing l., holding tiller and cornucopiae, mon. to l., ΑΣ (=201) in ex.; all within laurel-wreath. *B.M.C.* 2. **Plate VII**
VF £45; EF/VF £75

2232 *Caracalla.* Æ 29. MAP ΑVP ANTONINOC. Laur. bust r. Ɓ. ΤΡΙΠΟΛΙΤΩΝ. Altar of Zeus Hagios, in the form of tetrastyle building with pediment, containing flaming altar and figures of Sun and Moon: in ex., ΖΚΦ (=527=215 A.D.). *B.M.C.* 83 .. F £7

2233 *Elagabalus.* Æ 27. Latin legend: laur. bust r. Ɓ. ΤΡΙΠΟΛΙΤΩΝ. Temple containing figure of Astarte. *B.M.C.* 118 .. .. *fair*/F 50/-

2234 **Tyre** (Sur). 332-275 B.C. Æ *stater* or *didrachm.* Melqarth r., riding on hippocamp above waves; below, dolphin r. Ɓ. Owl standing r., crook and flail over shoulder; Phoenician letters in field. *B.M.C.* 26 .. .. *good* F £25

2235 *After* 126 B.C. Æ *tetradrachm* or *shekel.* Head of Melqarth, r. Ɓ. ΤΥΡΟΥ ΙΕΡΑΣ ΚΑΙ ΑΣΥΛΟΥ. Eagle standing l., palm over shoulder: in field, ΗΙ (=109/8 B.C.) and ΖΒ. *B.M.C.* 85 .. .. F/VF £15

2236 1st Cent. A.D. Æ 20. Head of Tyche r. Ɓ. ΤΥΡ in monogram: galley l. *B.M.C.* 252-267 .. .. *fair* 22/6

2237 2nd Cent. A.D. Æ 15. *Obv.* as preceding. Ɓ. ΤΥΡ (mon.) ΙΕΡΑΣ and date. Palm-tree. *B.M.C.* 275 .. .. F 25/-

2238 Æ 20. *Obv.* as preceding. Ɓ. ΗΛΣ ΤΥΡ (mon.) ΙΕΡΑΣ ΜΗΤΡΟΠΟΛΕWΣ. Galley l. *B.M.C.* 315 .. .. F 32/-

2239 *Elagabalus.* Æ 29. IMP CAES M AV ANTONINVS AVG. Laur. bust r. Ɓ. ΤVRIORVM. Astarte, wearing turreted crown, standing facing, with r. hand on trophy: to r., Nike l. on column, holding wreath: to l., palm-tree. *B.M.C.* 397 .. .. F/VF £8

2239A *Gordian III.* Æ 30. Latin legend. Bust r. Ɓ. COL ΤΥΚ ΜΕΤR. Kadmos r., hurling stone at serpent. *B.M.C.* 425 .. .. *fair* 52/6

2239A   2239B   2239C

2239B *Philip II.* Æ 30. Similar. Ɓ. COL ΤVRO ΜΕΤRO. Dido building Carthage: workmen and arched gate of city; palm-tree behind her .. .. .. *fair* £5

2239C *Gallienus.* Æ 29. As before but rad. bust and *rev.* type, eagle before standard inscribed LEG / III / GAL. *B.M.C.* 492 .. .. F £6/10/-

2240 **Imperial Provincial Coinage** (struck at Tyre). *Trajan.* Æ (base) *tetradrachm.* ΑΥΤΟΚΡ ΚΑΙC ΝΕΡ ΤΡΑΙΑΝΟC CEB ΓΕΡΜ ΔΑΚ. Laur. head r.: below, club and eagle. Ɓ. ΔΗΜΑΡΧ ΕΞ ΙΑ ΥΠΑΤ Ε. Head of Melqarth r., laur., with lion-skin around neck. *B.M.C.* 14 .. .. F 30/-; VF 85/-

PALESTINE

2441 **GALILAEA: Diocaesareia-Sepphoris** (about 5 miles north of Nazareth). Æ 21. *Trajan.* Greek legend; his laur. head r. Ɓ. ΣΕΠΦΩΡΗΝΩΝ. Palm-tree. *B.M.C.* 5
fair £6

2442 **Tiberias.** *Trajan.* Æ 19. Greek legend; laur. bust r. Ɓ. ΤΙΒΕΡ ΚΛΑΥ ΕΤ V. Palm-branch between crossed cornucopiae. *B.M.C.* 17 .. .. .. *fair* 85/-

2443 **SAMARIA : Caesareia.** *Trajan.* Æ 25. Latin legend; his laur. head r. ℞. COL. PRI . FL . AVG . CAESARENSIS. The emperor standing l. pouring libation on altar. *B.M.C.* 42 .. .. F £6

2444 *Trajan Decius.* Æ 27. Similar, but laur. bust r. ℞. COL . PR . F . AVG . F . C . CAES . METR P. Nike advancing l. *B.M.C.* 156 .. .. *fair* 90/-

2444A **Diospolis-Lydda.** *Caracalla.* Æ 26. As last. ℞. Λ CEΠ CΘO ΔI. City-goddess in tetrastyle temple, foot on river-god; in ex., ϵT I. *B.M.C.* 4 .. .. *RR, fair* £8

2444B **Joppa.** Æ 20. As before. ℞. ΦΛΑΟVIO IOΠΠHC. Athena stg. *RRR, fair* £6

2444C **Neapolis.** *Domitian.* Æ 20. Greek legend. His laur. bust dr. r. ℞. ΦΛΑΟVI NEAΠOΛI ΣAMΑΛΑI divided by palm-tree. *B.M.C.* 13 .. .. F £10

2444C 2445A

2445 *Commodus.* Æ 19. Greek legend; his laur. bust r. ℞. ΦΛ NEAC CYPI Π. Tyche standing l., foot on prow, holding spear. *B.M.C.* 80 .. .. *fair* 75/-

2445A *Philip I.* Æ 27. Latin legend; laur. bust r. ℞. COL SERG NEAPO. Silenus stg. l.; before him, eagle supporting Mount Gerizim. *B.M.C.* 120 .. .. *R, fair* £6

2446 *Trebonianus Gallus.* Æ 25. Greek legend; his bust r., laur. ℞. ΦΛNEAC / ΠOΛEWC / EΠICHMO / NEWKOP / OV, above Mount Gerizim between star and crescent; all in wreath. *B.M.C.* 154 .. .. *fair* 90/-

2446A **Nysa Scythopolis.** *Gordian III.* Æ 25. Greek legend; laur. bust r. ℞. NVC CKV IEPACV. City-goddess seated r. on throne nursing Dionysos; in ex., ΔT (=304); in field r., kantharos. *B.M.C.* 8 .. .. *fair* £5

2446B **Sebaste** (the ancient Samaria). *Domitian.* Æ 24. Latin legend. Laur. head r.; countermarked, LXF (the mark of the Xth legion). ℞. LΘP (=84/5 A.D.) CEBACTHNUN. City-goddess stg. l. *B.M.C.* 2 .. .. *fair* £7/10/-

2447 *Julia Maesa.* Æ 22. MAESA AVGVSTA. Diad. bust dr. r. ℞. COL . L . SEP . SEBASTE. Rape of Persephone: Hades in galloping quad. r., carrying Persephone in r. arm; above, Eros flying r.; below, overturned basket. *B.M.C.* 16 .. .. £7/10/-

2448 **JUDAEA: Aelia Capitolina** (Jerusalem). *Hadrian.* Æ 24. Latin legend. Laur. bust dr. r. ℞. COL . AEL . KAPIT and in ex., COND. The Founder, Hadrian, ploughing r. with bull and cow; in background, vexillum. *B.M.C.* 2 .. .. .. *fair* £5

2448 2448A

2448A — Æ 28. Similar. ℞. Temple of Jupiter Capitolinus as illustration. Jupiter seated l. between Minerva and Juno. *B.M.C.* 1 .. .. .. *fair* £7/10/-

2448B *Elagabalus.* Æ 22. Latin legend; his bust r. ℞. COLA . CC . PF. Quadriga facing, containing the conical stone of Elagabal. *B.M.C.* 89 .. .. .. *fair* 85/-

2448C *Herennius Etruscus.* Æ 24. Similar, ℞. COLAEL COMPF; she-wolf r. suckling twins. *B.M.C.* 104 .. .. *fair* 95/-

2448D **Anthedon.** *Sev. Alexander.* Æ 24. Greek legend. Laur. bust dr. r. ℞. ANΘ-HΛONOC ETOVC . Z (=7=228 A.D.). City-goddess seated l. *B.M.C.* 2 *RR, fair* £8

2449 **Ascalon.** *Domitian.* Æ 16. Greek legend; his laur. head r. ℞. AC ⊕ΠΡ (189=85/6 A.D.). War-deity Phanebal standing l., with harpa, shield and palm-branch. *B.M.C.* 129 .. .. *fair* 75/-

2449A **Eleutheropolis.** *Caracalla.* Æ 25. Greek legend. Laur. bust dr. r. ℞. Λ CEΠ CEOV EΛEVΘE. Jupiter Heliopolitanus stg. between two bulls; in field, EH (=8=206/7 A.D.). *B.M.C.* 3 .. .. *RR, fair* £8

2450 **Gaza.** 4th Cent. B.C. Æ *drachm.* Janiform head, face to l. bearded, face to r. beardless. ℞. Owl standing facing, wings closed, within spray of olive. *RR,* F £50

2451 *Hadrian.* Æ 24. AYT KAI TPA AΔPIAN. Laur. bust r. ℞. ΓAZA Γ EΠI BYP. City-goddess standing l., with sceptre and cornucopiae: beside her, heifer l. *B.M.C.* 35 *R,* F £8

2452 **Nicopolis-Emmaus.** *M. Aurelius.* Æ 23. Greek legend; his laur. bust dr. r. ℞. NEIKOΠOΛIT ѠN. Zeus seated l., holding sceptre and Nike; below, ETYA (=162 A.D.). *Hunter* 1 .. .. *R, fair* £5

2452A **Raphia.** *Sept. Severus.* Æ 24. As last. ℞. PAΦIA AΞC (=261=201/2 A.D.). Apollo stg. *B.M.C.* 4 .. .. *R, fair* £6

COINS OF THE JEWS.

2453 **HASMONAEAN DYNASTY. John Hyrcanus.** 135-104 B.C. Æ 14. Hebrew legend in wreath: above, A. ℞. Poppy-head between two cornuacopiae. *B.M.C.* 2-14 F 75/-

2454 As preceding, without A on *obv. B.M.C.* 15-44 .. .. F 60/-

2455 **Judas Aristobulos.** 104-103 B.C. Æ 14. Types similar to previous. *B.M.C.* 1 *RRR,* F £25

2456 **Alexander Jannaeus.** 103-76 B.C. Æ 15. Anchor in circle, inscr. around. ℞. Flower, inscr. around. *B.M.C.* 1-8 .. .. F 90/-

2456   2458

2457 Æ 15. Hebrew legend in wreath. ℞. as No. 2453. *B.M.C.* 11-39. *Restruck on earlier coin* .. .. F 50/-

2458 Æ 15. Similar, not re-struck. *B.M.C.* 30-38 .. .. F 60/-

2459 Æ 15. Similar, different *obv.* legend. *B.M.C.* 39-60 .. .. F 60/-

2459A Æ 15. ΒΑΣΙΛΕΩΣ ΑΛΕΞΑΝΔΡΟΥ. Anchor. ℞. Traces of Hebrew inscription within spokes of a wheel. *B.M.C.* 61-8.. .. .. F 60/-

2460 **Imitations of coins of Alexander Jannaeus.** 76-40 B.C. Æ 12. Anchor, inscr. around. ℞. Wheel, inscr. around. *B.M.C.* 1-16. *This is the coin usually known as the " Widow's mite "; the legends are always incomplete and the fabric barbarous* *fair* 27/6; F 60/-

2461 **Antigonus Mattathias.** 40-37 B.C. Æ 20. Hebrew legend. Cornucopiae. ℞. ΒΑCΙΛΕѠC ΑΝΤΙΓΟΝ within wreath. *B.M.C.* 33-55 .. .. .. *RR, fair* £20

2462 **THE HERODIAN DYNASTY. Herod I.** 37-4 B.C. Æ 23. ΒΑΣΙΛΕΩΣ ΗΡΟΔΟΥ. Tripod-lebes. ℞. Head-dress between palm-branches. *B.M.C.* 1-10. *Illustrated at top of next page* .. .. *fair* £12

2463 Æ 20. Legend as preceding: helmet. ℞. Circular shield. *B.M.C.* 11-13 *fair* £15

2464 Æ 18. Legend as preceding: wreath enclosing x. ℞. Tripod between palm-branches. *B.M.C.* 20-39 .. .. F £20

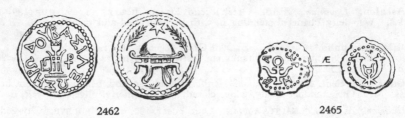

2462   2465

2465 Herod I. Æ 14. BACI HPⲰ or similar inscr.: anchor. ℞. Caduceus between two cornuacopiae. *B.M.C.* 40-65 .. .. F £5

2466 Æ 14. Legend in border of dots. ℞. Anchor within circle, from which project V-shaped ornaments. *B.M.C.* 66-69 .. .. *fair* 60/-

2467 Æ 14. BACIΛ HPⲰΔ. Cornucopiae. ℞. Eagle standing r. *B.M.C.* 70-74 F £7

2467A Herod Philip II. 4 B.C.-A.D. 34. Æ 22. Greek legend both sides. Head of Augustus. ℞. Temple of four columns, LIB (=12=8/9 A.D.). *B.M.C.* 1
R, *fair* £35

2467B Herod Antipas. 4 B.C.-A.D. 39. Æ 19. HPⲰΔOY TETPAPXOY. Palm-branch; L ΛZ (=37=33/4 A.D.). ℞. TIBE PIAC in wreath. *B.M.C.* 6 .. .. RR, *fair* £30

2468 Herod Archelaus. 4 B.C.-6 A.D. Æ 16. HPⲰΔOY. Bunch of grapes. ℞. EΘNAPXO. Crested helmet. *B.M.C.* 10-25 .. .. F £10

2468   2469

2469 Herod Agrippa I. 37-44 A.D. Æ 18. BACIΛEⲰC AΓPIΠA. Umbrella with fringe. ℞. Three ears of barley between L S. *B.M.C.* 1-19 M 17/6; *fair* 27/6; F 47/6

2470 Agrippa II. 50-100 A.D. Æ 20. Greek legend: head of Domitian, laur., r. ℞. [ETOYHI BA] AΓPIΠIΠA. Nike r., inscribing shield. *B.M.C.* 31 .. .. M £5

2471 PROCURATORS OF JUDAEA. Coponius. 6-9 A.D. Æ 16. KAICAPOC. Ear of barley. ℞. Palm-tree; in field, L ΛS (=36=5/6 A.D.). *B.M.C.* 1-8 .. F £5

2472 — Æ 17. Similar but date L ΛΘ (=39=8/9 A.D.). *B.M.C.* 9-16.. .. *fair* 50/-

2473 M. Ambibulus. Æ 18. Similar but L M (=40=9/10 A.D.). *B.M.C.* 17-9 F £5

2474 — Æ 17. Similar but L MA (=41=10/11 A.D.). *B.M.C.* 21-7 .. .. *fair* 50/-

2475 Valerius Gratus. 15-26 A.D. Æ 16. KAICAP within wreath. ℞. TIB LB (=2 =15/16 A.D.) over cornucopiae. *B.M.C.* 1 .. .. F £5

2476 Æ 16. IOYΛIA within wreath. ℞. Branch of eight leaves between L B. *B.M.C.* 4
fair 60/-

2477 Æ 16. TIB KAI CAP within wreath. ℞. Palm-branch dividing IOY ΛIA and LΔ. (=4) *B.M.C.* 31 .. .. *fair* 50/-

2478 — Similar, with date L ϵ (=5). *B.M.C.* 38 .. .. M 22/6; *fair* 50/-; F £5

2479 — Similar, with date L IA. (=11) *B.M.C.* 46 .. .. .. M 25/-; *fair* 60/-

2480 Pontius Pilate. 26-36 A.D. Æ 17. IOYΛIA KAICAPOC. Three ears of barley bound together. ℞. TIBEPIOY KAICAPOC L IS (=16=29/30 A.D.). Vessel resembling sim-pulum. *B.M.C.* 54. *Legends incomplete* .. .. *fair* £6

2481 Æ 15. *Obv.* legend as preceding: lituus. ℞. LIZ or LIH (=17 or 18) within wreath. *B.M.C.* 69-82 .. .. M £60; *fair* £5

2482 **Antonius Felix.** 52-60 A.D. Æ 16. ΙΟΥΛΙΑ ΑΓΡΙΠΠΙΝΑ within wreath. ℞. ΤΙ ΚΛΑΥΔΙΟC ΚΑΙCAP ΓΕΡΜ LIΔ. Crossed palm-branches. *B.M.C.* 1. *Legends incomplete nearly* F 60/–

2483 Æ 17. ΝΕΡΩ ΚΛΑΥ ΚΑΙCAP. Two oblong hexagonal shields and two spears crossed. ℞. ΒΡΙΤ ΚΑΙ L ΙΔ. Palm-tree. *B.M.C.* 21-33. *This coin bears the names of Nero and Britannicus Caesars: the legends are rarely complete* .. M 21/–; *fair* 50/–; F £5

2484 Æ 16. L Ε ΚΑΙCAPOC. Palm branch. ℞. ΝΕΡΩΝΟC within wreath. *B.M.C.* 1-28 M 18/6; *fair* 35/–; F 75/–

2485 **FIRST REVOLT.** 66-70 A.D. Æ *shekel* of Year 2. Hebrew inscr., "shekel of Israel": chalice with pearled rim. ℞. Hebrew inscr., "Jerusalem the Holy": triple lily. *B.M.C.* 7 .. .. *R, good* F £200

2486 — Similar, of slightly smaller and thicker fabric, year 3. *B.M.C.* 13-16 VF £200

2487 Æ *half-shekel* of Year 3. Similar. *B.M.C.* 12-16 .. .. .. *R,* VF £160

2488 Æ 16. Hebrew legend, "year 2": amphora. ℞. Hebrew legend "deliverance of Zion": vine-leaf and tendril. *B.M.C.* 22-41 .. .. F £5

2489 Æ 18. Similar but amphora with lid, "year 3." *B.M.C.* 42 .. *R,* F £10

2490 **"JUDAEA CAPTA."** *Titus.* Æ 24. ΑΥΤΟΚΡ ΤΙΤΟΣ ΚΑΙΣΑΡ. Laur. head r. ℞. ΙΟΥΔΑΙΑΣ ΕΑΛΩΚΥΙΑΣ. Trophy between captive and shield. *B.M.C.* 10 .. *fair* £7

2491   2496

2491 **SECOND REVOLT.** 132-135 A.D. Æ *shekel.* Screen of the Tabernacle with the Ark of the Covenant, represented by building with four columns containing arched structure: around, Hebrew inscr., "Simeon." ℞. Hebrew inscr., "Deliverance of Jerusalem." Bundle of twigs and citron. *B.M.C.* 11 .. .. *RR,* VF £350

2492 Æ *quarter-shekel* or *denarius.* Hebrew inscr. "Simeon" in wreath. ℞. Hebrew inscr. "Year two of the Deliverance of Israel." Ewer r.; in front, palm-branch. *B.M.C.* 6-13 .. .. *R,* VF £175

2493 — Another, with similar legends, but with bunch of grapes. ℞. Palm-branch. *B.M.C.* 21-27 .. .. F £90

2494 Æ 25. Hebrew inscr., "Second year of the Deliverance of Israel": vine-leaf. ℞. Hebrew inscr., "Simeon": palm-tree. *B.M.C.* 29-60. **Plate VII** *good* F £12

2495 Æ 21. Similar, but *obv.* legend "Deliverance of Jerusalem." *B.M.C.* 66-92 M 85/– : F £8

2496 Æ 20. Hebrew inscr. "Year four". Bundle of twigs between two citrons. ℞. Hebrew inscr. "For the redemption of Zion." Chalice. *B.M.C.* 10 *good* F £15

FURTHER ASIA.

MESOPOTAMIA.

For map see page 167

2497 Anthemusia. *Caracalla.* Æ 17. His laur. hd. r. ℞. ΑΝΘΕΜΟΥΣΙΑ. Turreted bust of city-goddess r., veiled. *B.M.C.* 1 .. .. *fair, RR* 45/-

2498 Carrhae (Haran). *Caracalla.* Æ 19. Laur. head of emperor r. ℞. COL MET ANTONIN-IANA AVR ALEX. Bust of Tyche r. *B.M.C.* 17 .. .. .. *fair* 25/-

2498A *Severus Alexander.* Æ 24. Radiate bust of emperor r. ℞. ΜΗΤ ΚΟ ΚΑΡΡΗΝΩΝ. Tyche seated l.: in front, small altar: below, river-god swimming l. *B.M.C.* 52
fair 30/-

2499 Edessa (Urfa, Turkey). *Septimius Severus.* Æ 22. Laur. bust of emperor r. ℞. ΑΒΓΑΡΟC ΒΑCΙΛΕ. Bust of Abgar VIII, wearing tiara, r. *B.M.C.* 16 .. .. *fair* 35/-

2500 *Elagabalus.* Æ 22. His laur. bust dr. l. with shield and spear. ℞. ΚΟΛ Μ ΕΔΕCCΑ. Two busts of city-goddess face to face; below, temple. *B.M.C.* 69 .. .. *fair* 30/-

2501 ~~2501~~ *Gordian III.* Æ 28. Radiate head r. ℞. ΜΗΤ ΚΟΛ ΕΔΕCCΗΝΩΝ. Bust of Tyche l.: in field, l., small figure of Aquarius r., on pedestal, and small altar. *B.M.C.* 126 .. F 50/-

2502 Æ 24. Laur. head r., star in field. ℞. ΑΒΓΑΡΟC ΒΑCΙΛΕVC. Bust of Abgar X, wearing tiara, r. *B.M.C.* 148 .. .. *fair* 17/6; *fair/F* 25/-

2503 Nisibis (Nusaybin). *Severus Alexander.* Æ 27. Laur. bust of emperor r. ℞. CEΠ ΚΟΛΟ ΝΕCΙΒΙ ΜΗ. Bust of Tyche r.: in front, star: above, ram leaping r., looking back. *B.M.C.* 4 .. .. *fair* 35/-

2504 *Gordian III.* Æ 26. Radiate head of emperor r. ℞. Similar to preceding. *B.M.C.* 13 .. .. *fair* 30/-

2505 *Philip I.* Æ 25. Laur. bust of emperor r. ℞. ΙΟΥ CEΠ ΚΟΛΩ ΝΕCΙΒΙ ΜΗΤ. Figure of Tyche seated facing within tetrastyle temple. *B.M.C.* 17 .. .. *fair* 30/-

2506 Rhesaena. *Trajan Decius.* Æ 25. Radiate bust of emperor r. ℞. CEΠ ΚΟΛ ΡΗCΑΙΝΗCΙΩΝ L III Ρ. Founder of colony ploughing r. with yoke of oxen. *B.M.C.* 11
nearly F 45/-

2507 Æ 25. As last but *rev.* type: Temple seen in perspective, three-quarter l.: within, eagle with wreath in beak: below, river-god swimming. *B.M.C.* 16 .. .. F 70/-

2508 Seleuceia ad Tigrim (25 m. S. of Baghdad). 1st Cent. B.C. Æ 12. Head of Tyche r. ℞. ΔΚΣ/ΔΙΟΥ/Α. *B.M.C.* 19 .. .. *fair* 20/-; *good* F 50/-

2509 Singara. *Gordian III* and *Tranquillina.* Æ 31. Busts of Gordian, r. and Tranquillina, l., facing each other. ℞. ΑVΡ CEΠ ΚΟΛ CΙΝΓΑΡΑ. Tyche seated l. on rock, holding branch: before her, river-god swimming l.: above, centaur l., drawing bow. *B.M.C.* 8 .. .. *fair* 45/-; *VF* £12/10/-

2507   2509A

ARABIA.

2509A **Kings of Nabathaea.** Aretas III. 87-62 B.C. Æ 20. Diad. hd. r. ℞. ΒΑΣΙΛΕΩΣ ΑΡΕΤΟΥ ΦΙΛΕΛΛΗΝΟΣ. Nike as city-goddess stg. l. *B.M.C.* 1 .. .. *R, fair* 50/-

2510 Obodas III. 30-9 B.C. Æ *drachm.* Jugate busts of king and queen r. ℞. Bust of Obodas r. *B.M.C.* 2 .. .. F £7/10/-

2511 Aretas IV with Queen Huldu. 9 B.C.-7 A.D. Æ *drachm.* King's bust r. ℞. Queen's bust r. *B.M.C.* 3 .. .. F £6/10/-

2512 — with Queen Shaqilath. 9-40 A.D. Æ 18. Their jugate busts r. ℞. Two cornuacopiae. *B.M.C.* 20 .. .. VF 65/

2513 Malichus II with Shaqilath II. 40-71 A.D. Æ 16. Similar. *B.M.C.* 5. F 32/6

2514 Rabbel with Gamilath. 71-106 A.D. Æ 15. Similar. *B.M.C.* 3 VF/F 50/-

2515 **Sabaeans.** 3rd-2nd Cent. B.C. Æ *drachm.* Imitation of the older Attic type: head of Athena r. ℞. Owl r., ΑΘΕ. *B.M.C.* 6 .. .. F £12

2516 **Himyarites.** 1st Cent. B.C. Æ *drachm.* Male head l. ℞. Bucranium. *B.M.C.* 7 .. .. VF £8

2517 Æ 25 *unit.* Arab head r. within wreath. ℞. Owl l. on amphora; mon. Hodur to l. and Yadail to r. *B.M.C.* 24 .. .. VF/F £12

2518 1st-2nd Cent. A.D. Amdan Bayyin Yanaf. Æ *drachm.* Beardless male head r. ℞. Small head r. *B.M.C.* 3 .. .. VF £6

2518A **Arabia Petraea : Adraa.** *Gallienus.* Æ 26. Greek legend; rad. bust r ℞. ΑΔΡΑΗΝΩΝ PN(=150=255/6 A.D.). Baetyl on altar. *B.M.C.* 2.. *fair, RR* 45/-

2519 **Bostra** (Busra, Syria). *Julia Mamaea.* Æ 18. Latin legend; her dr. bust r. ℞. COLONIA BOSTRA. Bust of Tyche l. *B.M.C.* 34 .. .. F 60/-

2519A Æ 31. Similar. ℞. N. TR. ALEXANDRIANAE around temple of four columns, city-goddess within between two small bulls; in ex., COL. BOSTR. *B.M.C.* 31 F £6

2519B **Charach-Moba** (El-Kerak, Jordan). *Elagabalus.* Æ 22. Greek legend; laur. bust dr. r. ℞. ΧΑΡΑΧ ΜWΒΑ. City-goddess stg. l. *B.M.C.* 1 .. .. *R, fair* 60/-

2519C **Esbus** (Hesbân, Jordan). *Elagabalus.* Æ 24. Latin legend; laur. bust dr. r. ℞. A V above temple in which city-goddess stg. l.; in ex., ΕϹΒΟΥϹ. *B.M.C.* 3 *R, fair* 65/-

2519D **Medaba** (Mâdebâ, Jordan). *Caracalla.* Æ 25. Greek legend; laur. bust dr. r. ℞. ΜΗΔΑΒΥΝ ΤΥΧΗ. City-goddess stg. r.; in field, ΡΕ (= 105 = 210/11 A.D.). *B.M.C.* 2 *fair, R* 65/-

2520 **Petra.** *Antoninus Pius.* Æ 15. Greek legend; his laur. head r. ℞. ΠΕΤΡΑ / ΜΗΤΡΟ / ΠΟΛΙϹ in laurel-wreath. *Hunter* 1 .. .. F 45/-

2521 **Philippopolis.** *Philip II.* Æ 26. Greek legend; his laur. bust dr. r. ℞. ΦΙΛΙΠ-ΠΟΠΟΛΙΤΩΝ ΚΟΛΩΝΙΑϹ. Roma seated l.; in field, SC. *B.M.C.* 10 .. .. *fair* 40/-

2522 **Rabbath-Moba.** *Julia Domna.* Æ 29. Greek legend; her draped bust r. ℞. ΡΑΒΑΘΜ Ω. War-god Ariel facing, standing on plinth. *B.M.C.* 4 .. .. *fair* 50/-

182

PERSIA, ETC.

2523 **PERSIAN EMPIRE.** Darius I. 521-485 B.C. Æ *siglos*. King r. in kneeling running attitude holding bow and spear: slight figure. ℞. Oblong irregular incuse. *Babelon*, i, 12. **Plate VIII** .. .. VF £15

2524 Xerxes. 485-465 B.C. Æ *siglos*. Similar, but kildaris usually low; beard more flowing. *B.M.C.* 72 .. .. F £7/10/-

2525 Artaxerxes I. 465-425 B.C. N *daric*. Similar, but coarse features, nose large, beard shaggy. *B.M.C.* 40 .. .. *nearly* VF £120

2526 Æ *siglos*. Similar. *B.M.C.* 47 .. .. F £6; *good* F £10

2527 Darius II. 424-405 B.C. Æ *siglos*. Similar; slim figure, with straight nose. *B.M.C.* 56 .. .. F £6; *good* F £10

2528 Artaxerxes II. 405-359 B.C. Æ *siglos*. Similar, but king drawing bow, no spear. *Bab.* ii, 10 .. .. F £6

2529 Arses. 338-337 B.C. Æ *siglos*. Similar, but king holds dagger and bow F £10

2530 Darius III. 337-330 B.C. Æ *siglos*. Similar, but king drawing bow .. *fair* £5

2531 **BABYLONIA** (Alexandrine Empire of the East). 331-312 B.C. Æ *tetradrachm*. Baal seated l. ℞. Lion l., Γ above. *B.M.C.* xxii, 1 .. .. F/*good* F £20

2532 Æ *didrachm*. Similar, but anchor above. *B.M.C.* xxii, 13 .. .. F £15

2533 Æ *hemiobol*. Similar, no symbol. *B.M.C.* xxi, 6 .. .. VF £10

2534 **PARTHIA** (Attributions according to A. V. Petrowicz). Tiridates I, 248-210 B.C. Æ *drachm*. Beardless bust l., wearing pointed helmet. ℞. ΒΑΣΙΛΕΩΣ ΜΕΓΑΛΟΥ ΑΡΣΑΚΟΥ. Arsaces seated r. on omphalos holds bow. *B.M.C.* i, 9 .. VF £10

2535 Æ *obol*. Similar. *B.M.C.* i, 13 .. .. RR, *fair* £6

2536 2540A

2536 Arsaces II. 210-191 B.C. Æ *drachm*. Diademed bust l., long pointed beard. ℞. Similar. *B.M.C.* iii, 3 .. .. *good* VF £6/10/-

2537 Æ 15. Similar. ℞. Horse r. *B.M.C.* iii, 6 .. .. F 35/-

2538 Phriapatius. 191-176 B.C. Æ *drachm*. Diademed bust l., pointed beard. ℞. Similar to No. 2534, but the legend has in addition ΦΙΛΑΔΕΛΦΟΥ. *B.M.C.* v, 4 *good* VF £8

2539 Phraates I. 176-171 B.C. Æ *drachm*. Diademed bust l., close beard. ℞. Similar to No. 2534. *Petrowicz* 1 .. .. *good* VF £10

2540 — Another, similar, but ΤΑΜ behind head. ℞. Similar, ΘΕΟΠΑΤΟΡΟΣ in addition. *Petrowicz* 16 .. .. *nearly* VF £6

2540A Mithradates I. 171-138 B.C. Æ *tetradrachm*. Diad. hd. r. ℞. ΒΑΣΙΛΕΩΣ ΜΕΓΑΛΟΥ ΑΡΣΑΚΟΥ ΦΙΛΕΛΛΗΝΟΣ. Herakles stg. l.; mon. on l.; in ex., ΓΟΡ (= 173 = 140/39 B.C.). *B.M.C.* 55. (Here we have taken the *B.M.C.* attribution; Petrowicz puts it to Valarsaces of Armenia) .. .. VF £200

2541 Æ *drachm*. Diademed bust l., short beard. ℞. Similar to No. 2534 and ΕΠΙΦΑΝΟΥΣ in addition. *B.M.C.* vi, 6 .. .. F/VF 75/-

2542 — Another, similar, but ΣΩΤΗΡΟΣ instead of ΕΠΙΦΑΝΟΥΣ. *Petrowicz* 1-2 RR, *nearly* VF/VF £12/10/-

2543 — Another, similar, long beard. ℞. Similar to No. 2541. *B.M.C.* vi, 8   EF   £8

2544 — Another, with helmeted bust l., star on helmet. ℞. Similar, but legend ΒΑΣΙΛΕΩΣ ΒΑΣΙΛΕΩΝ ΜΕΓΑΛΟΥ ΑΡΣΑΚΟΥ ΕΠΙΦΑΝΟΥΣ. *B.M.C.* viii, 2   ..   ..   F/VF   60/–

2545 Æ 15. Similar to No. 2543. ℞. Horse's head r. *B.M.C.* vii, 2   .. VF   45/–

2546 Phraates II. 138-128 B.C. Æ *tetradrachm*. Diademed bust l., small head, aquiline nose, short pointed beard. ℞. Similar to No. 2534 with addition of ΘΕΟΠΑΤΟΡΟΣ ΕΥΕΡΓΕΤΟΥ ΕΠΙΦΑΝΟΥΣ ΦΙΛΕΛΛΗΝΟΣ; to r., mgr. *B.M.C.* viii, 12
fine style, good VF   £75

2547 Æ *drachm*. Diademed bust l., close beard. ℞. Similar, but legend ends with ΕΥΕΡΓΕΤΟΥ. *B.M.C.* ix, 5   ..   ..   *good* VF   £6/10/–

2548 Artaban I. 128-123 B.C. Æ *drachm*. Helmeted bust l., horn on helmet. ℞. Similar to No. 2534, but legend ends with ΘΕΟΠΑΤΟΡΟΣ ΝΙΚΑΤΟΡΟΣ. *B.M.C.* xi, 10
VF   £6

2549 Æ 14. Similar. ℞. Pegasos r. *B.M.C.* xi, 12   ..   .. VF   45/–

2550 Mithradates II. 123-88 B.C. Æ *drachm*. Helmeted bust l., horn on helmet. ℞. Similar to No. 2534, legend ending ΕΥΕΡΓΕΤΟΥ ΕΠΙΦΑΝΟΥΣ ΦΙΛΕΛΛΗΝΟΣ; to r. mgr. *B.M.C.* xi, 2 ..   ..   VF   £5

2551 — Another, but bust diademed, thick wavy beard. *Cf. B.M.C.* x, 8   ..   F   50/–

2552 Æ 17. Diademed bust l. ℞. Pegasos r. *B.M.C.* x, 14   ..   .. VF   40/–

2553 Artaban II. 88-77 B.C. Æ *drachm*. Bust l. in spiked helmet with triple spray device. ℞. Similar to No. 2546, no mgr. *B.M.C.* xi, 15   ..   ..   F/VF   £7/10/–

2554 Sinatruces. 77-70 B.C. Æ *drachm*. Bust l., helmet with star device. ℞. Similar to No. 2534, legend ending ΑΥΤΟΚΡΑΤΟΡΟΣ ΦΙΛΟΠΑΤΟΡΟΣ ΕΠΙΦΑΝΟΥΣ ΦΙΛΕΛΛΗΝΟΣ. *B.M.C.* x, 3 ..   ..   *good* VF   £7/10/–

2555 Æ 12. Similar. ℞. Bow in case. *B.M.C.* x, 7   ..   ..   VF/F   30/–

2556 Phraates III. 70-57 B.C. Æ *drachm*. Diademed bust l., close beard. ℞. ΒΑΣΙΛΕΟΝΤΟΣ ΒΑΣΙΛΕ ΩΝ ΜΕΓΑΛΟΥ ΑΡΣΑΚΟΥ ΔΙΚΑΙΟΥ ΕΠΙΦΑΝΟΥΣ ΘΕΟΥ ΕΥΠΑΤΟΡΟΣ ΚΑΙ ΦΙΛΕΛΛΗΝΟΣ. Arsaces seated r. on omphalos. *B.M.C.* xiii, 8   ..   .. VF   £10

2557 Æ 13. Similar, star behind. ℞. Elephant's head r. *B.M.C.* xiii, 15   F   25/–

2558 Mithradates III. 57-54 B.C. Æ *drachm*. Bust facing, diademed. ℞. Similar to No. 2546. 7-line legend. *B.M.C.* xii, 1   ..   .. VF   £8

2559 — Another. Bust l., diademed, short beard. ℞. Similar, but legend ending ΦΙΛΟΠΑΤΟΡΟΣ ΕΥΕΡΓΕΤΟΥ ΕΠΙΦΑΝΟΥΣ ΦΙΛΕΛΛΗΝΟΣ. *B.M.C.* xii, 8   ..   .. VF   £6

2560 Æ 14. Bust facing, diademed. ℞. Nike r. *B.M.C.* xii, 2   ..   F/VF   30/–

2561 Orodes I. 57-37 B.C. Æ *tetradrachm*. Diademed bust l. ℞. Tyche l., kneeling before enthroned king, mon. in field; in ex., month ΠΕ (Peritius). *B.M.C.* xiv, 11
VF   £50

2562 — Another, crescent in *rev.* field; month ΞΑΝ (Xandicus) in ex. *B.M.C.* xiv, 12
F/VF   £20

2562A — Another without Tyche, crescent or month. *B.M.C.* xv, I   ..   *nearly* VF   £40

2563 Æ *drachm*. Diademed bust l., no symbols. ℞. ΒΑΣΙΛΕΩΣ ΒΑΣΙΛΕΩΝ ΑΡΣΑΚΟΥ ΕΥΕΡΓΕΤΟΥ ΔΙΚΑΙΟΥ ΕΠΙΦΑΝΟΥΣ ΦΙΛΕΛΛΗΝΟΣ. Arsaces enthroned r. *B.M.C.* xv, 6
VF   60/–

2564 — Another, similar, with crescent behind head. *B.M.C.* xvi, 3 ..   .. VF   60/–

2565 — Similar, but star in front, crescent behind head. *B.M.C.* xvi, 15   F/VF   40/–

2566 — Similar, but star in front, crescent and star behind, and on *rev.*, anchor behind throne. *B.M.C.* xvii, 12   ..   .. VF   70/–

2567 **Orodes I.** Æ *obol.* Diademed bust l., no symbols. ℞. As 2563 but shortened legend. *B.M.C.* xviii, 9 .. .. VF/F £6

2568 Æ 12. Similar. ℞. Gateway with four towers. *B.M.C.* xv, 14 .. .. F 25/-

2569 Phraates IV. 37-2 B.C. Æ *tetradrachm.* Legend as No. 2563. Bust l., diad., star on cuirass. ℞. Tyche l., presents palm to the enthroned king; in ex., ΖΠΣΔΕΙ (=287= 26/25 B.C.). *B.M.C.* 21 .. .. F £7/10/-

2570 — Another, similar, star and eagle on cuirass. ℞. Similar, but Athena instead of Tyche presenting diadem; date in ex. 288, month ΥΠΕΡΒ (Hyperberetaius). *B.M.C.* 39
VF £20

2571 — Another. ℞. King enthroned l., holding Nike; date under throne 285, month ΔΑΙΣΙ (Daisius). *B.M.C.* 17 .. .. VF £17/10/-

2572 Æ *drachm.* Diademed bust l.; eagle behind head. ℞. Similar to No. 2563. *B.M.C.* xx, 6. **Plate VIII**.. .. .. VF 45/-

2573 — Another, similar, but star in front, eagle behind. *B.M.C.* xxii, 1 .. VF 50/-

2574 — Another, similar, but star and crescent in front, eagle behind. *B.M.C.* xxii, 10
F/VF 30/-

2575 Æ 9. Similar. ℞. Triform face of goddess. *B.M.C.* xxi, 11 F/VF 50/-

2576 Æ 10. Similar ℞. Humped bull r. *B.M.C.* xxi, 16 .. .. VF/F 25/-

2577 Phraates V or Phraataces. 2 B.C.-4 A.D. Æ *tetradrachm.* Bust l., diademed; to l. and r. figures of Nike flying to crown king. ℞. Legend as on No. 2563. Arsaces throned r., ΑΙΤ (=311), month ΑΡΤΕΜΙΖΙΟΥ (Artemisius). *B.M.C.* xxiii, 11 .. .. F £12

2578 Æ *drachm.* Similar. ℞. As Phraates IV. *B.M.C.* xxiii, 12 .. .. F 50/-

2579 — With Queen Musa. Æ 13. Similar ℞. Bust of Musa l. wearing tiara. *B.M.C.* xxiv, 4 .. .. F £7

2580 Vonones I. 8-12 A.D. Æ *drachm.* ΒΑCΙΛΕΥC ΟΝ ѠΝΗC. Bust l., diademed. ℞. ΒΑCΙΛΕΥC ΟΝ ѠΝΗC ΝΕΙΚΗCΑC ΑΡΤΑΒΑΝΟΝ. Nike r. *B.M.C.* xxiv, 7 R, F £5

2581 Artaban III. 10-40 A.D. Æ *drachm.* Diademed bust l., flowing hair. ℞. Similar to No. 2563. *B.M.C.* xxv, 7 .. .. *scarce,* F 45/-

2582 Vardanes I. 42-45 A.D. Æ *drachm.* Diademed bust l., diadem with 3 ends, pointed beard. ℞. Similar to No. 2563. *B.M.C.* xxvi, 3 .. .. F 25/-

2583 — Another, similar, but diadem with 5 ends, rounded beard. *B.M.C.* xxvi, 4
F 25/-

2584 Æ 12. Similar. ℞. Eagle r., within square, wings open. *B.M.C.* xxvi, 11
F 15/-

2585 Gotarzes. 40-51 A.D. Æ *tetradrachm.* Diademed bust l. ℞. Tyche l., offering diadem to enthroned king; in field, ΖΝΤ (=357=45/6 A.D.). *B.M.C.* xxvi, 12 F £7/10/-

2586 Æ *drachm.* Similar, square cut beard. ℞. Similar to No. 2563. *B.M.C.* xxvii, 2
VF 45/-

2587 Æ 13. Similar. ℞. Hand holding caduceus. *B.M.C.* xxviii, 7.. .. *fair* 7/6

2588 Vologases I. 51-61 A.D. Æ *drachm.* Diademed bust l. Pahlevi letters behind head. ℞. Similar to No. 2563. *B.M.C.* xxix, 1 .. .. F 21/-

2589 Æ 10. Similar. ℞. Horse head r.; in front, A. *B.M.C.* xxix, 4 .. *fair* 7/6

2590 Vardanes II. 55-58 A.D. Æ *tetradrachm.* As No. 2584, but rounded beard; date, ΗΕΤ (=368). *Petr.* 3 .. .. F £6

2591 Æ *drachm.* Helmeted bust, facing, star each side. ℞. Similar to No. 2563. *B.M.C.* xxix, 15 .. .. F 32/6

2592 Æ 12. Similar. ℞. Zeus r., within shrine. *B.M.C.* xxix, 17 .. .. *fair* 7/6

2593 Vologases II. 61-71 A.D. Æ *drachm.* Diademed bust l., long pointed beard, long neck. ℞. Similar to No. 2563. *B.M.C.* xxix, 7 .. .. F 25/-

2594 Æ 12. Similar. ℞. Eagle l., wreath in beak. *B.M.C.* xxxii, 13 .. *fair* 8/6

2596 Vologases III. 77-147 A.D. Æ *drachm.* Helmeted bust l., short beard, Pahlevi letters behind. R. Similar to No. 2563. *B.M.C.* xxxii, 12.. .. .. F 25/–

2596A Æ 16. Similar. R. Bust of Tyche r.: in front, ΑΛΥ. *B.M.C.* xxxiii, 4.. F 10/6

2597 Pacorus II. 78-110 A.D. Æ *drachm.* Diademed bust l., beardless. R. Similar to No. 2563. *B.M.C.* xxx, 5 .. .. F 27/6

2598 Æ 11. Helmeted bust l., close beard. R. Nike r., holds wreath. *B.M.C.* xxxi, 3 F 10/6

2599 Osroes. 106-130 A.D. Æ 15. Bust l., diademed, hair in bunches. R. Bust of Tyche r., turreted: in front, ΘΚΥ. *B.M.C.* xxxi, 14 .. .. F 15/–

2600 Mithradates VI. *ca.* 116 A.D. Æ *drachm.* Diademed bust l., diadem with 3 ends, long pointed beard. R. Similar to No. 2563. *B.M.C.* xxxiii, 9 .. .. F 25/–

2601 Æ *drachm.* Similar, but 2 ends. R. Similar, Pahlevi line at top. *B.M.C.* xxxiii, 11 F 21/–

2602 Vologases IV. 147-191 A.D. Æ *tetradrachm.* His bust l.; behind, Β; ΒΑCΙΛΕΥϹ ΒΑCΙΛΕΩΝ ΑΡCΑΚΟΥ ΕΠΙΦΑΝΟΥC ΦΙΛΕΛΛΗΝΟC, King seated l. receiving diadem from Tyche; in ex., ΑΠΕΛΑΙΟΥ; in field above, ΔΞΥ(= 464 = 152/3 A.D.). *B.M.C.* 8 *fair* 75/–

2603 Æ *drachm.* Similar, long thick beard. R. Similar to No. 2563, Pahlevi line at top. *B.M.C.* xxxiv, 7 .. .. F 25/–

2604 Vologases V. 191-208 A.D. Æ *drachm.* Bust facing, diademed, hair in large bunches. R. Similar to No. 2563, but Pahlevi line on top and the rest of legend barbarous. *B.M.C.* xxxv, 9 .. .. F £6

2605 Æ 10. Similar. R. Eagle l., wings open. *B.M.C.* xxxv, 12 .. *fair* 10/6

2606 Vologases VI. 208-222 A.D. Æ *drachm.* Helmeted bust l., diadem with 2 ends, long pointed beard, Pahlevi letters behind. R. Similar to No. 2604. *B.M.C.* xxxvi, 4 F 25/–

2607 Æ 10. Similar. R. Eagle l., wings open. *B.M.C.* xxxvi, 6 .. .. *fair* 10/6

2608 Artaban V. 213-227 A.D. Æ *drachm.* Helmeted bust l., diadem with 4 ends. R. Similar to No. 2604. *B.M.C.* xxxvi, 8 .. .. F 22/6

2609 Artavasdes. *c.* 227 A.D. Æ *drachm.* Somewhat as last. *B.M.C.* xxxvi, 15 RR, VF £10

2610 **ARMENIA.** Valarsaces. *c.* 139 B.C. Æ *obol.* Head r., diademed. R. Head r. helmeted. *Petr.* xxiv, 11 .. .. F £6

2611 Æ 21. Similar. R. Horse's head r. *B.M.C.* ii, 12 .. .. .. *fair* 17/6 See also 2540A

2612 Arsaces I. *c.* 124 B.C. Æ 15. Bust r., diademed. R. Nike r. *Petr.* xxv, 2 *fair* 22/6

Tigranes. 94-56 B.C. Æ *tetradrachm.* See 2127.

2614 **ELYMAIS** (Susiana). Kamnaskires III, with Queen Anzaze. 82-81 B.C. Æ *drachm.* Two jugate busts l. R. Greek legend; Zeus l., enthroned. *B.M.C.* xxxviii, 4 F £10

2615 Kamnaskires IV. *c.* 40 B.C. Æ *hemidrachm.* Diad. bust l., long beard. R. Corrupt Greek legend; bust l., short beard. *B.M.C.* xxxviii, 11 .. .. .. VF £10

2616 Æ (base) *obol.* As previous. *B.M.C.* xxxviii, 13 .. .. .. *fair* 25/–

2617 Kamnaskires V. Early 1st Cent. A.D. Æ 16 *drachm.* Similar. *B.M.C.* xxxix, 9 F 50/–

2618 Kamnaskires VI. Middle 1st Cent. A.D. Billon *tetradrachm.* Similar. R. Small bust l. *B.M.C.* xxxix, 11 .. .. VF/F £10

2619 Orodes I. *c.* 75 A.D. Æ 15 *drachm.* Bust l., helmeted, anchor behind. R. Bust of Tyche l. *B.M.C.* xxxix, 18 .. .. *fair* 15/–

2620 Orodes II. *c.* 90 A.D. Æ 14 *drachm.* Bust helmeted, facing; on r., anchor and star in crescent. R. Dashes. *B.M.C.* xl, 15 .. .. F 20/–

2621 Phraates. *c.* 100 A.D. Æ 13 *drachm.* Similar, but bust almost l. ℞. Artemis r. *B.M.C.* xli, 10 .. .. *fair* 12/6
2621A Orodes IV. *c.* 175 A.D. Æ 13 *drachm.* Bust l. ℞. Female bust l.; behind, anchor. *B.M.C.* xlii, 8 .. .. *fair* 12/6
2621B Uncertain king, *v.* 200-225 A.D. Æ 13 *drachm.* Bust l. ℞. Artemis r. *B.M.C.* xlii, 14 .. .. *fair* 10/6
2622 **CHARACENE.** Attambelos I. 44-39 B.C. Æ *tetradrachm.* Head r., diademed, thick beard. ℞. Greek legend. Herakles seated l., holds club; in ex., ΒΟΣ (=272=41 B.C.). *B.M.C.* lv, 12 .. .. VF/F £12/10/-
2623 Attambelos III. 53-71 A.D. Billon *tetradrachm.* Beardless young head r., diademed. ℞. Similar. *B.M.C.* xliii, 9 .. .. VF £7/10/-
2624 — Billon *tetradrachm.* Bearded head r., diademed; countermark on neck. ℞. Similar. *B.M.C.* xliv, 5 .. .. VF £7/10/-
2625 Maga. 2nd Cent. A.D. Æ *tetradrachm.* Bust r., wearing tiara, Aramaic inscrip. ℞. Bearded head r., hair in rolls. *B.M.C.* xlv, 6 .. .. .. VF/F £7/10/-
2626 **PERSIS.** Darius I. 150-100 B.C. Æ *drachm.* Head r., wearing kyrbasia, crescent behind. ℞. Fire temple. *B.M.C.* xxx, 13 .. .. .. *nearly* VF £8
2627 Autophradates II. 1st Cent. B.C. Æ *hemidrachm.* Bust r., diademed, crescent above. ℞. Similar. *B.M.C.* xxxii, 3 .. .. F 85/-
2628 Darius II. 1st Cent. B.C. Æ *obol.* Bust l., helmeted. ℞. King standing l. before altar. *B.M.C.* xxxii, 18 .. .. F 70/-

BACTRIA AND INDO-GREEKS.

2629 **Diodotus.** *c.* 246-237 B.C. Æ *drachm.* Diad. head r. ℞. ΒΑΣΙΛΕΩΣ ΔΙΟΔΟΤΟΥ. Zeus l., hurling thunderbolt, eagle at his feet. *B.M.C.* 6 .. .. .. *fair* £16
2630 **Euthydemus I.** *c.* 230-190 B.C. Æ *tetradrachm.* Diad. head r. ℞. ΒΑΣΙΛΕΩΣ ΕΥΘΥΔΗΜΟΥ. Herakles seated l. on rock, holding club resting on his knee. *B.M.C.* 13 F £40
2631 Æ 22. Head of Herakles r. ℞. Same legend; free horse prancing r. *B.M.C.* 15 *fair* 50/-; F £6
2632 **Demetrius I.** *c.* 190-166 B.C. Æ *obol.* His dr. bust r., wearing elephant's scalp. ℞. ΒΑΣΙΛΕΩΣ ΔΗΜΗΤΡΙΟΥ. Herakles standing facing crowning himself. *B.M.C.* 12 *fair*/F £6

2630   2635

2633 Æ 24. Head of Herakles r., club over shoulder. ℞. Same legend; Artemis, radiate, standing facing. *B.M.C.* 13 .. .. VF/F £6
2634 **Apollodotus I Soter.** *c.* 185-162 B.C. Æ square *drachm.* ΒΑΣΙΛΕΩΣ ΑΠΟΛΛΟΔΟΤΟΥ ΣΩΤΗΡΟΣ. Indian elephant moving to r. ℞. Indian legend. Humped Indian bull moving to r. *B.M.C.* 10 .. .. *fair* 15/-
2635 Æ 22 square. Same legend. Apollo standing facing. ℞. Tripod. *B.M.C.* 29 *fair*/F 25/-
2636 **Agathokles.** *c.* 175-165 B.C. Æ 25×16 rectangular. Indian legend. Dancing girl. ℞. ΒΑΣΙΛΕΩΣ ΑΓΑΘΟΚΛΕΟΥΣ. Maneless lion to r.; all within incuse square. *B.M.C.* 9 F 60/-
2637 **Eucratides.** *c.* 169-159 B.C. Æ *tetradrachm.* Diad. bust dr. r. ℞. ΒΑΣΙΛΕΩΣ ΕΥΚΡΑΤΙΔΟΥ. The Dioskuri charging r., with couched lances. *B.M.C.* 6. **Plate VIII** *good* F/VF £50
2637A — Another with bust of king wearing horned helmet. *B.M.C.* 9 .. VF £100
2638 Æ *obol.* Helmeted bust dr. r. ℞. Caps of the Dioskuri. *B.M.C.* 27 F 55/-; VF/*good* F £6
2639 Æ 22×20 rectangular. As last ℞. as No. 2637. *B.M.C.* 44 .. .. F 32/6

2637A   2640

2640 **Menander.** c. 166-145 B.C. Æ *tetradrachm.* ΒΑΣΙΛΕΩΣ ΣΩΤΗΡΟΣ ΜΕΝΑΝΔΡΟΥ. Helmeted bust r. ℞. Indian legend. Athena l., holding aegis and hurling thunderbolt. *B.M.C.* 4 .. .. F £10; VF £25

2641 Æ *drachm.* Diad. bust r. ℞. Similar. *B.M.C.* 13 .. .. .. F 17/6

2642 — Helmeted bust r. ℞. Similar. *B.M.C.* 6-12 .. .. F 17/6; VF 45/–

2643 — Bust l. thrusting with javelin. ℞. Similar but Athena r. *B.M.C.* 32
good F 32/6

2644 Æ 22 square. As last. *B.M.C.* 44 .. .. fair/F 60/–

2645 Æ 18 square. Helmeted bust of Athena r. ℞. Nike advancing r. *B.M.C.* 52
fair 15/–

2646 **Antimachus II Nikephoros.** c. 162-157 B.C. Æ *drachm.* ΒΑΣΙΛΕΩΣ ΝΙΚΗΦΟΡΟΥ ΑΝΤΙΜΑΧΟΥ. Nike advancing l. ℞. King on horseback galloping r. *B.M.C.* 1
F 35/–

2646A **Heliocles I.** c. 150 B.C. Æ *tetradrachm.* Diad. bust r. ℞. ΒΑΣΙΛΕΩΣ ΗΛΙΟΚΛΕΟΥΣ ΔΙΚΑΙΟΥ. Zeus stg. *B.M.C.* 1 .. .. VF £90

2646B Æ 27. Barbarous copy of last. *B.M.C.* 11 .. .. fair 90/–

2647 **Zoilus I Dikaios.** c. 155-140 B.C. Æ *drachm.* ΒΛΣΙΛΕΩΣ ΔΙΚΙΟΥ ΞΩΙΛΟΥ. Diad. and dr. bust r. ℞. Herakles standing facing. *I.M.C.* 3 .. .. VF £8/10/–

2648 **Agathokleia and Strato I.** c. 145-140 B.C. Æ 20 square. ΒΑΣΙΛΙΣΣΗΣ ΘΕΟΤΡΟΠΟΥ ΑΓΑΘΟΚΛΕΙΑΣ. Her helmeted bust r. ℞. Herakles l. seated on rock. *B.M.C.* 1 F £7

2649 **Strato I.** c. 140-100 B.C. Æ *tetradrachm.* ΒΑΣΙΛΕΩΣ ΣΩΤΗΡΟΣ ΚΑΙ ΔΙΚΑΙΟΥ ΣΤΡΑΤΩΝΟΣ. Helmeted bust dr. r. ℞. Athena l. hurling thunderbolt. *B.M.C.* 1 var. VF £90

2650 Æ *drachm.* ΒΑΣΙΛΕΩΣ ΣΩΤΗΡΟΣ ΣΤΡΑΤΩΝΟΣ. Diad. bust r. ℞. Similar. *B.M.C.* 6
VF £12

2651 Æ 24 square. Apollo facing holding arrow and bow. ℞. Tripod-lebes on stand. *B.M.C.* 13-16 .. .. nearly F 52/6

2652 **Heliocles II.** c. 140-125 B.C. Æ *tetradrachm.* ΒΑΣΙΛΕΩΣ ΔΙΚΑΙΟΥ ΗΛΙΟΚΛΕΟΥΣ. Diademed bust of the king r. ℞. Indian legend. Zeus facing, holding thunderbolt and sceptre. *B.M.C.* 22 .. .. VF £120

2653 Æ *drachm.* Similar. *B.M.C.* 23 .. .. VF £12

2654 Æ 21 square. Diad. bust r., bearded. ℞. Elephant l. *B.M.C.* 28 fair 35/–

2655 **Apollodotus II Philopator.** c. 135-120 B.C. Æ *tetradrachm.* ΒΑΣΙΛΕΩΣ ΜΕΓΑΛΟΥ ΣΩΤΗΡΟΣ ΦΙΛΟΠΑΤΟΡΟΣ ΑΠΟΛΛΟΔΟΤΟΥ. Diad. bust r. ℞. Indian legend. Athena l. hurling thunderbolt. *B.M.C.* 1 .. .. VF £45

2656 Æ *drachm.* Similar, but without ΜΕΓΑΛΟΥ. *B.M.C.* 2 .. .. .. VF £8

2657 Æ 28. Apollo standing r., holding arrow. ℞. Tripod. *B.M.C.* 9 fair 21/–

2658 **Lysias.** c. 125-120 B.C. Æ *drachm.* ΒΑΣΙΛΕΩΣ ΑΝΙΚΗΤΟΥ ΛΥΣΙΟΥ. Helmeted bust r. ℞. Indian legend. Herakles facing, holding club, palm and lion's skin, crowning himself. *B.M.C.* 6 .. .. VF £12/10/–

2659 Æ 20 square. Bust of Herakles r., club over shoulder. ℞. Elephant walking r. *B.M.C.* 9 .. .. R, nearly F £6

2660 **Antialcidas.** c. 125-95 B.C. Æ *drachm.* ΒΑΣΙΛΕΩΣ ΝΙΚΗΦΟΡΟΥ ΑΝΤΙΑΛΚΙΔΟΥ. Dr. bust r., wearing flat Macedonian kausia. ℞. Zeus enthroned l., holding Nike and sceptre; to l., forepart of elephant l. *B.M.C.* 11 .. .. VF £8

2660A Æ *tetradrachm.* Same legend. Diad. bust of king l., seen from behind, brandishing spear. ℞. Zeus l. conducting elephant with Nike on its head. **Plate VII**
RRR, EF £250

2661 Æ 17 square. Bust of Zeus r. ℞. Pilei of the Dioskuri with two palms between. *B.M.C.* 19 .. .. fair 37/6; F 75/–

2662 Archebius. *c.* 95-85 B.C. Æ 22 square. As last but ΒΑΣΙΛΕΩΣ ΔΙΚΑΙΟΥ ΝΙΚΗΦΟΡΟΥ ΑΡΧΕΒΙΟΥ. *P.M.C.* 230 .. .. *nearly* F £8

2663 Philoxenus. *c.* 90-80 B.C. Æ *drachm* square. ΒΑΣΙΛΕΩΣ ΑΝΙΚΗΤΟΥ ΦΙΛΟΞΕΝΟΥ. Helmeted bust r. Ƀ. King on horseback galloping r. *B.M.C.* 7   *good* F/VF £7/10/-

2663A Æ *tetradrachm* round. Similar type. *B.M.C.* 3. **Plate VIII** .. .. EF £100

2664 Æ 20 square. Tyche standing l. Ƀ. Bull r. *B.M.C.* 11 .. .. VF £5

2665 Hippostratus. *c.* 80 B.C. Æ *tetradrachm.* ΒΑΣΙΛΕΩΣ ΣΩΤΗΡΟΣ ΙΠΠΟΣΤΡΑΤΟΥ. Diad. bust r. Ƀ. King on horseback r., horse walking. *B.M.C.* 11/7 .. *nearly* VF £30

2666 Æ 22 square. Apollo r. Ƀ. Tripod. *B.M.C.* 14.. .. .. VF £6

2667 Hermaeus. *c.* 75-55 B.C. Æ *tetradrachm.* ΒΑΣΙΛΕΩΣ ΣΩΤΗΡΟΣ ΕΡΜΑΙΟΥ. Diad. bust r. Ƀ. Zeus enthroned l. *B.M.C.* 3 .. .. VF £20

2668 Æ *drachm.* Somewhat similar but square omikron. *B.M.C.* 22 .. .. VF 75/-

2669 Æ 26. Similar. *B.M.C.* 26 .. .. *fair* 17/6; *good* F/F 65/-

2670 INDO-SCYTHIANS. Maues. *c.* 90 B.C. Æ *tetradrachm.* ΒΑΣΙΛΕΩΣ ΒΑΣΙΛΕΩΝ ΜΕΓΑΛΟΥ ΜΑΥΟΥ. Zeus standing l. holding sceptre. Ƀ. Indian legend. Nike advancing r. *B.M.C.* 3 .. .. *nearly* VF £25

2671 Æ 14 square. Apollo l. Ƀ. Tripod. *B.M.C.* 26 .. .. *fair* 20/-; VF £5

2672 Azes I. *c.* 90-40 B.C. Æ *tetradrachm.* ΒΑΣΙΛΕΩΣ ΒΑΣΙΛΕΩΝ ΜΕΓΑΛΟΥ ΑΖΟΥ. King on horseback r. Ƀ. Athena facing crowning herself. *B.M.C.* 70 .. VF £16

2673 — Another. Athena r. holding shield and spear. *B.M.C.* 92   VF/*good* F £10

2674 Æ *drachm.* King on horseback r., holding spear. Ƀ. Tyche l., holding brazier and palm. *B.M.C.* 109 .. .. F 80/-

2675 Æ 29. Demeter enthroned l., holding cornucopiae. Ƀ. Hermes l., holding caduceus. *B.M.C.* 127 .. .. *good* F 50/-

2676 Æ 21. Humped bull r. Ƀ. Lion r. *B.M.C.* 138-153 .. .. F 27/6

2677 Azilises. *c.* 40-15 B.C. Æ *tetradrachm.* ΒΑΣΙΛΕΩΣ ΒΑΣΙΛΕΩΝ ΜΕΓΑΛΟΥ ΑΖΙΛΙΣΟΥ. King on horseback r., holding couched lance. Ƀ. Indian legend. Similar to No. 2674. *B.M.C.* 7 .. .. VF/F £15

2678 — Another, but *rev.* two Dioskuri standing facing. *B.M.C.* 3 .. .. F £12

2679 Azes II. *c.* 15-5 B.C. Æ *tetradrachm.* Legend as No. 2672, but square omikron. King on horseback r., holding whip. Ƀ. Athena r., holding spear and shield. *B.M.C.* (Azes) 90. **Plate VIII** .. .. F 65/-; *nearly* VF £6

2679A Æ *drachm.* King r. on horseback. Ƀ. Zeus l. *B.M.C.* 28 .. .. F 15/-

2679B — Similar. Ƀ. Athena r. *B.M.C.* 83 .. .. VF 50/-

2680 INDO-PARTHIANS. Gondophares. 20-60 A.D. Billon *tetradrachm.* ΒΑCΙΛΕ ΩC ΒΑCΙΛΕ ΩΝ ΜΕΓΑΛΟΥ ΥΝΔΟΦΕΡΡΟΥ (often corrupt). Similar to No. 2679. *B.M.C.* 3
F 65/-

2681 Æ 23. Diad. bust r. Ƀ. Nike r. *B.M.C.* 13 .. .. F 20/-

2682 Pakores. *c.* 70-75 A.D. Æ 23. Diad. bust l., hair in large tuft. Ƀ. Nike to r. *B.M.C.* 1 .. .. VF/F 65/-

2683 Soter Megas *c.* 100 A.D. Billon *tetradrachm.* ΒΑCΙΛΕΥC ΒΑCΙΛΕ ΩΝ C ΩΤΗΡ ΜΕΓΑC. As No. 2679. Ƀ. Zeus r., holding long sceptre. *B.M.C.* 1 .. .. *fair* 20/-

2684 Æ 21. Bust r., radiate, holding lance. Ƀ. King r. on horseback. *B.M.C.* 2
fair 10/6

2685 Æ 14. Similar. *B.M.C.* 13 .. .. *fair* 10/6

2686 SOGDIANA. Early 2nd Cent. B.C. Æ *tetradrachm.* Barbarous copy of Euthydemus I of Bactria. 1st type. Bust r. Ƀ. Corrupt Greek legend. Herakles seated l. on rock, holding club resting on his knee. *Morgan,* fig. 531 .. .. *good* F £12/10/-

2687 Middle 2nd Cent. B.C. Another as last. 2nd type. Similar, but mixed Greek and Aramaic legend. *Morgan,* fig. 532 .. .. VF/F £10

2688 Hyrcodes. 1st Cent. B.C. Æ *drachm.* ΥΡΚ ΩΔΟΥ. Bust r. Ƀ. ΜΑΚΑΡΟΥ ΑΡΔΘΡΟΥ. King or deity standing facing, holding spear. *B.M.C.* 3 .. .. .. F £6

2689 Æ *hemidrachm.* ΥΡΚ ΩΔ. Bust r. Ƀ. ΥΡΚ ΩΔ. Forepart of horse r. *B.M.C.* 21
fair 40/-; F £6

2690 **KUSHANS. Kujula Kadphises I.** 50-85 A.D.   With the name of Hermaeus. Æ 22. ΒΑΣΙΛΕΩΣ ΣΤΗΡΟΣ ΣΥ ΕΡΜΑΙΟΥ. Bust of Hermaeus r., diad. ℞. Indian legend with the name of Kujula. Herakles facing, holding club and lion's skin. *B.M.C.* 1 F 22/6

2691 **Kadphises II.** 85-120 A.D. Æ 27. ΒΑΣΙΛΕΥϹ ΒΑΣΙΛΕ ΩΝ ϹꞶΤΗΡΜΕΓΑϹ ΟΟΗΜΟΚΑΔ-ΦΙϹΗϹ. King l., sacrificing at altar ℞. Indian legend. Siva facing, bull r. behind. *B.M.C.* 12 .. .. F 25/-

2692 **Kanishka.** 120-150 A.D. N *stater*. ΡΑΟΝΑΝΟΡΑΟΚΑΝΗΡΚΙ ΚΟΡΑΝΟ. Helmeted and diad. king standing l., holding ankus over altar and spear. ℞. ΟΚΡΟ. Nimbate Siva l., holding in his four hands vase, drum, trident and goat. *B.M.C.* 25   VF £22/10/-

2693 Æ 22. ΡΑΟΚΑΝΗΡΚΙ. Similar to No. 2691. ℞. ΜΙΟΡΟ. Sun-god Mithras l. *B.M.C.* 46 .. .. *fair* 10/6; F 25/-

2694 **Huvishka.** 150-180 A.D. N *stater*. ΡΑΟΝΑΝΟΡΑΟ ΟΟΗΡΚΙ ΚΟΡΑΝΟ. Upper part of king, helmeted, diad. and nimbate, emerging from clouds, holding ear of corn and spear. ℞. ΑΡΔΟΧΡΟ. Female deity r., holding cornucopiae. *B.M.C.* 6 .. .. EF £40

2695 Æ 21. King riding on elephant r., holding spear and ankus. ℞. ΜΑΟ. Moon-god l., crescent behind shoulders. *B.M.C.* 147 .. *fair* 10/6; F/*fair* 25/-

2696 **Vasu Deva I.** 180-220 A.D. N *stater*. ΡΑΟΝΑΝΟΡΑΟ ΒΑΖΟΔΗΟ ΚΟΡΑΝΟ. Similar to No. 2691. ℞. ΟΚΡΟ. Three-faced Siva facing, holding wreath and trident; behind him, bull l. *B.M.C.* 5 .. .. VF £20

2697 Æ 23. Similar to No. 2691. *B.M.C.* 25 .. .. .. *fair* 12/6; F 32/6

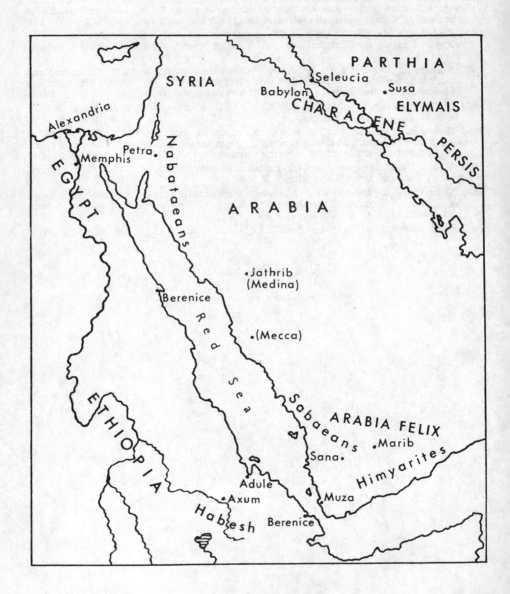

EGYPT.

2698 **Ptolemy I.** 323-284 B.C. As Governor. Æ *tetradrachm.* Head of Alexander the Great, with horn of Ammon, wearing diadem, elephant's skin and aegis. ℞. ΑΛΕΞ-ΑΝΔΡΟΥ. Athena Promachos r., with javelin and shield: in field, r., ΕΥ and eagle r. on thunderbolt. *B.M.C.* 11 .. .. EF £30

2699 — Similar, but in *rev.* field r., two monograms. *B.M.C.* 41-44 .. VF/F £12

2700 **Ptolemy I or II.** Æ *tetradrachm.* Head of Ptolemy I, diademed, r. ℞. ΠΤΟΛΕΜΑΙΟΥ ΒΑΣΙΛΕΩΣ. Eagle, with wings closed, standing l. on thunderbolt: in field, l., P and monogram. *B.M.C.* 9 .. .. VF £10

2701 Æ 27. Head of Zeus, laur., r. ℞. Legend and type as preceding, but eagle has wings open. *B.M.C.* 29 .. .. F 35/-

2702 N *pentadrachm.* Head of Ptolemy I, diad., r. ℞. ΠΤΟΛΕΜΑΙΟΥ ΒΑΣΙΛΕΩΣ. Eagle with closed wings standing l. on thunderbolt; to l., H and club. *B.M.C.* (Ptol. 1) 74; *Svor.* 636 .. .. VF £150

2703 **Ptolemy II.** 284-247 B.C. N *tetradrachm.* ΑΔΕΛΦΩΝ. Jugate busts of Ptolemy II and Arsinoë II dr. r. ℞. ΘΕΩΝ. Jugate busts of Ptolemy I and Berenice I dr. r. *B.M.C.* 4-5. **Plate VIII** .. .. VF £100

2704 N *octadrachm.* Veiled head of Arsinoë II wearing stephane; behind, Θ. ℞. ΑΡΣΙΝΟΗΣ ΦΙΛΑΔΕΛΦΟΥ. Double cornucopiae, a bunch of grapes hanging down on each side. *B.M.C.* Arsenoë 9 .. .. EF £250

2705 Æ *dekadrachm.* As last but no letters behind. *B.M.C.* 33. **Plate VIII**
VF, *but for some corrosion* £120

2706 Æ *tetradrachm* of *Sidon.* As No. 2700, but in *rev.* field l., ΣΙ. *B.M.C.* 32
F/*fair* 65/-; VF £10

2707 — of *Tyre,* similar, but in field, l., club and monogram ΤΥΡ. *B.M.C.* 37 *good* F £8

2708 Æ 27. As No. 2701. *B.M.C.* 19 .. .. *good* F 45/-

2709 **Ptolemy III.** 247-222 B.C. Æ 24. Head of Zeus, laur., r. ℞. As No. 2701, but in field, shield and two monograms. *B.M.C.* 5 .. .. *fair* 18/6

2710 Æ 23. Bust of Ptolemy III, laur., r. ℞. ΠΤΟΛΕΜΑΙΟΥ ΒΑΣΙΛΕΩΣ. Eagle l. on thunderbolt, wings closed: to l., cornucopiae. *B.M.C.* 99 .. .. .. F 35/-

2711 Æ 40. Head of Zeus, laur., r. ℞. As last, but ΔΙ between legs. *B.M.C.* 107
good F 65/-

2712 **Ptolemy IV.** 222-204 B.C. Æ 39. Head of Zeus, diad., r. ℞. ΠΤΟΛΕΜΑΙΟΥ
ΒΑΣΙΛΕΩΣ. Eagle, wings closed, on thunderbolt l., head r.: cornucopiae on shoulder
and E between legs. *B.M.C.* 37 ..   ..   VF £5

2713 Æ 21. Similar, but two eagles, wings closed, on thunderbolt, r.   *Svoronos* 1158
                                                      F 30/-

2714 Æ 25. Head of Alexander the Great, wearing elephant's skin, r.   ℞. as No. 2712.
B.M.C. 41 ..   ..   F 37/6

2715 Æ 28. Head of Cleopatra I, as Isis, r., hair in long curls.   ℞. ΠΤΟΛΕΜΑΙΟΥ ΒΑΣ-
ΙΛΕΩΣ. Eagle, wings open, on thunderbolt, l.   *Svor.*, xl, 11. **Plate VIII** *nearly* F 65/-

2716 **Ptolemy V.** 204-181 B.C. Æℛ *tetradrachm.* Bust of Ptolemy V r., wearing diadem
adorned with ear of corn.   ℞. ΠΤΟΛΕΜΑΙΟΥ ΒΑΣΙΛΕΩΣ. Eagle on thunderbolt l., wings
closed: in field, l., palm, on monogram TP (Tripolis): between eagle's legs, NI. *B.M.C.* 52
                                                         RR, VF £100

2718 Æ 24. Head of bearded Herakles, wearing lion-skin, r.   ℞. As preceding, but eagle
has closed wings. *B.M.C.* 8 ..   ..   VF/*good* F 75/-

2719 Æ 22. Head of Ptolemy I r.   ℞. ΒΑΣΙΛΕΩΣ ΠΤΟΛΕΜΑΙΟΥ. Head of Libya r.:
to r., cornucopia. *B.M.C.* 84 ..   ..   F 35/-

2720 Æ 17. Similar, smaller module. *B.M.C.* 87 ..   ..   F 27/6

2721 **Ptolemy VI.** 181-146 B.C. Æℛ *tetradrachm.* Head of Ptolemy I r.   ℞. ΠΤΟ-
ΛΕΜΑΙΟΥ ΒΑΣΙΛΕΩΣ. Eagle, wings closed, on thunderbolt, l.: in field, ΛΚΗ (year 28) and
ΠΑ (Paphos). *Cf. B.M.C.* 38 ..   ..   *good* VF £10

2722 Æ 29. Head of Zeus, laur., r.   ℞. Legend as preceding: two eagles, wings closed,
on thunderbolt, l.: in field, l., cornucopiae ..   ..   VF 75/-

2723 Æ 20. Similar, smaller module   ..   ..   F 27/6

2725 **Ptolemy VIII.** 170-117 B.C. Æℛ *tetradrachm.* *As illustration* ..   ..   VF £10

2726 — Similar, with ΛΑΒ and ΠΑ in *rev.* field. *B.M.C.* 59   ..   ..   VF £8

2727 ℛ *didrachm.* Similar to 2725. *B.M.C.* 23 ..   ..   ..   *R,* VF £12/10/-

2728 — Similar, with P and club in *rev.* field. *Cf. B.M.C.* 26 ..   ..   *R,* EF/VF £15

2729 Æ 29. Head of Herakles, wearing lion-skin, r.   ℞. Similar to No. 2722 *fair* 21/-

2730 Æ 20. Head of Zeus r.   ℞. ΒΑΣΙΛΕΩΣ ΠΤΟΛΕΜΑΙΟΥ ΕΥΕΡΓΕΤΟΥ. Eagle, wings
open, l.   *B.M.C.* 82 ..   ..   F 27/6

2731 **Ptolemy X.** 117-81 B.C. Æℛ *tetradrachm.* Types as No. 2725: in *rev.* field, ΛΙ and
ΠΑ. *B.M.C.* 63 ..   ..   VF/*good* F £5

2732 Æ 18. *Obv.* as No. 2730.   ℞. ΠΤΟΛΕΜΑΙΟΥ ΒΑΣΙΛΕΩΣ. Double cornucopiae. *B.M.C.*
43 ..   ..   F 30/-

2733 **Ptolemy XI.** 114-88 B.C. Æℛ *tetradrachm.* Types as No. 2725: in *rev.* field, ΛΙΒ Θ
and ΠΑ. *B.M.C.* 20 ..   ..   F/VF 65/-; VF £5

2734 ℛ *didrachm.* Bust of Ptolemy XI as Dionysos, r., wearing wreath of ivy. ℞. Legend
as preceding: eagle l., wings open. *B.M.C.* 17   ..   ..   *R, fair* 75/-

2735 **Ptolemy XIII.** 81-52 B.C. Æℛ *tetradrachm.* Types as No. 2725, but palm over eagle's
shoulder, and in *rev.* field ΛΒ, symbol of Isis, and ΠΑ. *B.M.C.* 2
                                                     good F 60/-; VF 90/-

2736 **Ptolemy, King of Cyprus.** 81-58 B.C. Æℛ *tetradrachm.* Types as No. 2725: in
rev. field, ΛΚ and ΠΑ. *B.M.C.* 39 ..   ..   VF/F 85/-

2737 **Cleopatra VII** (*wife of Mark Antony*). 52-30 B.C. Æ 27. Head of queen r.   ℞.
ΚΛΕΟΠΑΤΡΑΣ ΒΑΣΙΛΙΣΣΗΣ. Eagle on thunderbolt, wings closed, l.: in field cornucopiae
and Π. *B.M.C.* 4. **Plate VIII** ..   ..   ..   M £5; F/*fair* £25

EGYPT — Alexandria

In the following list, coins marked " Tet." are billon tetradrachms, the earlier issues being large and containing a good proportion of silver. The tetradrachm, however, gradually declined both in silver content and size, and the latest examples are small pieces of bronze with only about 4% of silver in their composition. Where the obverse is not described, it may be assumed to bear the emperor's or empress's head with appropriate Greek legend, except for the very small Æ pieces which usually have no inscr. on the obv.

2738 **Augustus.** Æ 27. Head of emperor r. ℞. Eagle on thunderbolt l. *B.M.C.* 1 *R, fair* 35/-

2739 Æ 13. ℞. ΛΑΘ in wreath. *B.M.C.* 13 .. .. *fair* 21/-

2740 Æ 20. ΣΕΒΑΣΤΟΣ. Altar between laurel branches. ℞. ΚΑΙΣΑΡΟΣ in wreath. *B.M.C.* 17 .. .. F/VF 45/-

2740A **Livia.** Æ 24. ℞. ΛΑΘ in wreath. *B.M.C.* 20 .. .. *fair* 35/-

2740B — Æ 14. ℞. ΛΔ. Ears of corn and poppy-heads. *B.M.C.* 61 .. *fair* 27/6

2741 **Tiberius.** *Tet.* ΤΙΒΕΡΙΟΣ ΚΑΙΣΑΡ ΣΕΒΑΣΤΟΣ. Laur. head r., ΛΖ in front. ℞. ΘΕΟΣ ΣΕΒΑΣΤΟΣ. Radiate head of Augustus r. *B.M.C.* 38 .. *fair*/F 65/-; VF/F £6

2742 — As preceding, but *obv.* type l. *B.M.C.* 41 .. .. F 85/-

2743 **Germanicus.** Æ 12. ℞. ΤΙ ΛΔ in wreath. *B.M.C.* 63 .. R, F 45/-

2744 **Caligula.** Æ 15. Phoenix (Numidian crane) l. ℞. Apis-bull r.: above, ΛΒ. *B.M.C.* 2632 .. .. F 40/-

2745 **Claudius.** *Tet.* ΤΙ ΚΛΑΥΔΙ ΚΑΙΣ ΣΕΒΑ ΓΕΡΜΑΝΙ ΑΥΤΟΚΡ. Laur. head r.; in front, date ΛΒ. ℞. ΑΝΤΩΝΙΑ ΣΕΒΑΣΤΗ. Dr. bust of **Antonia** r. *B.M.C.* 65 .. F 75/-

2746 — Similar, but date ΛΓ. ℞. ΜΕΣΣΑΛΙΝΑ ΚΑΙΣ ΣΕΒΑΣ. **Messalina** standing l. holding two small figures and ears of corn. *B.M.C.* 71 .. .. F 50/-

2747 Æ 26. ℞. ΑΥΤΟΚΡΑ. Bust of Nilus r. *B.M.C.* 82 .. .. .. F/VF 55/-

2748 Æ 15. ℞. Crocodile r.: above, ΛΙ. *B.M.C.* 87 .. .. F 32/6

2749 Æ 26. ℞. ΑΥΤΟΚΡΑ. Ears of corn and caduceus. *B.M.C.* 100 .. *fair* 15/-

2750 Æ 20. ℞. Clasped hands. *B.M.C.* 107 .. .. *fair* 15/-

2751 **Agrippina Junior.** Æ 27. ΑΓΡΙΠΠΙΝΑ ΣΕΒΑΣΤΗ. Bust r., wearing corn wreath. ℞. ΕΥΘΗΝΙΑ L ΙΒ. Bust of Euthenia r. *B.M.C.* 110 .. .. R, *fair* 42/-

2752 **Nero.** *Tet.* ΝΕΡΩ ΚΛΑΥ ΚΑΙΣ ΣΕΒ ΓΕΡ ΑΥ. Radiate head of Nero l. ℞. ΘΕΟΣ ΣΕΒΑΣΤΟΣ. Rad. head of Augustus r. *B.M.C.* 112-3 .. .. F 30/-

2753 — ℞. ΤΙΒΕΡΙΟΣ ΚΑΙΣΑΡ. Laur. head of Tiberius r. *B.M.C.* 114 .. F 30/-

2754 — ℞. ΑΓΡΙΠΠΙΝΑ ΣΕΒΑΣΤΗ. Bust of **Agrippina** r. *B.M.C.* 116 .. F 45/-

2755 — ℞. ΟΚΤΑΟΥΙΑ ΣΕΒΑΣΤΟΥ. Bust of **Octavia** r. *B.M.C.* 119-121 .. F 50/-

2755   2756

2756 — ℞. ΠΟΠΠΑΙΑ ΣΕΒΑΣΤΗ. Bust of **Poppaea** r. *B.M.C.* 122 *fair* 22/6; F 50/-; VF £5

2757 — ℞. ΔΙΟΣ ΟΛΥΜΠΙΟΥ. Head of Zeus Olympius r. *B.M.C.* 126-8 .. F 25/-

2758 — ℞. ΗΡΑ ΑΡΓΕΙΑ. Bust of Hera r. *B.M.C.* 135 .. .. .. VF/F 35/-

2759 — ℞. ΔΗΜΗΤΕΡ. Demeter standing l., holding corn-ears and sceptre. *B.M.C.* 138 F 25/-

2760 — ℞. ΑΠΟΛΛΩΝ ΑΚΤΙΟΣ. Bust of Apollo r., trident on shoulder. *B.M.C.* 144 F 27/6

2761 — ℞. ΔΙΚΑΙΟΣΥΝΗ. Dikaiosyne standing l., holding scales. *B.M.C.* 145/6 F 30/-

2762 — ℞. ΙΡΗΝΗ. Eirene r., holding caduceus and helmet. *B.M.C.* 148 F 25/-

2763 **Nero.** *Tet.* ℞. ΟΜΟΝΟΙΑ. Homonoia seated l., holding patera. *B.M.C.* 150　F　25/–

2764 — ℞. ΑΥΤΟΚΡΑ. Bust of Sarapis, wearing modius, r. *B.M.C.* 157　..　VF　50/–

2765 — ℞. ΑΥΤΟΚΡΑ. Bust of Alexandria, wearing elephant-skin head-dress, r. *B.M.C.*
163　　..　　..　　..　　..　　..　　..　　..　　F　30/–

2766 — ℞. ΝΕΟ . ΑΓΑΘ . ΔΑΙΜ. Agathodaemon serpent r. *B.M.C.* 174　..　F　35/–

2767 **Galba.** *Tet.* ℞. ΡΩΜΗ. Bust of Roma r. *B.M.C.* 198　..　.. *fair*　30/–

2768 **Otho.** *Tet.* ℞. ΕΛΕΥΘΕΡΙΑ. Eleutheria stg. l. against column. *B.M.C.* 208　F　£5

2768A **Vitellius.** *Tet.* ℞. Nike advancing l. *B.M.C.* 218　..　..　F　75/–

2769 **Vespasian.** *Tet.* ℞. Nike l., with wreath and palm. *B.M.C.* 236　..　F　35/–

2770 — ℞. ΑΛΕΞΑΝΔΡΕΙΑ. Alexandria standing l. *B.M.C.* 242　..　..　F　37/6

2771 Æ 25. ℞. Bust of Isis r. *B.M.C.* 264　..　..　..　..　F　37/6

2772 Æ 21. ℞. Hawk r., crowned with skhent. *B.M.C.* 275　..　.. *fair*　20/–

2772A **Titus.** *Tet.* ℞. ΟΜΟΝΟΙΑ. Homonoia seated l. *B.M.C.* 279　..　F　50/–

2773 **Domitian.** Æ 26. ℞. ΕΤΟΥΣ ΤΡΙΤΟΥ. Bust of Sarapis r. *B.M.C.* 300
fair　F　20/–

2774 Æ 19. ℞. Griffin seated r., fore-paw on wheel. *B.M.C.* 324　..　..　F　40/–

2775 Æ 17. ℞. Hawk standing r. *B.M.C.* 332 ..　..　..　.. *fair*　21/–

2776 Æ 35. ℞. Emperor in biga of centaurs r. *B.M.C.* 338　..　.. *fair*/F　50/–

2777 **Nerva.** *Tet.* ℞. Bust of Sarapis r. *B.M.C.* 351　..　..　F　45/–

2778 **Trajan.** *Tet.* ℞. Bust of Zeus r. *B.M.C.* 356　..　..　..　F　30/–

2779 — ℞. Dikaiosyne l., with scales and cornucopiae. *B.M.C.* 362　..　F　30/–

2780 — ℞. Bust of Nilus r. *B.M.C.* 378　..　..　..　F　30/–

2781 Æ 35. ℞. Zeus seated l., holding sceptre and thunderbolt: before him, eagle. *B.M.C*
399　..　..　..　..　..　..　..　..　F　75/–

2782 Æ 34. ℞. Elpis l., holding flower. *B.M.C.* 435　..　..　..　F　70/–

2783 Æ 35. ℞. Triumphal arch, on which emperor in chariot, trophies, etc. *B.M.C.*
545　　..　　..　　..　　..　　..　　..　R, F　£6

2784 Æ 34. ℞. Modius, containing corn, in biga of oxen r. *B.M.C.* 553　F/*fair*　60/–

2785 **Hadrian.** *Tet.* ℞. Head of Zeus Ammon r. *B.M.C.* 572　..　.. *fair*　15/–

2786 — ℞. Demeter standing l., with corn-ears and torch. *B.M.C.* 579　*good* F　37/6

2787 — ℞. Bust of Helios, radiate, r. *B.M.C.* 584　..　..　*good* F　45/–

2788 — ℞. Pronoia standing l., holding Phoenix and sceptre. *B.M.C.* 600　F/*fair*　18/6

2789 — ℞. Tyche standing l., with rudder and cornucopiae. *B.M.C.* 604　*fair*/F　15/–

2790 — ℞. Bust of Sarapis r., wearing modius. *B.M.C.* 609　..　..　F　27/6

2791 — ℞. Sarapis seated l., Cerberus before　*B.M.C.* 617　..　.. *nearly* VF　45/–

2792 — ℞. Nilus seated l., holding reed and cornucopiae. *B.M.C.* 649.　**Plate VIII**
fair/F　20/–; *good* VF　75/–

2793 Æ 34. ℞. Zeus recumbent l.　*B.M.C.* 675　..　..　.. F/*fair*　45/–

2794 Æ 33. ℞. The Dioskuri standing facing, heads turned inwards, each holding
spear and sword. *B.M.C.* 708　..　..　..　.. *fair*/F　52/6

2795 Æ 33. ℞. Tyche reclining on couch l. *B.M.C.* 730　..　.. *fair*　32/6

2796 Æ 32. ℞. Isis Pharia standing r., holding with hands and l. foot inflated sail. *B.M.C.*
754　　..　　..　　..　　..　　..　　..　　.. *fair*/F　37/6

2797 Æ 33. ℞. Type as preceding; to r., Pharos. *B.M.C.* 755　.. *fair*/F　40/–

2798 Æ 33. ℞. Harpokrates standing l., r. hand to mouth, l. holding club. *B.M.C.* 767
R, *good* F　£6

2799 Æ 33. ℞. Nilus reclining l., holding cornucopiae and reed, and with l. hand on
crocodile r. *B.M.C.* 783/5　..　..　..　..　..　.. F/*fair*　50/–

2800 Æ 34. ℞. Similar, but elephant under l. arm, no crocodile. *B.M.C.* 786
nearly F　50/–

2801 Æ 32. ℞. Nilus seated l. on rocks, otherwise as No. 2799. *B.M.C.* 788
good F　£6

2802 Æ 24. ℞. Bull r. *B.M.C.* 814　..　..　..　..　.. F　47/6

2803 Æ 18. ℞. Dolphin twisted around anchor. *B.M.C.* 817 *var.*　.. *fair*/F　27/6

2804 Æ 14. ℞. Rhinoceros r. *B.M.C.* 835　..　..　..　*fair*/F　25/–

2805 Æ 34. ℞. Emperor in quadriga of elephants r. *B.M.C.* 861　.. F/*fair*　65/–

2806 Æ 32. ℞. Statue of Nilus seated l. within tetrastyle temple. *B.M.C.* 881　*fair*　30/–

2807 Æ 14. ℞. Headdress of Isis. *B.M.C.* 901　..　..　..　.. F　22/6

2808 **Sabina.** *Tet.* ℞. Sabina as Demeter seated l. *B.M.C.* 916 .. .. F 80/-
2809 **Aelius.** Æ 34. ℞. Homonoia seated l. *B.M.C.* 923 .. .. .. *fair* 57/6
2809A **Antinous.** Æ 34. ℞. Antinous as Hermes on horseback r. *B.M.C.* 925.
RRR, F £42
2810 **Antoninus Pius.** *Tet.* Dikaiosyne seated l., with scales and cornucopiae. *B.M.C.*
955 .. .. VF 60/-
2811 — ℞. Elpis l., holding flower. *B.M.C.* 962 .. .. *fair* 14/-
2812 — ℞. Phoenix (Numidian crane), radiate, r. *B.M.C.* 1004 .. *good* F 50/-
2813 Æ 31. ℞. Kybele seated l. between lions, holding patera. *B.M.C.* 1042
fair/F 45/-
2814 Æ 34. ℞. Herakles r., carrying the Erymanthian boar on his shoulders. *B.M.C.*
1046 .. .. R, F £6
2815 Æ 34. ℞. Bust of Selene r., on crescent moon; below, crab. *B.M.C.* 1082
fair 35/-
2816 Æ 33. ℞. Bust of Zeus Sarapis, wearing modius, l. *B.M.C.* 1094 .. F 80/-
2817 Æ 32. ℞ Sarapis seated l. within distyle shrine. *B.M.C.* 1193 *fair*/F 35/-

2817A Æ 34. Isis seated l. before altar, with Harpokrates on her lap about to be suckled
F 75/-
2817B *Tet.* ℞. Veiled bust of **Faustina I** r. *B.M.C.* 1213 .. .. RR, *fair* 60/-
2818 **M. Aurelius.** *Tet.* ℞. Tyche seated l., sacrificing at altar and holding sceptre.
B.M.C.—; *Feuardent* 2004 .. .. VF 75/-
2819 Æ 19. ℞. Serpent, wearing horned-disk headdress, l. *B.M.C.* 1250 .. *fair* 20/-
2820 **Faustina II.** *Tet.* ℞. Asklepios stg. facing, head r., holding patera over altar and
snake-encircled staff. *B.M.C.* 1315 .. .. VF 80/-
2821 **L. Verus.** Æ 34. ℞. Semasia on horseback l., holding whip. *B M.C.* 1381
F £8
2822 **Commodus.** *Tet.* ℞. Head of Zeus, laur., r. *B.M.C.* 1394 .. .. F 20/-
2823 — ℞. Zeus seated l., holds thunderbolt and sceptre. *B.M.C.* 1400 .. F 20/-
2824 — ℞. Bust of Selene l.; in front, large crescent. *B.M.C.* 1404 .. .. F 25/-
2825 — ℞. Sarapis seated l. *B.M.C.* 1421 .. .. F 22/6
2826 — ℞. Emperor in quadriga r. *B.M.C.* 1429 .. .. VF 65/-
2827 **Pertinax.** *Tet.* ℞. Zeus seated l. *B.M.C.* 1450 .. RRR, *fair* £8
2828 **Septimius Severus.** *Tet.* ℞. Trophy. *B.M.C.* 1463 .. .. F 50/-
2829 **Julia Domna.** *Tet.* ℞. Dikaiosyne standing l., with scales and cornucopiae.
B.M.C. 1466 .. .. F 75/-
2829A **Geta.** *Tet.* ℞. ΝΕΙΚΗ ΚΑΙ ΒΡΕΤΑΝ. Nike advancing l. *B.M.C.* 1481. *An*
interesting type referring to victories in Britain .. .. F £12
2830 **Elagabalus.** *Tet.* ℞. Zeus standing l., with patera and sceptre. *B.M.C.* 1486
F 45/-
2831 — ℞. Athena seated l. *B.M.C.* 1493 .. .. VF 85/-
2832 **Julia Paula.** *Tet.* ℞. Helmeted bust of Athena r. *B.M.C.* 1526 *good* F £6
2832A **Aquilia Severa.** *Tet.* ℞. Nike seated l. *B.M.C.* 1545 .. .. F £5
2833 **Annia Faustina.** *Tet.* ℞. Ares standing l., holding spear and sword. *B.M.C.*
1551 .. .. F £8
2834 **Julia Soaemias.** *Tet.* ℞. Homonoia standing l., holding double cornucopiae.
B.M.C. 1560 .. .. F £5
2834A **Julia Maesa.** *Tet.* ℞. Dikaiosyne stg. l. *B.M.C.* 1569 .. .. F 70/-

2835 **Severus Alexander**, *as Caesar. Tet.* ℞. Sarapis standing facing, head r. *B.M.C.* 1585 ..   ..   R, F 65/-

2836 *As Augustus. Tet.* ℞. Bust of Zeus r. *B.M.C.* 1591 ..   ..   ..   F 45/-

2837 — ℞. Rad. bust of Helios r. *B.M.C.* 1599..   ..   ..   F 47/6

2838 — ℞. Bust of Athena r. *B.M.C.* 1601/2 ..   ..   ..   *good* F 60/-

2839 — ℞. Jugate busts of Sarapis and Isis r. *B.M.C.* 1666 ..   ..   F 65/-

2840 — ℞. Alexandria l., holding corn-ears and vexillum. *B.M.C.* 1687   *good* F 60/-

2841 **Julia Mamaea.** *Tet.* ℞. Homonoia l., as on No. 2834. *B.M.C.* 1737 F 50/-

2842 **Maximinus I.** *Tet.* ℞. Bust of Hermanubis r. *B.M.C.* 1798..   ..   F 45/-

2843 — ℞. Nilus reclining l. on hippopotamus. *B.M.C.* 1802..   ..   F 45/-

2844 — ℞. Trophy between captives. *B.M.C.* 1809 ..   ..   ..   F 40/-

2844A **Maximus.** *Tet.* ℞. Nilus reclining l., as 2843. *B.M.C.* 1821   ..   F 80/-

2844B **Gordian I.** *Tet.* ℞. Zeus seated l.; at feet, eagle. *B.M.C.* 1824 ..   F £10

2844C **Gordian II.** *Tet.* ℞. Nike seated l. *B.M.C.* 1833 ..   ..   ..   F £10

2844D **Balbinus.** *Tet.* ℞. Tyche stg. l. *B.M.C.* 1845 ..   ..   ..   F £10

2844E **Pupienus.** *Tet.* ℞. Nike advancing l. *B.M.C.* 1837 ..   ..   F £12

2845 **Gordian III.** *Tet.* ℞. Zeus seated l., with patera and sceptre; at feet, eagle. *B.M.C.* 1857 ..   ..   F 35/-

2846 — ℞. Dikaiosyne l., with scales and cornucopiae. *B.M.C.* 1869   ..   F 25/-

2847 — ℞. Nike seated l., with wreath and palm *B.M.C.* 1885   ..   ..   F 25/-

2848 — ℞. Tyche l., with rudder and cornucopiae. *B.M.C.* 1889   ..   ..   F 25/-

2849 — ℞. Nilus reclining l. *B.M.C.* 1902 ..   ..   ..   *good* F 40/-

2850 — ℞. Eagle with wreath in beak. *B.M.C.* 1907 ..   ..   VF 40/-

2851 — ℞. Eagle facing, holding wreath in claws. *B.M.C.* 1912   ..   F 20/-

2852 **Tranquillina.** *Tet.* ℞. Homonoia l., as on No. 2834. *B.M.C.* 1927 R, F £5

2853 **Philip I.** *Tet* ℞. Nike r., placing shield on column. *B.M.C.* 1971 *good* F 30/-

2854 — ℞. Bust of Isis l. *B.M.C.* 1983 ..   ..   F 32/6

2855 — ℞. Alexandria standing l. *B.M.C.* 1988   ..   ..   ..   VF 42/6

2856 — ℞. Eagle, wings closed, wreath in beak. *B.M.C.* 1995   ..   ·.   VF 37/6

2857 Æ 33. ℞. Homonoia stdg. l., holding double cornucopiae. *Not in B.M.C.*   R, F £7

The bronze issues of the Alexandrian mint almost cease about the time of Caracalla, but Philip I struck a limited number, possibly as part of his celebrations of the millennium of Rome in 248.

2858 **Otacilia Severa.** *Tet.* ℞. Athena l., holding Nike. *B.M.C.* 2008 ..   F 50/-

2859 — ℞. Eusebeia l., sacrificing at altar. *B.M.C.* 2015 ..   ..   ..   VF 90/-

2860 **Philip II.** *Tet.* ℞. Eagle, wings closed, wreath in beak. *B.M.C.* 2051   *good* F 45/-

2861 — ℞. Homonoia l., as on No. 2857. *B.M.C.* 2058   ..   *good* F 50/-

2862 **Trajan Decius.** *Tet.* ℞. Nike r., with wreath and palm. *B.M.C.* 2076 ..   F 30/-

2863 — ℞. Eagle, wings closed, wreath in beak. *B.M.C.* 2083   ..   VF 50/-

2863A **Etruscilla.** *Tet.* ℞. Eusebeia sacrificing over altar. *B.M.C.* 2089 ..   F 50/-

2863B **Trebonianus Gallus.** *Tet.* ℞. Dikaiosyne seated l. *B.M.C.* 2102   ..   F 45/-

2863C **Volusian.** *Tet.* ℞. Tyche stg. l. *B.M.C.* 2112 ..   ..   ..   F 55/-

2863D **Aemilian.** *Tet.* ℞. Nike advancing r. *B.M.C.* 2117 ..   ..   F £5

2864 **Valerian.** *Tet.* ℞. Type as 2863. *B.M.C.* 2145-9   ..   ..   VF 37/6

2865 **Gallienus.** *Tet.* ℞. Eirene l., with olive-branch and sceptre. *B.M.C.* 2177   VF 35/-

2866 — ℞. Homonoia seated l. *B.M.C.* 2190 ..   ..   VF 37/6

2867 — ℞. Nike, with wreath and palm. *B.M.C.* 2196..   ..   ..   VF 35/-

2868 — ℞. Eagle l., wings closed and wreath in beak. *B.M.C.* 2227 ..   ..   VF 30/-

2869 — ℞. ΔΕΚΑ ΕΤΗΡΙ CΚV PIOV in wreath. *B.M.C.* 2240 ..   ..   R, F/VF 50/-

2870 **Salonina.** *Tet* ℞. Eirene l., with branch and sceptre. *B.M.C.* 2250 VF 37/6

2871 — ℞. Elpis l., holding flower. *B.M.C.* 2252/3 ..   ..   *good* VF 45/-

2872 — ℞. Tyche stdg. l., with rudder and cornucopiae. *B.M.C.* 2263   *good* VF 45/-

2873 — ℞. Tyche reclining l. *B.M.C.* 2266 ..   ..   VF 40/-

2874 **Saloninus Caesar.** *Tet.* ℞. Eagle l., wings closed and wreath in beak. *B.M.C.* 2293/7 .. .. VF 85/–

2875 **Macrianus.** *Tet.* ℞. Eagle l. *B.M.C.* 2301 .. VF/*good* F £10

2875A **Quietus.** *Tet.* ℞. Homonoia stg. l. *B.M.C.* 2302 .. .. *good* F/VF £10

2876 **Claudius II Gothicus.** *Tet.* ℞. Dikaiosyne l. *B.M.C.* 2316 .. .. F 12/6

2877 — ℞. Nike l., with wreath and palm. *B.M.C.* 2323 .. .. VF 25/–

2878 — ℞. Bust of Anubis r.; in front, caduceus and palm. *B.M.C.* 2327 .. VF 35/–

2879 — ℞. Eagle r., wings closed and wreath in beak. *B.M.C.* 2332 *good* VF 25/–

2880 **Quintillus.** *Tet.* ℞. As preceding. *B.M.C.* 2338 .. .. VF 65/–

2881 **Aurelian.** *Tet.* ℞. Eirene l., with olive-branch and sceptre. *B.M.C.* 2346 VF 25/–

2882 — ℞. Eagle l., wings open and wreath in beak. *B.M.C.* 2360 .. .. VF 21/–

2883 **Severina.** *Tet.* ℞. Eagle as last. *B.M.C.* 2380.. .. .. VF 40/–

2884 **Aurelian and Vabalathus.** *Tet.* Bust of Aurelian r. ℞. Bust of Vabalathus r. *B.M.C.* 2384 .. .. *fair* 12/6; F/VF 35/–

2884A **Zenobia,** Queen of Palmyra and mother of Vabalathus. ℞. Homonoia stg. l. *B.M.C.* 2400 .. .. F £40

2885 **Tacitus.** *Tet.* ℞. Elpis l. *B.M.C.* 2404 .. .. .. VF 45/–

2886 **Probus.** *Tet.* ℞. Athena seated l., holding Nike. *B.M.C.* 2409 .. VF 20/–

2887 — ℞. Dikaiosyne l. *B.M.C.* 2412 .. .. VF 17/6

2888 — ℞. Eirene l., with branch and sceptre. *B.M.C.* 2415 .. .. VF 17/6

2889 — ℞. Elpis l., holding flower. *B.M.C.* 2417 .. .. .. VF 17/6

2890 — ℞. Eagle facing, wings open. *B.M.C.* 2434 .. .. .. VF 15/–

2891 **Carus.** *Tet.* ℞. Dikaiosyne l. *B.M.C.* 2441 .. .. .. VF 35/–

2892 — (After death). *Tet.* ℞. ΑΦΙΕΡШϹΙϹ. Flaming altar. *B.M.C.* 2446 .. VF 40/–

2893 **Carinus.** *Tet.* ℞. Tyche l. with rudder and cornucopiae. *B.M.C.* 2448 VF 25/–

2894 — ℞. Elpis l., holding flower. *B.M.C.* 2453/4 .. .. .. VF 25/–

2895 — ℞. Eagle l., wings closed and wreath in beak. *B.M.C.* 2459 .. .. VF 21/–

2896 **Numerian.** *Tet.* ℞. Eagle between standards. *B.M.C.* 2463 .. VF 30/–

2897 — ℞. Athena seated l., holding Nike. *B.M.C.* 2464 .. .. VF 35/–

2898 — ℞ Eirene l., with branch and sceptre. *B.M.C.* 2466 .. .. VF 30/–

2899 — ℞. Nike r., with wreath and palm. *B.M.C.* 2467/9 .. .. VF 30/–

2900 **Diocletian.** *Tet.* ℞. Elpis l., with flower. *B.M.C.* 2503 .. .. VF 15/–

2901 — ℞. Eusebeia l., sacrificing. *B.M.C.* 2510 .. .. .. VF 20/–

2901A **Domitius Domitianus.** *Tet.* ℞. Nike stg. l. *B.M.C.* 2626 F £17/10/–

2902 **Maximianus I.** *Tet.* ℞. Elpis l., with flower. *B.M.C.* 2556 .. VF 15/–

2903 — ℞. Alexandria l., holding head of Sarapis. *B.M.C.* 2591 .. .. VF 20/–

2904 **Constantius I.** *Tet.* ℞. Elpis l., with flower. *B.M.C.* 2604 .. .. VF 35/–

2905 — ℞. Nike r., with wreath and palm. *B.M.C.* 2610 .. .. VF 40/–

2906 **Galerius.** *Tet.* ℞. Elpis l., with flower. *B.M.C.* 2615 .. .. VF 35/–

2907 — ℞. Athena seated l., holding Nike. *Not in B.M.C.* .. .. VF 45/–

2908 — ℞. Head of Zeus r. *Not in B.M.C.* .. .. .. R, VF 65/–

THE NOMES OF EGYPT.

2909 **Menelaïte Nome.** *Antoninus Pius.* Æ 32. Head of Antoninus, laur., r. ℞. MEN-ΕΛΑΕΙΤ. Harpokrates, with crocodile body, l., holding cornucopiae: in ex., LH. *B.M.C.* 35
RR, M/*fair* £7/10/-

2909A **Prosopite Nome.** *Hadrian.* Æ 20. Head of Hadrian, laur., r. ℞. ΠΡΟCⲰ. Harpokrates stg. l., holding club; in field, LIA. *B.M.C.* 51 .. .. *RR,* M/*fair* £6

2910 **Saïte Nome.** *Antoninus Pius.* Æ 34. Head of Antoninus, laur., r. ℞. CAEI-THC. Athena l., holding owl: in field, LH. *B.M.C.* 55 *var.* .. *RRR,* F £15

2911 **Upper Sebennyte Nome.** *Antoninus Pius.* Æ 33. Head of Antoninus, laur., r. ℞. CEBENNYTHC. Ares standing l., with spear and parazonium; in field, LH. *B.M.C.* 60
RR, F £15

2912 **Herakleopolite Nome.** *Trajan.* Æ 35. Head of Trajan, laur., r. ℞. HPAK-ΛΕΟΠΟΛΕΙΤΗC. Herakles-Harpokrates standing l., holding club: in field, LIΓ. *B.M.C.* 77 *var.* .. .. *RR,* M/*fair* £7/10/-

2912A *Hadrian.* Æ 14. His laur. hd. r. ℞. Griffin r.; in ex., HPA; in field, LIA. *B.M.C.* 80 .. .. *RR,* F £10

2913 **Oxyrynchite Nome.** *Antoninus Pius.* Æ 34. Head of Antoninus, laur., r. ℞. ΟΞVΡVΝΧΙΤΗC. Athena standing l., holding double-axe and figure of Nike; in field, LH. *B.M.C.* 90 .. .. *RR,* *fair* £9

CYRENAICA.

2914 **CYRENE.** *c.* 525-480 B.C. Æ *Asiatic drachm.* Silphium fruit. ℞. Similar to *obv.* but in square incuse. *B.M.C.* 35 .. .. VF £32/10/-

2915 — — Two fruits set base to base, four pellets above and below. ℞. Lion's mask, facing. *B.M.C.* 38 .. .. VF £40

2916 *c.* 480-435 B.C. Æ *Attic tetradrachm.* Silphium plant. ℞. KVPA. Head of Zeus Ammon r. *B.M.C.* 42 .. .. VF £200

2917 Æ *Asiatic hemidrachm.* Similar type, but without legend. *B.M.C.* 57 .. F £8

2918 375-308 B.C. N *stater.* KVPANAION. Quadriga driven by Nike r. ℞. ΠΟΛΙΑΝΘΕΥΣ. Zeus Ammon standing l., hand extended over thymiaterion. *B.M.C.,* pl. xiv, 4
RR, F £70

2919 N *hemidrachm.* Triple silphium plant. ℞. XAIPI. Head of Athena l. *B.M.C.* 135 *var.* .. .. *RRR,* F £40

2920 N *Attic tenth.* KYΔ downwards behind head of Carneius r. ℞. Female head (? Cyrene) r., hair rolled. *B.M.C.* 151 .. .. F £20

2921 Æ *Asiatic drachm.* Head of Carneius l. ℞. Silphium plant. *B.M.C.* 167-8
VF £15

2922 Before 308 B.C. Æ 24. Head of Carneius, horned, r. ℞. Silphium plant. *B.M.C.* 174-6 .. .. VF £5

2923 Æ 22. Head of Apollo r. ℞ as preceding. *B.M.C.* 183-6 .. .. F 40/-

2924 Æ 17. Horse prancing r. ℞. Six-spoked wheel seen in perspective. *B.M.C.* 189 .. .. F 45/-

2925 Æ 16. Head of Carneius r. ℞. Silphium plant. *B.M.C.* 199-201 .. *fair* 30/-

2926 Æ 10. Head of Libya r. ℞. Gazelle r. *B.M.C.* 208-9 .. .. *fair* 25/-

2927 **Magas,** Governor, 308-277 B.C. N *obol.* Head of Ammon r., with short hair. ℞. Female head r., hair rolled. *B.M.C.* 215 .. .. *R,* VF £30

2928 Æ *didrachm.* Head of Apollo Carneius r. ℞. KYPA. Silphium plant. *B.M.C.* 228-36 .. .. *good* F/F £11; *good* VF £30

2929 Æ 18. Head of Ammon r. ℞. KYPAI. Palm tree; to r., silphium. *B.M.C.* 316
F/VF 50/-

2930 Æ 16. Head of Apollo Myrtous r. ℞. ΚΥΡΑ. Lyre. *B.M.C.* 319 .. F 30/-
2931 Æ 14. *Obv.* as preceding. ℞. ΚΥ. Horse prancing r.: above, star; below, crab. *B.M.C.* 344 .. .. F 20/-
2932 **" Koinon " Issue.** *c.* 250 B.C. Æ 25. Head of Zeus Ammon r. ℞. ΚΟΙΝΟΝ. Silphium plant. *B.M.C.* 23 .. .. F 37/6; VF 85/-
2933 **Regal Issues. Magas in revolt.** 277-261 B.C. (?). Æ 19. Head of Ptolemy I r. ℞. Winged thunderbolt. *B.M.C.* 14 .. .. F 27/6
2934 Æ 18. *Obv.* as preceding. ℞. Eagle, wings open, standing l. *B.M.C.* 19-24
F 25/-
2935 Æ 17. *Obv.* as preceding. ℞. Forepart of winged horse l. *B.M.C.* 27 F 32/6
2936 Æ 12. *Obv.* as preceding. ℞. Horse galloping l. *B.M.C.* 28 .. .. F 27/6
2937 **Ptolemy IV.** 222-204 B.C. Æ 13. *Obv.* as preceding. ℞. Head of Libya r. *B.M.C.* 45-6 .. .. F 22/6
2938 Æ 22. Types as preceding. *B.M.C.* 47 .. .. nearly F 30/-
2939 **Ptolemy V.** 204-181 B.C. Æ 15. Types as preceding. *B.M.C.* 64
almost VF 50/-
2940 **Ptolemy VII-Ptolemy Apion.** *c.* 140-96 B.C. Æ 11. Turreted female bust r. ℞. Caps of the Dioskuri. *B.M.C.*—. *First published in " Num. Chron.," 6th Series, Vol. VI,* 1944, pp. 105-113 .. .. fair 30/-
2941 **BARCE.** *c.* 480-435 B.C. Æ *tetradrachm.* Silphium plant. ℞. Head of Zeus Ammon r.; around, ΒΑΡΚ; all within incuse square. *B.M.C.* 8 .. .. F £50
2942 Æ *drachm. Obv.* as preceding. ℞. as preceding, but not in incuse square. *Cf. B.M.C.* 10-16 .. .. F £15

2942A 435-308 B.C. Æ *tetradrachm.* ΒΑΡΚΑΙ down each side of siliphium plant. ℞. ΑΚΕΣΙΟΣ. Facing head of Ammon. *B.M.C.* 32 .. .. nearly VF £250
2943 **EUHESPERIDES** (Benghazi). Late 4th Cent. B.C. Æ 17. Head of nymph r. ℞. Silphium plant. *B.M.C.* 8-10 .. .. F 60/-
2944 **CYRENAICA UNDER THE ROMANS :** Crassus. Æ 16. ΚΡΑ. Head of Libya r. ℞. Silphium plant. *B.M.C.* 26 .. .. F 50/-
2945 Scato. Æ 30. CAESAR TR POT AGRIPPA. Bare heads of Augustus and Agrippa face to face. ℞. SCATO PRO COS in laurel wreath. *B.M.C.* 37 .. .. R, fair/F £5
2946 Palikanus. Æ 28. IMP AVG TR POT in laurel wreath. ℞. *Sella castrensis* (magistrate's chair). *B.M.C.* 44-8 .. .. fair 60/-

LIBYA.

2946A 2nd cent. B.C. Æ *didrachm.* Hd. of Herakles l. ℞. ΛΙΒΥΩΝ in ex. Lion walking r., Punic letters above. *Müller* 349 .. .. RR, fair £20
2946B Æ 24. Similar but *rev.* type, bull butting r. *Müller* 354 .. RR, fair 75/-

SYRTICA.

2946C **Gergis** (Zarzis). *Augustus.* Æ 35. His hd. r., lituus before. ℞. PERM L. VOLVSI PRO COS GERG. Hd. of Athena r.; before, crab. *Müller* 65 .. .. RRR, fair £10
2947 **Leptis Magna** (Lebda). 146-27 B.C. Æ 19. Head of young Dionysos l. ℞. Phoenician inscr.: club: all within wreath. *Müller* 2 .. .. F 45/-
2948 *Augustus.* Æ 22. Bare head of Augustus r. ℞. Phoenician inscr.: peacock walking r., head l.: above, inverted, eagle r. *Müller* 18 .. .. R, fair 85/-
2949 **Oea** (Tripoli). *Livia.* Æ 25. Bust of Livia r. ℞. Bust of Athena, helmeted, l. before, Phoenician inscr. *Müller* 34 *Illustrated on p.* 201 .. .. R, F £12/10/-

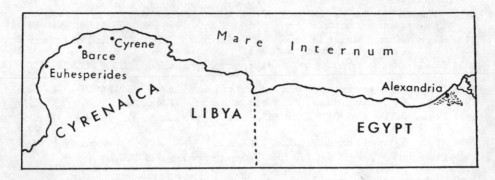

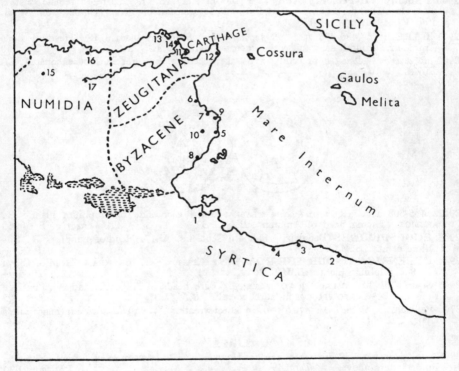

Syrtica	6 Hadrumetum	12 Clypea
1 Gergis	7 Leptis Minor	13 Hippo Diarrhytus
2 Leptis Magna	8 Thaena	14 Utica
3 Oea	9 Thapsus	*Numidia*
4 Sabrata	10 Thysdrus	15 Cirta
Byzacene	*Zeugitana*	16 Hippo Regius
5 Achulla	11 Carthage	17 Tipasa

2949   2950

2950 **Oea.** *Tiberius.* Æ 29. TI CAESAR AVGVSTVS. Bare head of Tiberius, l., between eagle and laurel-branch. ℞. Phoenician inscr.: head of Apollo r.: in front, lyre: all within laurel-wreath. *Müller 37* .. .. F £10

2951 **Sabrata.** *Augustus.* Æ 29. CAESAR. His bare head r.; in front, lituus; all within laurel-wreath. ℞. Phoenician legend. Head of bearded Herakles, laur., r. *Müller 54*
R, fair   75/–

BYZACENE.

2952 **Achulla.** *Augustus.* Æ 29. AVG . PONT . MAX . C . L. Bare head of Augustus l., between small heads of Caius and Lucius Caesars. ℞. ACHVLLA P . QVINCTILI . VARI. Head of Quinctilius Varus r. *Müller 7* .. .. .. R, fair £6

2953 **Hadrumetum** (Souse). 1st Cent. B.C. Æ 18. Head of Poseidon r., trident over shoulder. ℞. Radiate head of Helios l. *Müller 22* .. .. R, F 60/–

2953A **Leptis Minor** (Lamta). *Tiberius.* Æ 30. His hd. r. ℞. ΛΕΠΤΙC. Bust of Mercury l., B below. *Müller 18.* .. .. R, fair £5

2954 **Thaena.** *Augustus.* Æ 30. CAESAR DIVI F. His bare head r. ℞. Phoenician legend. Dr. bust of Astarte r. wearing high head-dress. *Müller 4* R, fair £5

2955 **Thapsus** (Ras Dimas). *Tiberius.* Æ 28. Roman legend. His bare head r. ℞. THAPSVM IVN . AVG. Veiled head of Livia l. *Müller 12* .. .. F £10

2955A **Thysdrus** (el Djem). Time of Augustus. Æ 23. Veiled hd. of Astarte r., sceptre behind. ℞. Punic inscription. Lyre. *Müller 34* .. .. RR, fair 65/–

ZEUGITANA.

2956 **Carthage** (near Tunis). 410-310 B.C. Siculo-Punic. Æ *tetradrachm.* Head of Persephone, l., as on Syracusan coins of Euainetos, wearing corn-wreath, ear-ring and necklace; around, four dolphins. ℞. Horse's head l.: behind, palm-tree; below, Phoenician legend. *Müller 14* .. .. EF £200

2957 Æ *tetradrachm.* Head of young Herakles r., wearing lion-skin, as on coins of Alexander the Great. ℞. Similar to preceding. *Müller 8* .. .. .. good VF £70

2958 Æ *tetradrachm,* probably struck at Heraclea Minoa. *Obv.* Similar to No. 2956. ℞. Quadriga galloping l.: above, Nike flying r., crowning charioteer. *B.M.C. 18*
good F £70

See also Siculo-Punic on page 59.

2959 N *trihemiobol.* Palm-tree. ℞. Horse's head r.; in front, ·.· . *Müller 82* VF £40

2960 340-242 B.C. N *stater.* Head of Persephone l. wreathed with corn and wearing necklace; head of good style and in high relief. ℞. Free horse r., ·.· before front feet. *Müller 45.* **Plate VIII** .. .. R, VF £125

2961 Æ 24. Similar. ℞. Horse r., looking back; palm in background. *Müller 220*
good F 55/–

2962 241-146 B.C. *Electrum stater.* Head of Persephone l. ℞. Horse standing r.
Müller 48 .. .. *good* VF £45

2963 Æ *didrachm.* Head of Persephone l. ℞. Horse standing r., looking back, in front
of palm-tree. *Müller* 107.. .. .. *good* F £20

2964 Æ *drachm.* Similar. ℞. Horse standing r., flaming disc above. *M.* 87
F £6; *good* VF £20

2965 — Another, without the flaming disc. *M.* 84 .. .. VF £14

2966 Æ *hemidrachm.* Similar. *M.* 86 .. .. .. *nearly* VF/*good* F £12

2967 Æ 31. Head of Persephone l., wearing wreath of corn. ℞. Horse standing r.: in
background, palm-tree: below horse, Phoenician letter in broken circle. *M.* 154
almost VF £8

2968 Æ 28. *Obv.* as preceding. ℞. Horse walking r. *M.* 244 .. .. *fair* 32/6

2969 Æ 25. *Obv.* as preceding. ℞. Horse standing r., looking back. *M.* 200
good F 45/-

2970 Æ 20. Similar types. *M.* 204 .. .. VF 50/-

2971 Æ 19. *Obv.* as preceding. ℞. Horse's head r.; in front, Phoenician letter. *M.* 266
VF 45/-

2972 Æ 16. *Obv.* as preceding. ℞. Horse standing r.: in background, palm-tree. *M.* 167
good F 35/-

2974 *Tiberius.* Æ 23. Head of Tiberius r. ℞. Livia seated r.: in field, P P D D: around,
magistrate's name. *M.* 328 .. .. R, F 70/-

2974A **Clypea.** (Kelibia). *Tiberius.* Æ 28. Bare hd. l. ℞. PERMISSV L. APRONI PROCOS
III . C . SEX . POM . CELSO. Ceres or Livia seated r., C P I in field. *M.* 332 *fair* 50/-

2974B **Hippo Diarrhytus** (Binsert). Time of Augustus. Æ 15. HIPPONE. Hd. of Ceres r.
℞. LIBERA. Hd. of Juno r. *M.* 375 .. .. F 50/-

2974C *Tiberius.* Æ 24. His hd. r. between lituus and simpulum. ℞. L. APRONIVS
HIPPONE LIBERA. Hd. of Drusus Junior r. *M.* 378 .. .. *fair* 60/-

2975 **Utica.** *Tiberius.* Æ 30. TI CAESAR DIVI AVG F AVG IMP VIII. Bare head of Tiberius
l. ℞. SEX TADIVS FAVSTVS IIV C VIBIO MARSO PR COS II. Livia seated r., holding patera
and sceptre: in field, M M and I V. *M.* 358 .. .. R, *good* F/*fair* 90/-

2976 Æ 30. *Obv.* as preceding. ℞. Type as preceding, but with DD and PP in field;
around, DR CAE Q PR T G RVFVS F C C VIB MARSO PR COS. *M.* 364 R, F £6

ISLANDS BETWEEN AFRICA AND SICILY.

2977 **Cossura** (Pantelleria). 2nd Cent. B.C. Æ 24. Female head r., wearing Egyptian head-
dress. ℞. Phoenician inscription within laurel-wreath. *Mayer* 13 *nearly* F/*good* F £5

2978 1st Cent. B.C. Æ 27. Similar, countermarked REG. ℞. COSSVRA and mon. within
laurel-wreath. *Hunter* 9 .. .. F £5

2979 **Gaulos** (Gozo). 1st Cent. B.C. Æ 18. Head of Astarte r.; in front, V; beneath, large
crescent. ℞. ΓΑΥΛΤΩΝ. Warrior standing r. *Hunter* 1 .. .. .. *fair* 45/-

2980 **Melita** (Malta). 2nd-1st Cent. B.C. Æ 25. ΜΕΛΙΤΑΙΩΝ. Bust of Isis l.: in front, corn-ear
℞. Four-winged figure of Osiris, kneeling r. *Hunter* 19 .. .. .. *fair* 45/-

2980　　　　　　　　　　　　　　　　　2981

2981 Æ 21. Head of Herakles r. ℞. Three Phoenician letters below sacrificial cap, all in wreath. *Hunter 1* .. .. *fair* 37/6

2982 Æ 15. Veiled female head r. ℞. Similar. Ram's head r. *Hunter 8* .. F 45/-

2983 Æ 20. ΜΕΛΙΤΑΙΩΝ. Veiled female head l. ℞. C ARRVNTANVS BALBVS PRO PR. Curule chair. *Hunter 30 var.* .. .. *fair* 45/-

2984 Æ 20. Veiled female head l. ℞. ΜΕΛΙΤΑΙΩΝ. Tripod. *Hunter 27* .. *fair* 40/-

2984   2985

NUMIDIA.

2985 **KINGS : Micipsa and his brothers.** 148-118 B.C. Æ 26. Bearded head r. ℞. Horse galloping l.: below, pellet. *Müller 32* .. .. F/*fair* 30/-

2986 As preceding, but with Phoenician letters below head and horse. *Müller 23* F 50/-

2987 **Jugurtha.** 118-105 B.C. Æ *drachm.* Male head l. ℞. Elephant advancing r. *Mazard 75* .. .. *RRR*, F £35

2988 **Hiempsal II.** 105-62 B.C. Æ *quinarius.* Male head r. ℞. Horse prancing r.; beneath, two letters. *Mazard 79* .. .. *RR*, F £20

2989 Æ 20. Veiled head of Demeter r. ℞. Horse galloping l., letter beneath, wreath above. *Mazard 82* .. .. *RRR*, F £9

2990 **Juba I.** 60-46 B.C. Æ *denarius.* REX IVBA. Bearded bust r., with sceptre. ℞. Temple. *Müller 50* .. .. F 90/-; *nearly VF* £8

2991 Æ 28. Head of Zeus Ammon r. ℞. Elephant walking r. *Müller 56* F £6

2992 **CITIES: Cirta** (Constantine). Æ 26. Hd. of Tyche r., CRTN in Phoenician behind. ℞. Phoenician legend. Horse r. *Mazard 527* .. .. *RR*, *fair* 75/-

2992A **Hippo Regius** (near Bône) **and Tipasa.** Æ 19. Phoenician legend. Young male head l. ℞. Phoenician legend. Panther bounding r. *Müller 65* R, *fair* 50/-

2990   2996

MAURETANIA.
For map, see page 26.

2993 **KINGS: Juba II.** 25 B.C.-23 A.D. Æ *denarius.* REX IVBA. Young head of king, diademed, r. ℞. Cornucopiae and sceptre in saltire. *Müller 25* .. .. VF £6

2994 — Another. REX IVBA. King's head r., wearing the lion-skin of Herakles, club on shoulder. ℞. Capricorn r., cornucopiae over shoulder and globe between forefeet: below, RXXXXII. *Müller 59.* **Plate VIII** .. .. EF £15

2995 — Another. *Obv.* as No. 2993. ℞. Elephant r. *Müller 20* .. .. VF £8

2996 — Another, similar. ℞. Lion's skin on club between bow and arrow; date, R XXXXV on r. *Müller 36* .. .. VF £8

2997 Juba II and Cleopatra (*The latter was daughter of Mark Antony and Cleopatra of Egypt*). *Æ denarius. Obv.* as preceding. ℞. BACIΛICCA ΚΛΕΟΠΑΤΡΑ. Star and crescent. *Müller* 95 .. .. *nearly* EF £10

2998 — As preceding, but *rev.* type, crocodile l. *Müller* 92 .. .. .. VF £10

2999 — As preceding, but *rev.* type, head-dress of Isis and sistrum side by side. *Müller* 91 VF £7/10/-

3000 As preceding, but *rev.* type, head of Cleopatra l. *Müller* 87 .. .. R, VF £25

3001 Juba II and Ptolemy (*his son*). *Æ denarius. Obv.* as preceding. ℞. REX PTOLEMAEVS REGIS IVBAE F. Diademed head of Ptolemy l. *Mazard* 379 .. R, VF/EF £20

3002 Ptolemy. 23-40 A.D. *Æ denarius.* REX PTOLEMAEVS. As last *rev.* ℞. R . A . VII . Club within wreath. *Müller* 161 .. .. F £12/10/-

3002A CITIES: Babba: *Claudius.* Æ 20. His laur. hd. r. ℞. C C I B D D. Bull swimming in waves. *Müller* 260 .. .. *fair* 45/-

3003 Caesarea, formerly **Iol.** *Æ denarius.* REX IVBA. Head of Juba II as Hercules wearing lion's skin. ℞. CAES / AREA in wreath. *Müller* 51 .. .. R, F £10

3004 Lix (Larache). 1st Cent. B.C. Æ 27. Head of divinity l., beardless, wearing high conical cap. ℞. Phoenician legend. Two bunches of grapes. *Müller* 234 R, *fair* 60/-

3005 Semes. 38 B.C.-23 A.D. Æ 22. Bearded head facing. ℞. Phoenician legend. Star between bunch of grapes and ear of corn. *Müller* 250 .. .. R, F 75/-

3002A

3006

3006 Tingis (Tangiers). 1st Cent. B.C. Æ 18. Bearded head r. ℞. Phoenician legend. Three ears of corn. *Müller* 224 .. .. F 50/-

ETHIOPIA.

(Coins of the Axumite Kings up to the 6th Century A.D., when Greek legends were replaced by Gheez).

3007 AXUM, Endybis. *Ca.* 250-275 A.D. *Æ* 15 millimetres. ΕΝΔΥΒΙC ↄ BACIΛEYC. Dr· bust of king r., wearing round close-fitting head-dress; the bust enclosed between two ears of corn. ℞. AΞWΜΙΤW ↄ BICIΔAX. Bust r., identical with that on obv. *Anzani* 1 *nearly* EF £140

3008 — *Æ* 15. Similar, but no ears of corn on obv. *Anz. Supplement, Pl. N.* 2 F/*good* F £40

3009 Afilas. *Ca.* 275-300 A.D. *Æ* 7. *Obv.* No legend. Similar to previous, but with crescent and star in front of bust. ℞. AΦI/ΛAC/BACI/ΛEY within circle of dots. *Anzani* 4 *var.* .. .. EF £125

3010 Ousanas. *Ca.* 300-310 A.D. *Æ* 14. OYCANA. Bust of king r., similar to 3008, within double plain circle. ℞. BACI (to r.) ЄYC (to l.). Similar bust within one thin and one thick plain circle. *Anz. Suppl. Pl. N.* 7 *var.*... .. .. .. *fair* £25

3011 Ezanas, as pagan. Before 330 A.D. *Æ* 12. HZA ↄ NAC. Similar to 3008. ℞. ↄ BACIΛEYC. As *obv.*, but smaller bust within circle of dots. *Anzani* — .. F £40

3012 — **after his conversion to Christianity.** After 330 A.D. *Æ* 17. + HZA + HAC + BACI + ΛEYC. Crowned and dr. bust of king r., holding sceptre, between two ears of corn. ℞. + AΞW + MITWN + BICI + ΛΛЄΗЄ. Dr. bust of king r., wearing round close-fitting head-dress, and holding branch; the bust enclosed between two ears of corn. *Anzani* 37 .. .. *nearly* EF/*good* VF £100

3013 Ezanas and his successors. *ca.* 350-400 A.D. Æ 15. BACIΛEYC. Similar to *rev.* of previous, but without branch, and bust within double circle. ℞. TOYTOAPECHTHXWPA. Cross within a plain circle. *Anz.* 45 .. .. F/*good* F 75/-

3014 **Wazeba II.** *Ca.* 380-395 A.D. Æ 17. + ovΛzнВΛC BΛCIΛEVC. Similar to *rev.* of 3012, but without branch. ℞. Legend similar to previous. Similar bust, but smaller within round shallow incuse; background inlaid with gold. *Anz.* 71 .. F 85/-

3015 **Kaleb.** *Ca.* 520-530 A.D. Ɲ 18. + ХΛΛНᗺ ᗺΛƏIΛƆVƏC +. Similar to 3012. ℞. ++ BΛCIΛEVC +. Similar to 3012. *Anz.* —.. .. .. VF £150

3016 **Kaleb and his successors.** *Ca.* 520-540 A.D. Æ 16. CΛХΛCΛ. Crowned and dr. bust of king r., holding sceptre surmounted by cross; in field l., cross. ℞. Legend similar to 3013. Cross, with circular incuse in centre, within circle of dots. *Anz.* 169 F 55/-

3017 **Nezana.** *Ca.* 540-545 A.D. Ɲ 17. ΘЕОY ЄYХΛPICTIΛ. Crowned, dr. and cuir. bust of king r., holding branch; bust flanked by two ears of corn. ℞. BΛƆIΛЄVC NЄIOШΛ. Similar to 3012, but head-dress surmounted by cross *Anz.* — .. .. EF £150

3018 — Æ 15. NЕZΛ (to r.) NΛВΛ (to l.). Dr. bust of king r., wearing round close-fitting head-dress. ℞. ΘЕ ОV ХΛ PI. Ornament, in shape of voided cross, within circle of dots, dividing the legend into four sectors of two letters each: centre of ornament inlaid with gold. *Anz.* 178 .. .. *slightly chipped, good* F £50

3019 **Ebana.** *Ca.* 565-575 A.D. Æ 14. ЄВΛNΛ. Crowned and dr. bust of king r. ℞. BΛ ΛC IΛ ЄY. Lozenge with crosslet points, dividing the legend into four sectors, containing two letters each: centre of lozenge inlaid with gold. *Anz.* 191 .. .. F £25

Semitic	Phoenician and Punic	Israelite	Aramaic	Greek early	Greek late	North Italian	Early Latin and Roman	English
✕	✶ ⼤ ⼤	⺌ ⼤	⼤ ⼦	⼤ ⼈ A	A A	⺉ ⺉ ⼈	⼈ ⼈ ⼈	A
⼃	⼃ ⼃ ⼃	⼃ ⼃ ⼤	⼤ ⼦	⼦ ⼤ B	B B	⼋ B	B	B
⼁	⼁ ⼁ ⼈	⼁ ⼁	⼈ ⼈	⼕ ⼈ ⼂	⼂	⼁ ⼂ ⼕	⼕ C G	C G
⼃	⼃ ⼃ ⼃	⼃ ⼁	⼤ ⼤	D D ⼃	⼃	⼹	D	D
⽬	⼃⼃ ⼃	⼃ ⼃	⼹ ⼸	⼗ ⼦ E	E E	⼹ ⼹ E	E E	Ĕ
Y	⼤ ⼤	⼤⼦ ⼦	⼁	⼕ ⼤ F		⼹⼸ ⼱	F F	F
‡	I ⼲	⼤	⼲	‡ I	Z I	⼸‡ I	Z	Z
⽇	⼫⼫ ⽇	⽇⽇	H	⼫⼫⽇	H	⽇⼑⽇	H	H(E)
	⊕ θ ⼇			⊞ ⊕ ◇	⽇ ⊙ θ	⊗ ⊙ ◇		Th
⼸	Z M ⼂	⼸ Z	⼸ Z	⼸ ⼃ I	I	I	I	I
⼸	⼈ ⼤ ⼈	⼈⼦	⼈⼈	K	K	⼃K	K	K
L	⼈ ⼁ ⼁	L	⼁⼁	⼈⼁	⼈	⼁⼈	L	L
⼴	⼴⼴ ✕	⼴⼸	⼴	⼴⼴M	M M	⼴⼴⼴	⼴ M	M
⼸	⼸⼹⼁	⼸⼸	⼸	⼈⼸N	N	⼸⼸⼸	N	N
‡	‡⼸		⼸	+⼫‡	⼸⼸⼸		X	X
O	O ∪	⊂ ∪	∪	�口◇O	O	O	◇OO	Ŏ
⼁	⼁⼁⼁	⼁⼁⼁	⼁⼁	Γ P C	Γ ⼇ ⼉	⼁⼁⼁	P P	P
	⼴⼸⼁	⼸⼸		M T				(san)
φ	φ φ ⼦	⼸ φ	⼦	φφY	φ		⼸ Q	Q
⼦	⼦⼸⼁	⼸⼦	⼸⼸	R D ⼁	P	⼦⼸R	D R	R
W	⼴⼸⼦	⼴⼴		⼦⼦S	⼁⼆⼸	⼸⼸⼦	⼦ S	S
⼗	✕⼦ ⼫	✕⼗	⼫⼫	⼗ T	T	⼗⼗⼸	T	T
				Y ⼈ Y	Y	Y ⼈ ⼸	⼈	U. V. W. Y.
				⊞ ⊙ ⊘	⼦ φ φ	⊙ ⊞		Ph
				⼷Y✕	✕	⼷Y		Kh
				⼷ ⼴	⼴			Ps
	⼁			O Ω	⼴ω Ω			Ō

ANCIENT ALPHABETS

INDEX

It was thought it would be useful to list most of those towns and many of the rulers not included in this catalogue and what better place could there be for this than the alphabetical index.

The ordinary numbers after a town refer to the page on which coins are listed or the town or person is mentioned. The italic numbers refer to the pages on which the town is shown on the maps.

Where no number is found it indicates that this town or ruler is not to be found in this catalogue but that coins were issued.

For Gaulish Tribes see pages 30 to 32.

Roman emperors and other Roman personages represented on the Greek Imperial series have been purposely omitted.

We have used as a guide in the compilation of these indexes " *Historia Numorum,* a manual of Greek Numismatics," by Barclay V. Head, 1910. This consists of over 950 pages of condensed information on the Greek series and every student or collector should possess a copy.

Is. or is.—island

TOWNS, DISTRICTS, &c.

RULERS.

(Roman Emperors and Princes are not included).

BOOKS OF REFERENCE ON GREEK COINS

The standard work on Greek Coins is the **British Museum Catalogue of Greek Coins** in twenty nine volumes. The reprinting of this important work was completed during the latter part of 1965. Each volume is uniformly priced at £9/5/- including postage. The complete set may be purchased for £225. = 5 vols free.

1. **Italy**—432 pp., line ills. in text.

2. **Sicily**—292 pp., line ills. in text.

3. **The Tauric Chersonese, Sarmatia, Dacia, Moesia, Thrace, etc.**—274 pp., line ills. in text.

4. **The Seleucid Kings of Syria**—122 pp., 27 plates.

5. **Macedonia etc.**—200 pp., 1 map, line ills. in text.

6. **The Ptolemies, Kings of Egypt**—229 pp., 32 plates.

7. **Thessaly to Aetolia**—234 pp., 32 plates.

8. **Central Greece, Locris, Phocis, Boeotia and Euboea**—220 pp., 24 plates.

9. **Crete and the Aegean Islands**—199 pp., 29 plates.

10. **Peloponnesus (excluding Corinth)**—238 pp., 37 plates.

11. **Attica, Megaris, Aegina**—243 pp., 26 plates.

12. **Corinth, Colonies of Corinth, etc.**—247 pp., 39 plates.

13. **Pontus, Paphlagonia, Bithynia, Kingdom of Bosphorus**—296 pp., 39 plates.

14. **Ionia**—509 pp., 1 map, 35 plates.

15. **Mysia**—252 pp., 1 map, 35 plates.

16. **Alexandria and the Nomes**—495 pp., 32 plates.

17. **Troas, Aeolis and Lesbos**—343 pp., 1 map, 32 plates.

18. **Caria, Cos, Rhodes, etc.**—443 pp., 1 map, 45 plates.

19. **Lycia, Pamphylia and Pisidia**—476 pp., 1 map, 44 plates.

20. **Galatia, Cappadocia and Syria**—432 pp., 1 map, 38 plates.

21. **Lycaonia, Isauria and Cilicia**—427 pp., 1 map, 40 plates.

22. **Lydia**—590 pp., 1 map, 45 plates.

23. **Parthia**—377 pp., 1 map, 39 plates.

24. **Cyprus**—203 pp., 1 map, 39 plates.

25. **Phrygia**—491 pp., 1 map, 53 plates.

26. **Phoenicia**—470 pp., 1 map, 45 plates and a table of the Phoenician alphabet.

27. **Palestine (Galilee, Samaria and Judaea)**—474 pp., 1 map, 42 plates and a table of the Hebrew alphabet.

28. **Arabia, Mesopotamia and Persia (Nabatea, Arabia Provincia, S. Arabia, Mesopotamia, Babylon, Assyria, Persia, Alexandrine Empire of the East, Elymais and Characene**—573 pp., 1 map, 55 plates.

29. **Cyrenaica**—429 pp., 47 plates.

COHEN, H. **Médailles Imperiales.** Description Historiques des Monnaies frappées sous l'Empire Romain. Reprint (1955) of the London-Paris Edition of 1880. 8 vols. containing in all 4213 pages, all the original illustrations in the text, each vol. 8½"×5½"   £48
[*Although this is the standard work on coins of the Roman Empire, all the Greek Imperial coins with Roman legends are included*].

CORPUS NUMMORUM PALAESTINENSIUM.
> VOL. I.   **The Coins of Aelia Capitolina,** by Leo Kadman.   Jerusalem, 1956. 191 pp., 17 plates, 1 plan   52/6

> VÖL. II.   **The Coins of Caesarea Maritima,** by Leo Kadman.   Jerusalem, 1957.   243 pp., 19 plates   80/-

> VOL. III.   **The Coins of the Jewish War of 66-73,** by Leo Kadman. 203 pp., 5 plates, 2 plans   70/-

> VOL. IV.   **The Coins of Akko Ptolemais, by** Leo Kadman.   Jerusalem, 1961.   240 pp., 19 plates   80/-
> [*Each volume is cloth bound, 9¾"×6¾"*]

GARDNER, P.   **Archaeology and Greek Coin Types.**   (Reprint 1965).   217 pp., 15 plates, cloth, 10¼"×8½".   *With a new introduction by Margaret Thompson*
£5/10/-

HEAD, B. V.   **Historia Numorum.**   (Reprint 1964).   964 pp., 399 ills. in text, cloth, 10"×6½"   £9/9/-
[*The Standard General work on Greek Coins*]

KLAWANS, Z. H.   **An Outline of Ancient Greek Coins.**   U.S.A., 1964.   208 pages, many illustrations in text   30/-

JENKINS, G. K., and LEWIS, R. B.   **Carthaginian Gold and Electrum Coins.** London, 1963.   140 pp., 38 plates, cloth.   10"×7½"   £5/5/-

MULLER, L.   **Numismatique d'Alexandre le Grand.**   (Reprint 1957).   40 plates and tables, cloth, 9¼"×8½"   50/-

REIFENBERG, A.   **Ancient Jewish Coins.**   Jerusalem, 1965.   (4th Ed.).   66 pp., 16 plates, cloth, 9¾"×7"   25/-
[*A useful introduction to Jewish Coins*].

SELTMAN, C.   **Greek Coins.**   London, 1955.   311 pp., 64 plates, cloth, 9"×5½"
70/-

[*The best general introduction to Greek Coins*].

SELTMAN, C.   **Masterpieces of Greek Coins.**   128 pp., many fine enlargements of Greek coins, cloth   25/-

SVORONOS, J. N.   **Synopsis de mille coins faux de faussaire C. Christodoulos.** Athens, 1922 (Reprint 1963).   16 pp., 17 plates, paper covers, 10½"×7"   45/-

SEABY'S NUMISMATIC PUBLICATIONS

ANCIENT COINS

ROMAN COINS AND THEIR VALUES *by* D. R. Sear

The third and enlarged edition of our general catalogue on
Roman Coinage; 376 pages, 13 plates. **£2·40**

ROMAN SILVER COINS *by* H. A. Seaby

A comprehensive catalogue with values.

Vol. I	Republic—Augustus	**£2·00**
Vol. II	Tiberius—Commodus	**£2·25**
Vol. III	Pertinax—Balbinus and Pupienus	**£2·40**
Vol. IV	Gordian III—Postumus	**£2·50**

A DICTIONARY OF ROMAN COINS *by* S. W. Stevenson

A reprint of the 1889 dictionary which contains a wealth of
information on Roman life and coinage; 929 pages with
several hundred illustrations in text. **£6·00**

THE COINAGE OF ROMAN BRITAIN *by* Gilbert Askew

A history and catalogue of the coins struck in the Roman
province of Britannia and of coins that refer to campaigns
fought in Britain. **88p**

GREEK COINS AND THEIR VALUES *by* H. A. Seaby

Gives a representative listing of coins of all the city states and
kingdoms of the Hellenic world, including the Greek coins
struck during the Roman period; 218 pages, 18 maps, 8 plates
and 375 illustrations in text. **£1·50**

THE COINAGE OF ANCIENT BRITAIN *by* R. P. Mack

The standard work of reference on the Celtic coins found in
Britain. **£3·50**

COIN AND MEDAL BULLETIN

*A monthly magazine and price list for all interested in
Numismatics.*

This contains articles on coins and medals, letters, answers to
questions, reviews of numismatic publications and news
from numismatic societies.

The coins and medals listed for sale are well catalogued and
provide a useful guide to the collector both as to value and
the cataloguing of a collection.   *Subscription* (*12 months*)   **£1·40**

B. A. SEABY LTD.

Dealers in Coins and Medals, Numismatic Publishers and Booksellers

AUDLEY HOUSE, 11 MARGARET STREET, LONDON, W1N 8AT

SOME OTHER SEABY PUBLICATIONS

Coins of the British Isles

STANDARD CATALOGUE OF BRITISH COINS. Parts 1 & 2: ENGLAND AND UNITED KINGDOM. (10th. ed.)   **£1·25**

ENGLISH COINS IN THE BRITISH MUSEUM: Anglo-Saxon Coins. By CHARLES KEARY and HERBERT GRUEBER. 2 vols.   **£10·00**

ENGLISH SILVER COINAGE from 1649. By H. A. SEABY and P. A. RAYNER (3rd. ed.)   **£2·25**

BRITISH COINS 1816-1969. Ed. P. J. SEABY   **62p**

BRITISH COPPER COINS and their Values. By P. J. SEABY and MONICA BUSSELL (1969-70 ed.)   **75p**

BRITISH TOKENS and their Values. By P. J. SEABY and MONICA BUSSELL (1970)   **£1·50**

TRADE TOKENS issued in the 17th Century. By G. C. WILLIAMSON. 3 vols.   **£12·50**

THE PROVINCIAL TOKEN COINAGE of the 18th Century. By RICHARD DALTON and SAMUEL HAMER   **£14·50**

THE NINETEENTH CENTURY TOKEN COINAGE. By W. J. DAVIS   **£6·00**

THE SILVER TOKEN COINAGE 1811-12. By RICHARD DALTON, with supplement by FRANK PURVEY   **£3·50**

COINS AND TOKENS OF IRELAND. By P. J. SEABY   **£1·20**

Medals

COLLECTING MEDALS AND DECORATIONS. By ALEC C. PURVES. *Revised edition ready Spring* 1971   **£2·00**

THE WHITE RIBBON: a medallic record of British Polar exploration. By NEVILLE W. POULSOM   **£3·75**

BRITISH GALLANTRY AWARDS. By PETER ABBOTT and JOHN TAMPLIN. A superb new comprehensive standard work—produced in conjunction with Guinness Superlatives Ltd. *Ready Spring* 1971   **£6·00**

B. A. SEABY LTD.
11 MARGARET STREET, LONDON, W1N 8AT

PLATE I

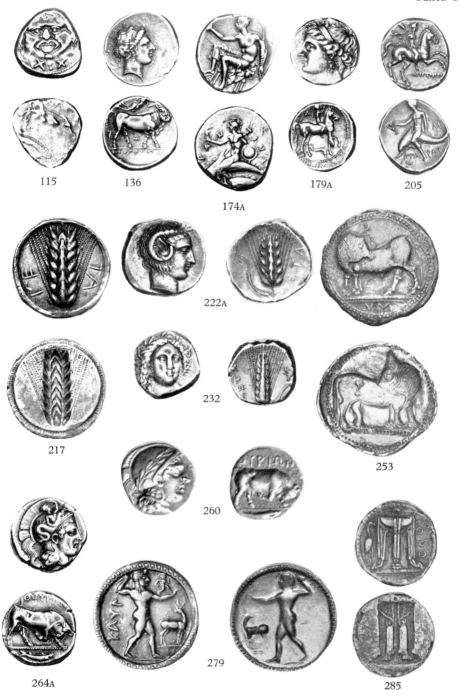

115 136   179A 205

174A

222A

232

217

253

260

264A   279 285

PLATE II

288

299

311

320

331

376

414A

388

427A

431

418

432

PLATE III

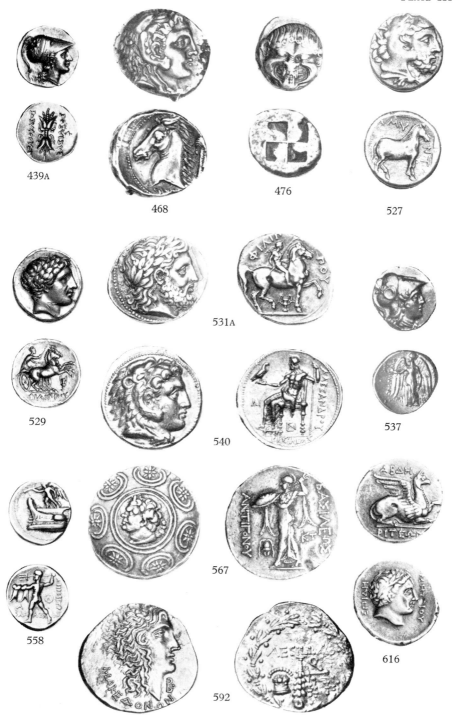

439A

468

476

527

529

531A

540

537

558

567

592

616

PLATE IV

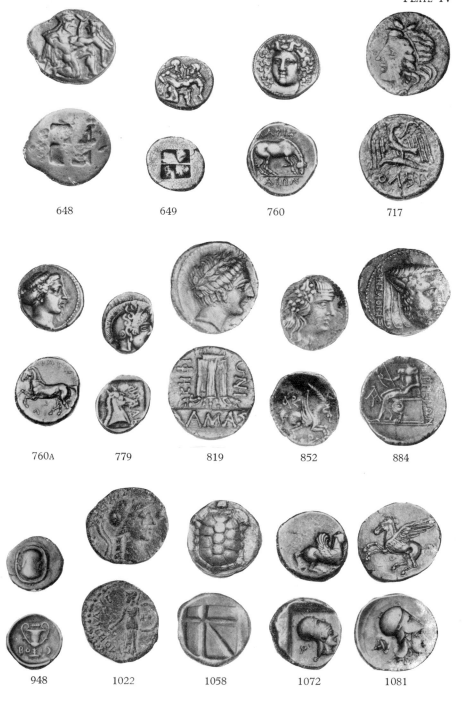

648   649   760   717

760A   779   819   852   884

948   1022   1058   1072   1081

PLATE V

1164   1168A   1223   1274   1415

1323   1316   1325   1242

1424   1440   1454   1503   1506A

PLATE VI

1532c

1590a

1533

1610a 1610b 1625 1777a 1812b 1815

1780 1980 1985 1988 2095

PLATE VII

1996

2011

2042

2097A

2043

2049

2108

2171

2231

2494

2660A

PLATE VIII

2637

2572

2679

2703

2663A

2792

2715

2737

2960

2705

2994